Atmospheric Diffusion

ATMOSPHERIC DIFFUSION

The Dispersion of Windborne Material
from
Industrial and other Sources

F. PASQUILL, D.SC.,

Meteorological Office, Bracknell, Berkshire

D. VAN NOSTRAND COMPANY LTD
LONDON

TORONTO   NEW YORK
PRINCETON, NEW JERSEY

D. VAN NOSTRAND COMPANY LTD
Windsor House, 46 Victoria Street, London, S.W.1

D. VAN NOSTRAND COMPANY INC.
120, Alexander Street, Princeton, New Jersey
24, West 40 Street, New York 18, New York

D. VAN NOSTRAND COMPANY (CANADA) LTD
25, Hollinger Road, Toronto 16, Canada

Library of Congress Catalog Card No. 61–13476

First Published 1962
Reprinted   1968

C

Reproduced photolitho in Great Britain by
J. W. Arrowsmith Ltd., Bristol 3

Preface

The varying capacity of the atmosphere for transferring and diluting gases, small particles or droplets, is a matter of practical importance in operations or events involving the release or escape of such materials. Problems arising in this field have been among the greatest stimuli to the detailed study of diffusion processes in the atmosphere, especially in the layers close to the ground. An authoritative general discussion of these processes, covering the classical background and the development up to 1950, is provided in Sir Graham Sutton's *Micrometeorology*.

During the last decade interest in atmospheric diffusion has been heightened by the increasing attention given to air pollution in general, to the new hazards introduced by the products of nuclear processes, and to the possibilities of augmenting rainfall by large-scale cloud-seeding. As a result, the theoretical and observational aspects of this problem have continued to be investigated in a number of directions, and a considerable addition to the volume of literature has accumulated, both in the form of isolated papers in the regular journals and collected papers in the proceedings of symposia, notably those held on an international basis at Boston, U.S.A., in 1951 and at Oxford, England, in 1958. The time therefore seemed appropriate for a review and re-assimilation of the ideas and information available. That which is attempted here is not claimed to be encyclopaedic, but it includes those features which seem to me to be most significant in the description and estimation of the diffusion of material released in the atmosphere. The presentation is in chapters dealing in a fairly self-contained way with obvious divisions into theoretical and practical interest, the repetition of previous integrated discussions being kept to the minimum essential for balance in the present specialized context. It is hoped that this arrangement will be useful to meteorologists, physicists and other workers actively concerned with diffusion in the atmosphere.

During the preparation of the book I have had the benefit of many technical discussions with colleagues and friends working in this field of research. I am especially indebted to Dr F. B. Smith of the Meteorological Office, for reading the whole draft, and for making many valuable suggestions.   I am also grateful to Professor H. A. Panofsky, Pennsylvania State University, and Mr R. A. McCormick, United States Weather Bureau, for reading and helpfully commenting on certain chapters.

For permission to reproduce diagrams and to quote other material I am indebted to the Director-General of the Meteorological Office, the Controller of Her Majesty's Stationery Office, the War Office, the United Kingdom Atomic Energy Authority, the Royal Meteorological Society, the Cambridge University Press, the Academic Press, the Pergamon Press, the United States Weather Bureau, the American Meteorological Society, the Air Pollution Control Association and the American Geophysical Union.

Finally, my thanks go to several colleagues, in the Meteorological Office and at C.D.E.E., Porton, who have been most helpful in many tedious but necessary tasks.

F. PASQUILL

War Department, Chemical Defence Experimental Establishment, Porton Down, Wiltshire, England.
    January 1961.

Introduction

This book is concerned with the physical problems arising in the wind-borne movement and dilution of material released deliberately or accidentally into the atmosphere over a localized area. There are related problems involving the removal and redistribution of water vapour and heat from the earth's surface, which are of great importance in meteorology and hydrology, and which involve the same physical processes of turbulent mixing. This second class of problems forms a large subject on its own and the progress made in it since the publication of Sutton's *Micrometeorology* has recently been summarized in Priestley's *Turbulent Transfer in the Lower Atmosphere*. Such references as are made here to this aspect will accordingly be restricted to a context and length essential to the particular interests of the present review.

In general the motion of the atmosphere may be said to be turbulent to some degree. The very definition of *turbulence* is a difficult matter on which there are considerable differences of view, as will be appreciated from a reading of the concluding discussions of the international symposia held at Boston, U.S.A., in 1951 and at Oxford, England, in 1958. In the present context one may perhaps be excused from attempting any precise definition, and be allowed to take the simple empirical view. On this view turbulence is that quality which is manifested in the random character of the velocity of a fluid (say at a fixed point as a function of time), in contrast to the constancy of such a velocity in steady stream-lined flow, or to the recognizable periodicities of a wave motion. It is on this turbulence, which varies greatly in time and space in the atmosphere, that atmospheric diffusion depends. Even in the controlled and simplified conditions of the laboratory or wind tunnel turbulent motion is extremely complex, and, when to this are added other complicating features which occur naturally in the open air, it is not surprising that the whole problem of atmospheric diffusion contains many features which are still relatively intractable. In the historical development of reliable usable methods of estimating the effects of atmospheric flow on diffusion in practical circumstances, which is one of the endpoints of interest in this book, it is clear that progress has depended upon following a middle course, avoiding undue dependence on empiricism, and yet not making treatments unproductive by too much insistence on a more rigorous approach.

A brief consideration of the typical 'plume' of smoke extending from a factory chimney on a fine day will serve to introduce the central problem which will be investigated, and discussed at length, in the various chapters which follow. The spreading of the smoke can be seen to occur in two distinct ways. Firstly, any given section of the plume spreads as it travels, and this spreading action is clearly a result of differences of velocity within the relatively small volume of air occupied by the smoke. In addition, the plume as a whole possesses irregularities arising from variations in the bodily displacement of its component sections. These variations in bodily displacement are evidently associated with variations in the general velocity of the larger volumes of air which transport the sections of plume without exerting any important effect on their rates of growth. The effects of turbulent fluctuations with a wide range of scales or, to use a conventional phrase, of eddies with a wide range of sizes, are thereby directly demonstrated. Most of the task of clarifying atmospheric diffusion problems consists of defining and describing these fluctuations, and expressing their action in redistributing the air and so dispersing the material carried with it.

In contrast with the early development of the theory of turbulent diffusion, with its avoidance of the detailed properties of the turbulence, and its preference for analysis in terms of a virtual diffusivity analogous to molecular diffusivity, the current tendency is increasingly to employ the statistical concepts of turbulence developed in the fields of fluid mechanics and aerodynamics. Accordingly, the first two chapters are respectively devoted to the technique of analysis of turbulence and to the description of those aspects of its structure which have been examined in the atmosphere, and which are particularly relevant to the process of diffusion. It should perhaps be emphasized that the treatment in the first chapter is confined to features which are relatively straightforward, and which have already made impact on analyses of atmospheric diffusion; much more elaborate discussions of the analysis and mechanics of turbulence are contained in works on fluid dynamics, but their significance and application in the present context have yet to be realized. Furthermore, the omission of a special discussion of the structure of free convection, as distinct from mechanical turbulence, is not to be interpreted as doubting the importance of this feature; but since the advances in this field are covered in Priestley's book, references are here confined to specific aspects which find appropriate place at the end of Chapter 3. This latter chapter deals generally with the theoretical treatments of diffusion, and in particular attempts to give due emphasis to the potentialities of the statistical approach.

With the first three chapters providing an essential background on the properties of the flow and the theoretical specification of its diffusive action, the way is prepared for a connected discussion of the many observations which are now available on the basic features of diffusion, namely the dimensions and shapes of the spatial distributions of tracer material released experimentally into the atmosphere. These observations are collected and put into perspective in Chapter 4, which completes the more fundamental side of the book. The remaining third of the book is concerned with practical applications. Chapter 5 comprises an outline of the utilization of the accumulated qualitative and quantitative experience, in forming estimates of the concentrations of material produced down-wind of idealized types of source, on the basis of meteorological data of a more or less specialized nature. This is written with the requirements of the operational meteorologist and engineer primarily in mind. Alternatively the systems may be used in reverse so as to estimate the allowable positions and strengths of sources, given a maximum permissible level of contamination. Finally, Chapter 6 reviews a number of separate practical interests arising in connection with the windborne distribution of material released into the atmosphere from real sources of various kinds, and where relevant examines these in relation to the earlier fundamental discussions.

Contents

1

Analysis of Turbulence

1.1 Early history

The mathematical treatment of turbulent flow is essentially based on the idea that the motion can be resolved into a fluctuating motion super-imposed on a 'mean flow'. Leaving until later the precise interpretation of the term 'mean', and taking the simplest view that this mean flow is constant in velocity, then components of velocity may be defined in the usual rectangular coordinate system with Ox, Oy in the horizontal plane and Oz vertical, as follows:

$$u = \bar{u} + u' \qquad \text{along } Ox$$
$$v = \bar{v} + v' \qquad \text{along } Oy \qquad\qquad (1.1)$$
$$w = \bar{w} + w' \qquad \text{along } Oz$$

Here $\bar{u}$, $\bar{v}$, $\bar{w}$ are the mean velocities, and the quantities identified by primes (u', etc.) are the fluctuations from these mean values, usually referred to as components of turbulence or eddy velocities. Physically, these velocities refer to a particle or small element of the fluid passing through the point x, y, z at time t, and in the *Eulerian* system of hydro-dynamics the velocities are specified at all positions in the field of flow at a given instant. An alternative system, with which we shall be greatly concerned later in the treatments of diffusion, uses velocities which refer to an individual *particle* or *element of fluid* as it moves in the field of flow, and this system is referred to as *Lagrangian*. In practice the above velocity specification is usually simplified by assuming the mean flow to be horizontal, so that $\bar{w} = 0$, and by taking the x axis to be in the direction of the mean flow, so that $\bar{v} = 0$.

If the values in (1.1) are substituted for u, v and w in the Navier-Stokes equations of incompressible motion (e.g. see Sutton, 1953, p. 63) the result is that the usual viscous stresses are augmented by virtual stresses (the *Reynolds stresses*) proportional to the mean values of the squares ($\overline{u'^2}$ etc) and products ($\overline{u'w'}$ etc) of the eddy velocities. These quantities are fundamental in any general statistical description of the turbulent flow, though in this and

1

the next chapter the discussion will be confined to the properties of the mean squares, rather than the mean products. The latter are particularly relevant to the transporting action of turbulence in the presence of a shear in the mean flow, and are referred to briefly in this context in Chapter 3.

Terms like $\overline{u'^2}$ represent the kinetic energy of the turbulent motion, and the ratios of the corresponding quantities $\sqrt{(\overline{u'^2})}$ to the mean wind velocity are normally used to specify the *intensity* of turbulence. These quantities provide a physically relevant specification of the scattering or mixing quality of the flow. However, it is clear from the most elementary considerations that such quantities alone are insufficient to define the flow and its actions, for the same value of $\overline{u'^2}$ may easily arise from quite different variations in the velocity u. Some further representation of the temporal and spatial variation of the flow is also required, and in the earliest attempts to provide a general theoretical framework it was assumed that the turbulent fluctuations were a consequence of the random motion of discrete independent masses of fluid. Theories of this nature were developed principally by Prandtl and G. I. Taylor, and in the work by the former the treatment took on its best-known form, that of the *mixing-length* theory. According to this, the separate masses of fluid, or eddies, were supposed to spring into existence in some undefined way and then, after moving unaltered over a certain path, were supposed to become once more indistinguishable from the surrounding fluid. In this way the life of an eddy was something like that of a molecule of gas between successive collisions. The idea of a mixing action in the fluid was implicit in this model, and the length of the path of the eddy, analogous to the mean free path of a molecule, was termed the 'mixing length'. Mixing-length theories are now mainly of historical interest, and we shall not be concerned with any discussion of them here, beyond noting that they provided a mechanistic picture of the transport of fluid properties, such as momentum, heat content and material content, at a rate proportional to the gradient of the particular quantity. It was obvious that the discontinuous action which was implied was quite artificial, and the modern treatment of turbulent motion emphasizes instead the continuous nature of the motion. The basis of this treatment, and those developments which are especially relevant to the analysis of the intensity and structure of atmospheric turbulence, are outlined in the following sections.

1.2 Correlation and spectrum properties

The breakaway from the old discontinuous representation and the essential step to the modern notions was provided by G. I. Taylor. The initial presentation of the idea (1921) was in terms of the velocity of a given particle or element of fluid, in an analysis which remains a fundamental basis of treatments of turbulent diffusion in a fluid.   Discussion of this Lagrangian representation will be reserved for a later and more appropriate section, and at this point it is sufficient to note that the fundamental idea lay in the recognition that the velocity should be regarded as varying *continuously*, in this case with time along the path of the particle.   This idea of continuous variation remained undeveloped for a considerable time until it was extended, again by Taylor (1935), to the Eulerian description of the spatial structure of turbulence.   It was evident that any ideas about the *size* of eddies would be more realistically formulated in terms of the differences in velocity existing instantaneously between one point and another in the fluid.   For example, small eddies as previously conceived would impose differences in velocity between two relatively close points, whereas large eddies would more often than not give velocities which would be similar at the two points.

The statistical expression of the latter idea is provided by the space-correlation coefficient between the velocities at two points a specified distance apart.   Clearly, if the eddy *sizes* are large compared with this distance the correlation coefficient will tend to be high, and vice versa.   Thus, if the turbulent components u'_1 and u'_2 are measured instantaneously at two points, one of which is kept fixed while the other is varied in distance x from it, then the correlation coefficient $R(x)$, defined by

$$R(x) = \overline{u'_1 u'_2}/\overline{u'^2} \tag{1.2}$$

should generally decrease with increase of spacing x.   In this expression of correlation *homogeneous* turbulence is implied in that the statistical properties $R(x)$ and $\overline{u'^2}$ are taken to be independent of position.   The sharpness of the decrease of $R(x)$ with x, which is obviously a reflection of the eddy sizes, can be represented by a length l, defined by the relation

$$l = \int_0^\infty R(x)\,dx \tag{1.3}$$

provided that the integral converges.   This quantity was suggested by Taylor as a possible definition of the 'average size of eddies', and is now commonly referred to as the *scale* of turbulence.   Similar scales along the y and z axes can likewise be defined in terms of the velocity components v' and w'.

A time-correlation coefficient, $R(t)$, usually referred to as an auto-correlation coefficient, may also be defined in terms of the eddy velocities at a fixed point at instants separated by t.   If the sequence of variations of u at a fixed point is assumed to be determined by the passage over the fixed point of an unchanging pattern of turbulence, it immediately follows that

$$R(t) = R(x) \quad \text{when } x = ut \tag{1.4}$$

This relation, the validity of which is discussed in the next chapter, was adopted by Taylor (1938) in the next important advance, namely the introduction into turbulence theory of the relation between the correlation coefficient and the *spectrum* of turbulence as contained in the variations of the turbulent velocity at a fixed point. If this variation is represented by the Fourier integral

$$u'(t) = 2\pi \int_0^\infty [I_1(n) \cos 2\pi nt + I_2(n) \sin 2\pi nt] \, dn \tag{1.5}$$

where n is frequency (cycles per second), it is a consequence of a theorem in harmonic analysis that the total variance, $\overline{u'^2}$, may be formally expressed as an integral of the Fourier coefficients $I_1(n)$ and $I_2(n)$ as follows:

$$\overline{u'^2} = 2\pi^2 \int_0^\infty \lim_{T\to\infty} \left(\frac{I_1^2(n)+I_2^2(n)}{T} \right) dn \tag{1.6}$$

where T is the time over which the turbulent variation is supposed to exist. The quantity

$$2\pi^2 \lim_{T\to\infty} \left(\frac{I_1^2(n)+I_2^2(n)}{T} \right) dn$$

thus represents the contribution made to the total variance by frequencies between n and $n+dn$, and may be denoted by $\overline{u'^2} F(n) \, dn$, where

$$\int_0^\infty F(n) \, dn = 1 \tag{1.7}$$

The plot of $F(n)$ against n forms the *energy spectrum* or *power spectrum* curve, and $\overline{u'^2}F(n)$ may be referred to as a *spectral density*. Using an analytical theorem due to Wiener, Taylor was able to show that $R(t)$ and $F(n)$ are related by the expression

$$R(t) = \int_0^\infty F(n) \cos 2\pi nt \, dn \tag{1.8}$$

and by comparison with the pair of formulae expressing the Fourier integral theorem it was seen that when Eq. (1.8) holds

$$F(n) = 4 \int_0^\infty R(t) \cos 2\pi nt \, dt \tag{1.9}$$

must also be true.   Thus, knowing $R(t)$, $F(n)$ can be calculated, and vice versa.   An experimental demonstration of the relations (1.8) and (1.9), with $R(x)$ and $R(t)$ assumed to be related as in Eq. (1.4), was provided by measurements of both $R(x)$ and $F(n)$ made by Simmons and Salter (see Taylor, 1938) in the turbulent flow downstream of a grid in a wind tunnel. The values of $F(n)$ were measured by passing the electrical signal representing $u'(t)$ through filter circuits.

The immediate practical importance of the above development is two-fold.   Firstly, it brings out the idea of a continuous range of eddy *sizes* (in so far as size can be identified with inverse frequency) and provides a way of identifying those sizes which are of most significance as regards kinetic energy.   Secondly, it provides a method of calculating the spectral distribution when measurements similar to those made by Simmons and Salter are impracticable, either because the *signal* representing $u'(t)$ is of inconvenient form, or because suitable electronic apparatus is not available.

It is instructive at this point to note the connection between the spectrum and the *scale* of turbulence l, defined in Eq. (1.3), in the simple case when the correlogram is assumed to decay exponentially, i.e. when

$$R(x) = \exp\left(-x/l\right) \tag{1.10}$$

As will be seen in the next chapter it has been found that correlograms in atmospheric turbulence can often be approximately represented in this way.   Substituting (1.10) in (1.9), again assuming Eq. (1.4), it follows that

$$nF(n) = \frac{2}{\pi(a+1/a)} \tag{1.11}$$

where $a = 2\pi n l/\bar{u}$.   Plotting $nF(n)$ against $\log n$ gives a form of spectrum curve which is much used in practice, for while using a scale which is more convenient when large ranges of frequency are involved, it retains the useful feature of representing the contribution to the total variance in specified frequency bands, since

$$\int_{n_1}^{n_2} nF(n)\ \mathrm{d}\log_e n = \int_{n_1}^{n_2} F(n)\ \mathrm{d}n \tag{1.12}$$

Plotted in this way Eq. (1.11) is a symmetrical curve (see Fig. 1.1) with a maximum value of $1/\pi$ at $n = \bar{u}/2\pi l$, or at an equivalent wavelength $\bar{u}/n = 2\pi l$, that is, the maximum variance contribution in a small interval of $\log n$ occurs at an equivalent wavelength equal to 2π times the scale of turbulence as originally defined.

2—A.D.

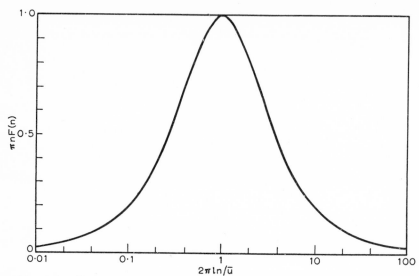

FIG. 1.1.   Energy spectrum curve corresponding to a correlogram of form
$$R(x) = \exp(-x/l)$$

1.3 Isotropic turbulence and the universal equilibrium theory

In the early work on the statistical representation and analysis of homogeneous turbulence Taylor introduced the further simplification of *isotropy*, i.e. the condition in which statistical properties such as $\overline{u'^2}$ are

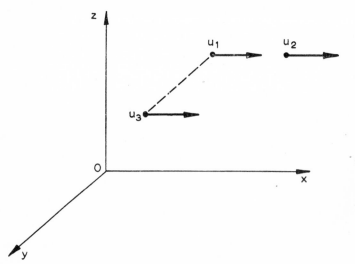

FIG. 1.2.   Longitudinal and transverse correlations

unaffected by rotation or reflection of the axes of reference. The quantities $\overline{u'^2}$, $\overline{v'^2}$ and $\overline{w'^2}$ then become equal, as well as uniform in space.

One of the important results which emerged from the detailed analysis of isotropic turbulence was the realization that the correlogram (and hence the scale) for a given component could be defined in a *longitudinal* sense or in a *transverse* sense. Thus, in Fig. 1.2 the correlation between u_1 and u_2 at points on a line parallel to the x-axis is longitudinal, while that between u_1 and u_3 on a line parallel to the y-axis is transverse. The term transverse is used here in preference to lateral, as the latter term is commonly used to describe the component of atmospheric turbulence (or of diffusion) in a horizontal cross-wind direction. In isotropic turbulence these two correlation functions are different, and, as first shown by von Kármán (see Taylor 1938, p. 484)

$$R_{\text{trans}} = R_{\text{long}} + \tfrac{1}{2} r \frac{dR_{\text{long}}}{dr} \qquad (1.13)$$

for a given separation distance r. As Taylor showed, this relation was verified by Simmons and Salter's measurements. The transverse correlation fell off much more rapidly with increasing separation x than did the longitudinal correlation, and took on small negative values before becoming zero and equal to the longitudinal value.

The difference in the longitudinal and transverse forms needs to be kept in mind constantly when interpreting the autocorrelation of a component of wind fluctuation at a fixed point. With Taylor's assumption as in Eq. (1.4), this can be transformed to a space-correlation [in the direction of the mean flow] which will be longitudinal for the u' component and transverse for the v' and w' components. Thus, using subscripts to denote the component involved,

$$R(t)_v = R(t)_w \neq R(t)_u \qquad (1.14)$$

and applying (1.13) in evaluating the apparent scale l from (1.3)

$$l_v = l_w = \tfrac{1}{2} l_u \qquad (1.15)$$

i.e. the scales derived for the v and w components of turbulence will be one-half of that observed for the u component. These differences in the longitudinal and transverse forms appear in the corresponding spectrum functions, for on applying the Fourier-transform (1.9) to (1.13) it follows that

$$F(n)_{\text{trans}} = \tfrac{1}{2} F(n)_{\text{long}} - \frac{n}{2} \frac{dF(n)_{\text{long}}}{dn} \qquad (1.16)$$

i.e. the spectral shapes derived from autocorrelation measurements are the same for the v and w components but different for the u component. This means that even though both $\overline{v'^2}$ and $\overline{w'^2}$ are equal to $\overline{u'^2}$ in isotropic turbulence the spectral densities for v' and w', although equal to each other, are in general different from the spectral density for u'.

In the atmosphere the condition of isotropy does not occur as a general rule, but its existence to an approximate degree has often been assumed in order to facilitate the analysis of problems of diffusion. Furthermore, the field of application of the laws of isotropic turbulence has been greatly extended by the development of the idea of *local isotropy*, i.e. isotropy which is confined to the small-scale structure of the motion. This development

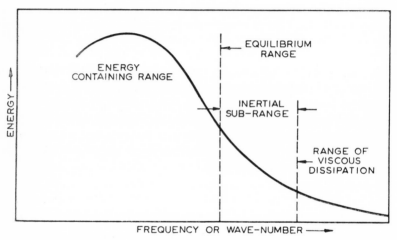

FIG. 1.3. Schematic representation of energy spectrum of turbulence

was suggested independently by several workers but it was put forward first, and in its most productive form, by A. N. Kolmogoroff. Kolmogoroff's theory, variously referred to as the *similarity theory* or *theory of universal equilibrium*, was published in 1941, but it was not until 1946 that it began to be widely known in journals printed in the English language, as a result of discussions by G. K. Batchelor (1946, 1947, 1950, 1953), and the brief outline given here is based on Batchelor's presentations of the work. The theory postulates that all turbulent motions, irrespective of their origins and of the form of the mean flow, and subject only to their occurrence with sufficiently large scale, possess local isotropy. In effect local isotropy means that statistical properties involving the *differences* of velocity between two points are independent of the choice of reference point, and of rotation or reflection of the axes of reference.   By using relative velocities, in place of the absolute velocities considered in general isotropy, attention is necessarily confined to the smaller eddies, i.e. to the high-frequency end of the spectrum.

The general physical picture is represented schematically in Fig. 1.3. It is supposed that most of the energy is contained in a definite group of 'energy-containing' eddies, of a scale characteristic of the distribution of mean velocity, and that there is a continual passage of energy from large to small scale (i.e. to high frequency) through the action of inertia forces. At all stages, but predominantly at high frequencies, there is a dissipation of energy by viscous forces, and the total amount so dissipated must be equal to the amount transferred from the mean flow.   The idea introduced by Kolmogoroff is that in this process of transfer of energy down the scale of eddies, the eddies successively concerned gradually lose all the original influence (e.g. the directional preference) of the energy-containing eddies, and ultimately a stage is reached when the motion of the succeeding eddies is isotropic.   For these small eddies the properties are conditioned firstly by an 'inflow' of energy which, because of the small viscous dissipation in the relatively large eddies, is equal to the energy transferred from the mean flow and ultimately dissipated by viscous action at a rate ϵ per unit mass of fluid, and secondly by the viscosity, ν, of the fluid, as governing this rate of dissipation.   Thus, for this *equilibrium range* Kolmogoroff's first similarity hypothesis states (see Batchelor 1950):

The average properties of the small-scale components of turbulence are determined uniquely by the quantities ϵ and ν.

When this equilibrium range is sufficiently wide it is further argued that the larger eddies in the range will contribute so little to the total viscous dissipation that a sub-range will exist in which the properties will be determined by the purely inertial transfer of energy.   This concept provides Kolmogoroff's second hypothesis:

At the large-eddy end of the equilibrium range there is an inertial sub-range in which the average properties are determined by the quantity ϵ.

The conditions assumed in the inertial sub-range lead to an important prediction about the relative velocities.   For a range of small separation x the difference in the velocities at the two points will depend only on x and ϵ and dimensional reasoning shows that

$$\overline{(u'_2 - u'_1)^2} \propto (\epsilon x)^{2/3} \tag{1.17}$$

or expanding and introducing $R(x)$ as defined in (1.2)

$$1 - R(x) \propto (\epsilon x)^{2/3} \tag{1.18}$$

A corresponding prediction can be made about the form of the energy spectrum.   In these developments, as in the whole of the formal treatment of turbulence, the spectrum analysis is more properly made in terms of space-variations, rather than time-variations at a fixed point, with frequency n replaced by *wave number* (inverse wavelength) κ.   The prediction is then that for a range of sufficiently high κ

$$F(\kappa) \propto \epsilon^{2/3}\kappa^{-5/3} \tag{1.19}$$

With the previous assumption of equivalence in the time and space variations $n = \bar{u}\kappa$, and for the equivalent frequency spectrum

$$F(n) \propto \epsilon^{2/3}n^{-5/3} \tag{1.20}$$

It is to be noted at this point that dimensional analysis directly in terms of frequency leads to a term n^{-2} in the form for $F(n)$.   This apparent inconsistency (see Charnock and Robinson, 1957) is a reflection of the fact that frequency alone can give no knowledge of a length parameter.

This outline of the formal representation of the properties of turbulence has been given in terms of a resolved component of the turbulent velocity, whereas a complete analysis brings in the three-dimensional vector character of the velocity field, with consequent elaboration of the mathematical techniques.   For the purpose of introducing the essential concepts, and indeed for much of the subsequent analysis in this book, the one-dimensional approach will be both convenient and adequate, and the reference to three-dimensional considerations will be confined to those points where this is essential to avoid erroneous results.   Furthermore, though it has already been observed that the Eulerian analysis should strictly be made in terms of space and wave-number, most observations of atmospheric turbulence are in the form of time-variation at a point, so that the time and frequency representation is usually imposed at the outset.   For certain problems *time* analysis *per se* is appropriate and there is no disadvantage, but inferences therefrom concerning space properties must be made with caution.

1.4   The statistical effects of finite sampling and averaging

We now consider in some detail the analysis of the variation with time of a turbulent velocity component at a fixed point in the field of flow.   If it is assumed that the frequency spectrum of the whole motion extends indefinitely on the low-frequency side, i.e. effectively that there is no upper limit to the size of the eddies, then it follows that for the specification of the whole turbulent motion quantities like the variance would have to be evaluated over an effectively infinite period of observation.   If the variation is considered only over some finite duration of *sampling*, τ (see Fig. 1.4), the effects of the slow variations will be partially excluded. In this case the magnitude of the turbulent component, say u', is expressed precisely as in Eq. (1.1), except that now the mean value is defined as

$$\bar{u}_\tau = \frac{1}{\tau} \int_{t'-\tau/2}^{t'+\tau/2} u \, dt \tag{1.21}$$

and then

$$u = \bar{u}_\tau + u' \tag{1.22}$$

The mean velocity is thus recognized as a purely arbitrary quantity, dependent on the duration, τ, and time of origin, t', of the sample of fluctuations.

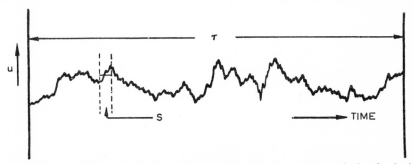

FIG. 1.4. Sampling-duration (τ) and averaging-time (s) in the analysis of velocity fluctuations

At the other end of the scale some of the fine structure of the variation will be smoothed out, since any individual observation must represent an average over some period s. Even if this averaging effect is not imposed deliberately in the process of 'reading' the variation, it will still exist as a consequence of the inertia of the measuring instrument. The effects of *sampling* duration τ and *averaging time* s on the apparent statistical properties are thus of great importance.

Considering the whole variation as a composition of sinusoidal components let the variation associated with a frequency n be represented by

$$y = a \sin 2\pi nt \tag{1.23}$$

The process of averaging over time interval s amounts to replacing y in the above by

$$y = \frac{1}{s} \int_{t'-s/2}^{t'+s/2} y \, dt = \frac{a}{\pi ns} \sin \pi ns \sin 2\pi nt' \tag{1.24}$$

and the original sinusoidal variation is replaced by a variation of the same

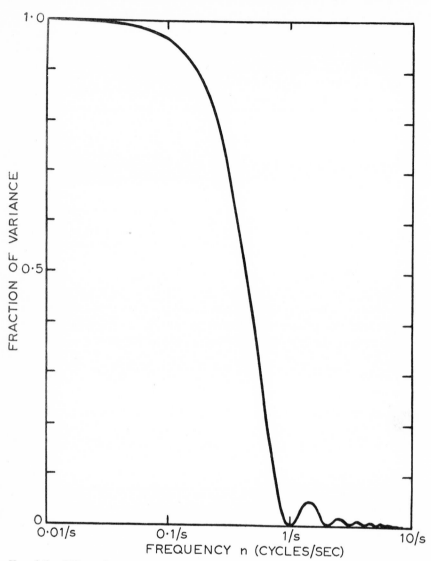

Fig. 1.5.   Effect of averaging, over a time s, on the variance of a sinusoidal fluctuation of frequency n

form but with an amplitude which is reduced to $\sin \pi n s / \pi n s$ of the original value.   This means that the variance contributed by the frequency n is reduced to $\sin^2 \pi n s / (\pi n s)^2$ of its original value.   The variation of this factor, shown in Fig. 1.5, is such that the variance contribution becomes very small when $n > 1/s$ i.e. when the periodic time $(1/n)$ of the component is less than s, and is virtually 100 per cent of the original value when the periodic time is greater than $10s$. Generalizing to the whole spectrum, the variance $\sigma^2_{\infty,s}$, obtained by averaging over time interval s and sampling for infinite time, is related to the whole variance $\sigma^2_{\infty,0}$, obtained with infinitesimal averaging time, by the equation

$$\sigma^2_{\infty,s} = \sigma^2_{\infty,0} \int_0^\infty F(n) \frac{\sin^2 \pi n s}{(\pi n s)^2} \, dn \qquad (1.25)$$

In effect the original spectrum is cut off by a weighting function of the shape shown in Fig. 1.5. As s is increased, and the curve is displaced to lower frequencies, more of the spectrum is cut off and $\sigma^2_{\infty,s}$ is reduced.

The complementary effect of sampling over a time τ while maintaining infinitesimal averaging time follows immediately from the definition of variance. Using the subscript notation introduced above for sampling and averaging

$$\sigma^2_{\infty,0} = \sigma^2_{\infty,\tau} + [\sigma^2_{\tau,0}]_\infty \qquad (1.26)$$

where the square bracket with subscript ∞ implies averaging the variances from consecutive periods τ over infinite time. Then by substituting for $\sigma^2_{\infty,\tau}$ the form equivalent to (1.25) equation (1.26) becomes

$$[\sigma^2_{\tau,0}]_\infty = \sigma^2_{\infty,0} - \sigma_{\infty,0} \int_0^\infty F(n) \frac{\sin^2 \pi n \tau}{(\pi n \tau)^2} \, dn \qquad (1.27)$$

and, remembering that by definition $\int_0^\infty F(n) \, dn = 1$, this may be written

$$[\sigma^2_{\tau,0}]_\infty = \sigma^2_{\infty,0} \int_0^\infty F(n) \left(1 - \frac{\sin^2 \pi n \tau}{(\pi n \tau)^2}\right) dn \qquad (1.28)$$

In other words if the fluctuating quantity is observed over time τ, the variance apparent in this sample will *on average* be equal to the variance of the whole spectrum modified by a function which has a shape complementary to that shown in Fig. 1.5. It is immediately evident that with a sampling duration τ contributions from a given frequency become small when the equivalent periodic time is greater than τ, and virtually 100 per cent when the periodic time is less than $\tau/10$. Correspondingly, as τ increases so also does the total variance.

The precise combined effect of averaging and sampling depends on the particular way in which averaging and sampling are applied. For the simple arrangement in which the data are averaged over consecutive intervals s, and sampled over consecutive intervals τ, each containing an integral number of intervals s, Eq. (1.26) applies when the zero averaging time is replaced by s.   From this and Eq. (1.25)

$$[\sigma^2_{\tau,s}]_\infty = \sigma^2_{\infty,0} \int_0^\infty F(n) \left(\frac{\sin^2 \pi n s}{(\pi n s)^2} - \frac{\sin^2 \pi n \tau}{(\pi n \tau)^2}\right) dn \qquad (1.29)$$

When τ/s is large equation (1.29) is the same as

$$[\sigma^2_{\tau,s}]_\infty = \sigma^2_{\infty,0} \int_0^\infty F(n) \left(1 - \frac{\sin^2 \pi n \tau}{(\pi n \tau)^2}\right) \frac{\sin^2 \pi n s}{(\pi n s)^2} dn \qquad (1.30)$$

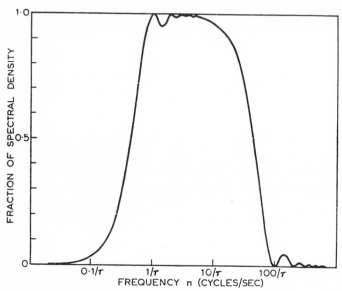

FIG. 1.6.   The *spectral window* equivalent to a sampling-duration τ and an averaging-time $\tau/100$

and the resultant weighting function is seen to be the product of the separate weighting functions for sampling and averaging.   Sampling and averaging for finite times may thus be regarded as equivalent to confining the observation of the spectrum to a *spectral window* of a form such as that shown in Fig. 1.6.   For example, if the spectrum is represented by plotting $nF(n)$ against $\log n$ the spectrum $nF(n) = $ constant would actually appear to have the shape given in this diagram.   This general aspect of the turbulence spectrum will be seen in later chapters to be particularly relevant to an appreciation of the diffusion processes.

In view of the intimate relation between the spectrum function and the correlation function there will be corresponding modifications of the latter, and indeed if it is accepted that the Fourier-transform procedure of Eq. (1.8) and (1.9) may be applied to the spectrum function modified as in (1.28) we have immediately:

$$[R(t)_\tau]_\infty = \int_0^\infty F(n)\left(1 - \frac{\sin^2 \pi n\tau}{(\pi n\tau)^2}\right)\cos 2\pi nt \, dn \qquad (1.31)$$

and

$$F(n)\left(1 - \frac{\sin^2 \pi n\tau}{(\pi n\tau)^2}\right) = 4\int_0^\infty [R(t)_\tau]_\infty \cos 2\pi nt \, dt \qquad (1.32)$$

where $[R(t)_\tau]_\infty$ is the average autocorrelation coefficient, at lag t, for finite sampling time τ. Using the modified spectrum function in (1.29) corresponding relations may be written for the case when both τ and s are finite. The result in (1.31) was derived by Ogura (1957) in the reverse manner, i.e. by forming the correlation function for a finite sampling time in terms of that for infinite sampling time, and then replacing the latter by the cosine-transform of $F(n)$. In comparing with Ogura's results it should be remembered that his correlation functions are actually *covariances* (i.e. formed from terms like $\overline{u'_1 u'_2}$), that his frequency is in radians/sec, and that his $F(n)$ is the absolute, not the fractional, contribution to the covariance. Taking these differences into account Ogura's equation (30) is identical with Eq. (1.31) above.

Ogura's analysis is of additional interest in showing that the correlation function satisfying (1.31) must be obtained by taking the velocities in the interval τ and combining *all* values with corresponding values at lag t, so that in fact the evaluation for sampling time τ requires a record of length $\tau+t$. Another noteworthy feature of Ogura's results is the relation between the variance for finite sampling time and the correlation function for infinite sampling time. In the present notation,

$$\sigma^2_{\infty,0} - [\sigma^2_{\tau,0}]_\infty = \frac{2\sigma^2_{\infty,0}}{\tau^2} \int_0^\tau (\tau - t) \, R(t)_\infty \, dt \qquad (1.33)$$

Since the left-hand side of Eq. (1.33) is equal to $\sigma^2_{\infty,\tau}$, i.e. the variance when the fluctuations are *averaged* over time τ, this equation is equivalent to Kampé de Fériet's form of the well-known Taylor equation involving Lagrangian correlation [see 3.4 and Eq. (3.41)]. A generalization of Eq. (1.33), taking into account the effect of first averaging the variable continuously over over-lapping periods s, has been derived by F. B. Smith in an unpublished analysis leading to Eq. (1.30). This form for $\sigma^2_{\tau,s}$, rather than Eq. (1.29), would therefore appear to be the correct form when a fluctuation is continuously averaged over s, and sampled over τ, in that order.

An equation similar to Eq. (1.33) has been obtained by Charnock and Robinson (1957) as a step in deriving a general form for the correlogram. For convenience the equation is multiplied by τ^2 and differentiated twice to give

$$\frac{1}{2} \frac{\partial^2}{\partial \tau^2} \left(\tau^2 [\sigma_{\tau,0}^2]_\infty / \sigma_{\infty,0}^2\right) = 1 - R(\tau)_\infty \qquad (1.34)$$

where $R(\tau)$ is the correlation coefficient for lag τ and infinite sampling time. Actually Charnock and Robinson's analysis is in terms of a finite series of discrete values. The fact that these values may be averages over some time interval has no effect on (1.33), provided σ and R are derived from the same values. Provided also that the length of the series is sufficient to give a constant value of the variance (i.e. effectively $\sigma_{\infty,0}^2$), then equation (6) in Charnock and Robinson's paper is exactly equivalent to (1.33) above.

A fundamental discussion of the effects of finite averaging time on the correlation properties of an effectively infinite record has been given by Kahn (1957). This leads to a *generalized average-correlation function* which is too cumbersome for practical use, but Kahn shows how the result can be used to derive special cases of practical value. Referring back to (1.34) it is interesting to note that Kahn's equations (38) and (34) lead to a relation for R, i.e.

$$\frac{1}{2} \frac{\partial^2}{\partial s^2} \left(s^2 \sigma_{\infty,s}^2 / \sigma_{\infty,0}^2\right) = R(s)_\infty \qquad (1.35)$$

Equations (1.34) and (1.35) are seen to be exactly complementary by putting $\tau = s$ and remembering that then (see Eq. (1.26))

$$\sigma_{\infty,s}^2 + [\sigma_{\tau,0}^2]_\infty = \sigma_{\infty,0}^2$$

Besides needing to be kept closely in mind, the effects of averaging time and sampling duration on the variance may actually be exploited, as for example in the next section. Furthermore, through Eq. (1.34) and (1.35) the correlogram may be obtained purely from calculations of variance, which are simpler than those of covariance. However, the advantage ultimately gained depends also on making satisfactory determinations of the second derivatives. In practice this may not be readily achievable graphically, but it may be possible to facilitate the process by obtaining suitable analytical approximations to the observed relation between variance and τ or s (e.g., see Charnock and Robinson, 1957).

1.5 Spectrum analysis of atmospheric turbulence

There are two important complications which arise in the analysis of atmospheric turbulence in contrast to turbulence in pipes and wind tunnels.

The first is that the atmospheric spectrum extends up to the large scales involved in the disturbances of the general circulation.   Consequently the statistical properties depend considerably on the sampling duration, and in many practical examples the variance and autocorrelation do not reach their respective constant or zero limiting values.   The second complication is that because of the effects of variable terrain, of diurnal heating and nocturnal cooling of the ground, and of the continually changing large-scale pattern of airflow, turbulence in the atmosphere is neither *homogeneous* nor *stationary*, i.e. the statistical properties depend also on the particular *place* and *time* at which the observations are made.   This feature is troublesome not only in the obvious sense that extensive observations are required before any representative description can be assembled, but also because the major developments in the theory of time-series analysis rely on the simplifying assumption that conditions are stationary.   This is particularly so, for example, in the case of the Fourier-transform relation between the autocorrelation and spectrum functions.   In this and other related aspects there are difficulties which have yet to be clarified and which are beyond the scope of this book.   In the meantime, as will be seen, the Fourier-transform method is used with various adjustments designed to eliminate gross error.

The methods by which a series of observations can be analysed to give a spectrum may be considered under four headings:

(a) Classical harmonic analysis.   (See for example Brooks and Carruthers, 1953).

(b) Numerical filter techniques.

(c) The use of electrical filters.

(d) The application of the Fourier-transform to the correlogram of the series.

(a) gives *periodogram* ordinates, corresponding to $I_1(n)$ and $I_2(n)$ in Eq. (1.5) for $N/2$ values of frequency, where N is the total number of observations. In practice adjacent ordinates are found to differ widely, and despite the already considerable numerical effort a reproducible smoothed spectrum is apparently not obtained without time-consuming smoothing procedures.

One of the simplest forms of (b) consists of applying different averaging times to the data.   From Fig. 1.5 this is equivalent (in electrical terms) to *low-pass* filtering with a cut-off at frequencies which are inversely proportional to the averaging time.   The difference in the variances obtained with two different averaging times s_1 and s_2 corresponds to a *spectral window*, the shape of which is obtained by subtracting the transmissions (i.e. the ordinates of Fig. 1.5) for the larger value of s from those for the smaller value.   For approximate purposes the total transmission through this window may be regarded as equivalent to 100 per cent transmission over the frequency range $0·44/s_1$ to $0·44/s_2$ (the frequencies for 50 per cent transmission through the separate filters).   A version of the technique has been used by Panofsky and McCormick (1952).   The complementary method, using different durations of sampling (i.e. *high-pass* filtering) has been employed by F. B. Smith (1961), the difference in variance for sampling durations τ_1 and τ_2 being assigned to the frequency band $0·44/\tau_1$ to $0·44/\tau_2$.   Departure of the filter shapes from an ideally sharp cut-off means that the spectrum obtained will be a distorted version, but certain broad features may be usefully and conveniently examined by these simple techniques. A 'sharpening' of the numerical filter to give a closer approach to a definite cut-off at a given frequency can be introduced by using suitably weighted averages, but the numerical work is then greatly increased and the procedure has apparently not been used in evaluating turbulence spectra.

Method (c), in which a continuous electrical signal representing the variable is fed into an electrical filter, is especially attractive in its avoidance of laborious extraction and computing processes.   However, for detailed resolution of the spectrum narrow band-pass filters with sharp cut-off characteristics are required.   In this case the electrical equipment is elaborate and intricate, especially when the low frequencies of atmospheric turbulence are concerned, and the method has not yet been widely adopted in this connection.   Examples of the use of this analogue computing technique have been described by McCready (1953a) and Businger and Suomi (1958), and it is noteworthy that in a later discussion Businger (1959) refers to the need frequently to test the accuracy of the results obtained.   If the requirement for sharp cut-off is relaxed, much simpler electrical filters may be used, yielding a resolution similar to that obtained by the simple numerical filter technique outlined above.   A combination of high-pass, electrical filtering of this quality, with high-pass numerical filtering by adopting specific sampling durations, is used in Smith's (1961) analysis. Further details of the simple electrical filter employed are given by Jones and Pasquill (1959, see also 2.7) in connection with an application in which electrical filters are actually used to represent the effect of specific sampling durations.

So far the method which has been used most widely is (d), especially with the increasing availability of automatic digital computing methods which facilitate the otherwise laborious process of deriving the auto-correlogram for large numbers of lags.   Moreover, there is the advantage (over (a)) that a relatively smoothed spectrum is obtained. One of the difficulties encountered in this method is that when very slow variations are contained in the velocity trace the autocorrelogram may retain a positive value over the range of lags employed. A formula for eliminating this effect has been given by Webb (1955). If the correlogram of the whole variation (fluctuation plus slow trend) is denoted by $R_q(t)$, and tends to a steady value R'_q at large t, the correlogram of the fluctuation alone is

$$R_s(t) \simeq \frac{R_q(t) - R'_q}{1 - R'_q} \tag{1.36}$$

The formula applies to the case of a linear trend, or more generally, to any slow variation uncorrelated with the relatively high-frequency fluctuation which it is required to analyse. The validity of applying it when the correlogram has reached a value which is not constant but merely diminishing very slowly, as may well occur with a wide continuous spectrum, has not been made clear. If it is applied in such a case it is presumably at least necessary that the spectrum from $R_s(t)$ should not be evaluated for frequencies lower than the reciprocal of the maximum lag.

The most comprehensive practical procedure which has yet been offered, for the Fourier-transform treatment of time-series of the type encountered in atmospheric turbulence measurements, is that developed by Tukey for the analysis of noise problems in electrical communications (Tukey 1949, Blackman and Tukey 1958). Summaries of the procedure in the present context have been given by Panofsky and McCormick (1954) and R. A. Jones (1957), and the outline which follows is based on the latter presentation. The method is intended to provide a realistic analysis of a finite series of discrete observations such as would be obtained by reading a velocity record at prescribed intervals. With N observations at intervals of time δt the first step is to form the covariances Q_k of the values X_i ($i = 1, 2, 3, \ldots, N$) for successive values of lag $k\delta t$, as follows,

$$Q_k = \frac{1}{N-k} \left[\sum_{i=1}^{N-k} X_i X_{i+k} - \frac{1}{N-k} \sum_{i=1}^{N-k} X_i \sum_{i=1}^{N-k} X_{i+k} \right] \quad k = 0, 1, \ldots, m \tag{1.37}$$

Since Q_k is known only at the $m+1$ specific lags it follows that the spectrum function is determined only for specific frequency bands centred at $n = 0, 1/2m\delta t, 2/2m\delta t, \ldots, 1/2\delta t$. The Fourier-transform equation (1.9) is accordingly evaluated in series form, with frequency n replaced by $h/2m\delta t$ and time-lag t by $k\delta t$, as follows:

$$L_0 = \frac{1}{2m}[Q_0 + Q_m] + \frac{1}{m}\sum_{k=1}^{m-1} Q_k$$

$$L_h = \frac{1}{m}Q_0 + \frac{2}{m}\sum_{k=1}^{m-1} Q_k \cos\frac{kh\pi}{m} + \frac{1}{m}Q_m \cos\pi h;$$

$$h = 1, 2, \ldots, (m-1) \qquad (1.38)$$

$$L_m = \frac{1}{2m}[Q_0 + (-1)^m Q_m] + \frac{1}{m}\left[\sum_{k=1}^{m-1} (-1)^k Q_k\right]$$

in which it is implicit that $\sum_{h=0}^{m} L_h$ is equal to Q_0, the variance of the series.

The quantities L_h are related to $F(n)$ by the equation

$$L_h = F(n)Q_0\Delta n \qquad (1.39)$$

the frequency-band width Δn being simply $1/2m\delta t$, except for the end values L_0, L_m, when it is $1/4m\delta t$. Experience has shown that additional smoothing of the results is necessary, by means of a 3-term weighted average as follows:

$$
\begin{aligned}
U_0 &= 0.54L_0 + 0.46L_1 \\
U_h &= 0.54L_h + 0.23(L_{h-1} + L_{h+1}) \quad \text{for } h = 1, 2, \ldots, (m-1) \\
U_m &= 0.54L_m + 0.46L_{m-1}
\end{aligned}
\qquad (1.40)
$$

These values of U_h are considered to be in effect averages of the spectral density $(F(n)Q_0)$ over overlapping frequency bands as illustrated in Fig. 1.7.

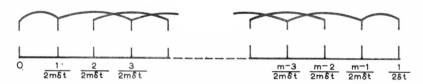

FIG. 1.7. Frequency-bands over which estimates of average spectral density are obtained from observations at intervals δt, following the procedure recommended by Tukey

The choice of number of lags is important. For resolution of the spectrum into narrow bands m should be as large as possible, but if it is too large the computational work involved may be prohibitive and, more important probably, the accuracy of the estimates decreases. Tukey suggests that m should be small enough in relation to N to make the number of degrees of freedom

$$f = \frac{2(N - m/4)}{m} \qquad (1.41)$$

satisfactorily large, and the values which have been commonly used are $6 < m < 30$ and $f > 30$. In round figures, if the number of lags is equal to $1/20$ of the N observations in a sample of duration τ, the spectrum is evaluated in $[(N/20) - 2]$ bands over the frequency range $10/\tau$ to $1/2\delta t$, and $f \simeq 40$. Assuming that the original data X_i have a Gaussian distribution the spectral estimates from different samples will have a χ^2/f distribution, and in the last example ($f = 40$) the 90 per cent confidence limits of the estimates will be 70 and 140 per cent of the values computed.

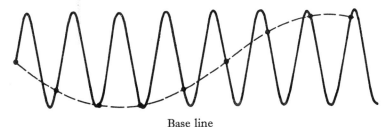

Base line

FIG. 1.8.   The *aliasing* of a high-frequency oscillation as a result of using discrete observations

The analysis amounts to subjecting the spectrum to band-pass filters which are imperfect in the sense of not having definite cut-offs, and an additional error is thereby introduced when the spectrum changes rapidly with frequency. To remedy this situation Tukey has suggested a *pre-whitening* procedure, by which the original time series is transformed to one not varying rapidly with frequency. For the case of a spectrum in which energy increases with decreasing frequency this procedure amounts to emphasizing the high-frequency fluctuations, and in practice is effected by the following linear transformation of X_i to a new series Y_i

$$Y_i = X_i - bX_{i-1} \qquad (1.42)$$

with b usually 0·75. The spectrum of the transformed series is evaluated as before, up to the stage of obtaining estimates V_h corresponding to U_h in Eq. (1.40), and the following reverse transformation

$$U_h = \frac{V_h}{1 + b^2 - 2b \cos (\pi h/m)} \qquad (1.43)$$

is then applied to give the estimates U_h appropriate to the original spectrum.

3—A.D.

Another source of error, known as *aliasing*, arises from the fact that with observations at discrete intervals the variations associated with a high frequency oscillation effectively appear at a lower frequency (see Fig. 1.8). This is reduced by making δt as small as possible, consistent with the averaging time of the observations, and by discarding the high-frequency end of the spectrum. It is also customary to apply a statistical correction for the effect of the finite averaging time s. From the previous discussion leading to Eq. (1.25) it follows that this is achieved by multiplying the spectral estimates by $(\pi ns)^2/\sin^2 \pi ns$.

2

The Statistics of Atmospheric Turbulence

Studies of turbulence in the atmosphere are complicated not only by the existence of a wide range of eddy sizes, but also by the thermal stratification of the atmosphere, as a result of which vertical motions tend to be augmented or suppressed by the buoyancy forces which are brought into play. Thus in any full analysis of atmospheric turbulence a knowledge of the conditions of stability is of fundamental importance. The specification of these conditions in terms of the vertical gradient of air temperature, alone or combined with the gradient of wind speed in the form of the Richardson number, is a standard feature of micrometeorological analysis (see Sutton, 1953, pp. 10, 61, 152) and no further introduction is needed here.

2.1 The historical development of measurements of atmospheric turbulence

The earliest systematic examination of data on wind fluctuations was provided by G. I. Taylor (1927) in his well-known study of the partition of eddy energy near the ground. This made use of the ribbon-like traces obtained with conventional wind speed and direction recorders, the semi-widths of the traces being taken to be extreme values of u' and $v'/\bar{u}$ respectively. From records referring to a height of 130 ft Taylor was able to demonstrate that the magnitudes of these components were approximately equal. With the addition of measurements of the vertical component from observations on the motion of a tethered balloon, it was further concluded that this equality applied to all three components, and hence that the turbulent motion not too close to the ground could be regarded as approximately isotropic. For investigations of the same feature much closer to the ground Taylor introduced the bi-directional vane. This differs from the conventional wind vane in having a universal pivot and a pair of fins set horizontally and vertically, and in being lighter and more responsive. The vane sets itself in the *vector* direction of the wind, and its vertical and lateral motion is traced out, by a pen hanging from the arm of the vane, on to a fixed vertical chart of cylindrical form. After the instrument has been operating for a short period the irregular tracing from the pen forms into a more or less compact ellipse or circle. The appropriate dimensions of the trace are taken as a measure of the magnitudes of $v'/\bar{u}$ and $w'/\bar{u}$, though, as in the analysis of the broad time-lapse trace from the conventional instrument, the precise specification and interpretation of the dimensions is in some doubt. In practice an oval is drawn enclosing all except the occasional very wide excursions of the pen, and the dimensions of this oval are measured. Observations taken with this type of instrument soon showed that in the first metre or so above ground the cross-wind component was usually much greater than the vertical component.

These observations were later greatly extended by Scrase (1930), and Best (1935), using bi-directional vanes and other instruments. Scrase's measurements were made in the first 20 m over open downland, with very small temperature gradient in the vertical and wind speeds usually greater than 3 m/sec, in which conditions buoyancy effects are negligible near the ground. One of the most important results was the demonstration of the close proportionality of the eddy components u', v', w' to the mean velocity $\bar{u}$. The components were found to be unequal at all heights, but for the vertical and lateral components there was a clear tendency for the inequality to decrease with height. The investigation included the first recorded attempt to obtain and analyse a high-speed time-lapse measurement of the turbulent components in the atmosphere. Although the sample of data was small it did give a clear indication of the existence of fluctuations with frequencies of 1 cycle/sec and more. From these and other data on a coarser scale the existence of a wide spectrum of eddies was apparent.

An important consequence of the wide spectrum is seen in the variation of the size of the bi-directional vane traces with the duration of the recording (see Fig. 2.1). There is a systematic growth of the trace, though the increase is rapid only in the first minute or two, and this led to the adoption of three minutes as a standard duration which could be expected to give a fairly complete measurement, at least in so-called steady winds. In relation to the previous discussion of the effects of *sampling* duration (see 1.4) it follows that most of the energy represented in these measurements came from frequencies of oscillation greater than about 0·01 cycles/sec. However, from the continued slow increase of the trace up to at least eight minutes it is evident that much lower frequencies were also present to some degree.

Best's measurements were concentrated on a lower range of heights, and were extended into conditions of appreciable temperature gradient in the vertical. They demonstrated the important role of thermal instability and stability in respectively increasing and decreasing the components of the intensity of turbulence, especially in light winds. Furthermore, measurements of much greater reliability than those obtained with the recording bi-directional vane were made at a number of heights with a hot wire anemometer. This was arranged (with the element vertical) to give

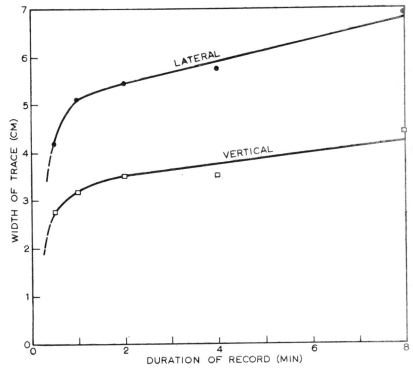

Fig. 2.1   Variation of the size of a bi-directional-vane trace with the duration of recording. Mean figures from two series of observation at a height of 2 m. (Scrase, 1930) (from *Meteorological Office Geophysical Memoirs No. 52*, *H.M.S.O.* Crown Copyright Reserved)

a close approximation to u', the component in the direction of the mean wind. Readings at 10-second intervals over a period of three minutes were used to evaluate mean deviations $\overline{|u'|}$. These results gave a fairly clear indication that the influence of stability and instability diminishes systematically with increasing wind speed and decreasing height. They also provided data on the probability distribution of the magnitude of the wind fluctuation, which will be summarized later with other similar data.

Best's investigation resulted in a very detailed description of the relative magnitudes, and variation with height, of the three components in the first 5 m above the surface, but the interpretation is complicated by the uncertain meaning of the values deduced from the bi-directional vane records. Moreover, as regards the variation with height the results are somewhat different from those previously obtained by Scrase. It is possible that this is partly a consequence of the different durations of recording which were employed (Scrase 1 min, Best 3 min).

At about the same time as Scrase's investigation of the fine structure of atmospheric turbulence, an examination on a rather larger scale was undertaken by Giblett and others (1932), in relation to the effects of wind-gusts on airships. This employed the conventional patterns of wind speed and wind direction recorders, with certain improvements introduced specially for the purpose, including provision for driving the charts at higher speeds so that the trace was drawn out into a single line from which definite readings could be taken at close intervals. Three sets of instruments were set up, at a height of 50 ft, at the corners of an equilateral triangle of side 700 ft, and a fourth set was placed in the middle of one side. A detailed study was made of the response of the instruments, and it was concluded that if the records were averaged over five seconds or more the effects of the inertia and resonance would be virtually eliminated.

From a qualitative examination of the records obtained it was concluded that the turbulence could be classified into four broad types, according to the general degree of thermal stability existing. The classification was of particular interest in containing the recognition not only that the amplitudes of the fluctuations increased with a change from stable to unstable conditions, but that the frequencies of the oscillations tended to decrease. The extreme cases were represented by conditions with cumulo-nimbus clouds, when the wind traces showed predominant large gusts at comparatively wide intervals, and clear-sky conditions at night, when any fluctuations which occurred were relatively small and rapid. In the former case the eddies were clearly of large scale, and thermal in origin, while in the latter they were relatively small and of mechanical origin.

A more quantitative expression of the 'quick-run' records was provided in the form of correlation analyses, examples of which are shown in Fig. 2.2 and 2.3. The first of these shows autocorrelations for both speed and direction, for time lags up to 60 and 40 seconds respectively. In the terms of the earlier discussion of the correlogram in 1.2 the initial decay of correlation implies an important scale of turbulence corresponding to about 10 seconds, which at the wind speed prevailing corresponds to 150 metres, but from the subsequent decrease of the speed correlation to a negative minimum at 50 seconds it was concluded that there was a pattern in the wind tending to repeat itself in about 100 seconds or 1500 metres.   Fig. 2.3 shows *cross-correlograms* of wind speed from pairs of instruments in line with the direction of the mean wind.   The two curves refer to the correlation between instrument C and instrument D separated by 350 ft, and between C and B separated by 700 ft.   The interesting feature is that the

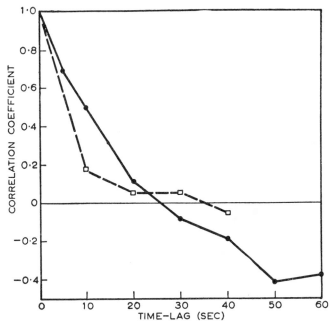

FIG. 2.2   Autocorrelations of wind speed (●) and direction (□) at a height of 50 ft.   Sampling-duration 10 min, averaging-time 5 sec; $u = 34$ miles/hr. (Giblett *et al.*, 1932)

interpolated maxima of the curves were estimated to be at 8 and 16 seconds time-lag respectively, and as the time taken to travel at the mean wind speed was $8\frac{1}{2}$ seconds from C to D, and 17 seconds from C to B, there seemed to be a clear indication of a pattern of motion travelling at approximately the mean wind speed.

Despite the lead provided by Taylor's theoretical work, and the promise contained in the investigation just described, the evolution to a detailed systematic study of the *structure* of atmospheric turbulence did not follow rapidly.   Progress was inhibited at first, not by any lack of recognition of the need, but by the sheer difficulty of recording the data in a suitable form and of dealing with the enormous volume of computing work entailed. With the removal of much of these difficulties by modern recording and computing techniques the subject has advanced fairly rapidly since about 1950.

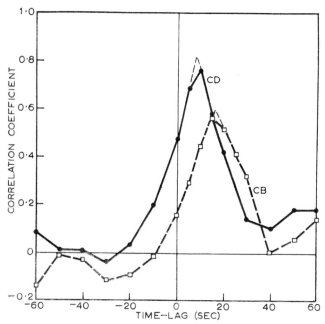

FIG. 2.3   Cross-correlations of wind speeds from anemometers spaced along the mean wind.   Separations 350 ft (● CD), 700 ft (▢ CB); sampling-duration 7½ min; averaging-time 5 sec; $u = 28$ miles/hr.   (Giblett et al., 1932) (from *Meteorological Office Geophysical Memoirs No. 54, H.M.S.O.*   Crown Copyright Reserved)

2.2   The broad features of 'time spectra' in the lower atmosphere

A major introduction to the knowledge of turbulence spectra in the first 100 metres of the atmosphere has been provided by Panofsky and his co-workers, using the observations made at the Brookhaven National Laboratory since 1951.   This laboratory is situated in slightly-rolling wooded country on Long Island, New York.   The records consisted of time-lapse traces of wind speed, direction and inclination, from instruments with free periods approximately $10/\bar{u}$ seconds, where $\bar{u}$ is the speed in m/sec. Samples of duration about an hour were employed, and, in keeping with the response characteristics of the instruments, averages over 5 or 10 seconds, estimated by eye from the traces, were used as the basic data.

A preliminary analysis of some of these data was carried out by the moving-average technique described by Panofsky and McCormick (1952). Panofsky (1953) applied this to single samples of the vertical component at 23 and 91 metres, and demonstrated that the energy contributions of the high-frequency components in the spectrum decreased with height, while those of the low-frequency components increased. This result was not unexpected, in view of the effect of the ground in restricting vertical motion. A more detailed study of all three components at 91 metres, using a total of fifteen samples, was later provided by McCormick (1954). The analysis included the estimation of the energy contributions in three broad bands of frequency centred roughly on 1, 0·15 and 0·02 cycles/min. In the low-frequency and medium-frequency bands the energies of the horizontal components (especially that along the mean wind) were substantially greater than that of the vertical component, but there seemed to be a definite trend towards equipartition in the high-frequency band.

For the subsequent and more detailed analysis of the Brookhaven data the relatively crude method was abandoned in favour of the Fourier-transform approach, the detailed procedure recommended by Tukey being followed (see 1.5). However, although the more elaborate analysis provides finer resolution, individual spectra differ one from another, and generally speaking a consistent picture usually emerges only from composite spectra in which several results in similar conditions have been averaged.

Panofsky and McCormick (1954) have given an account of such an analysis, using twenty samples of the w and u components at a height of 91 m. The quantity evaluated was the absolute spectral density $S(n)$ $(= \overline{w'^2}F(n)$, etc.) in units m^2/sec^2 per unit range of frequency, but this was then converted to $nS(n)$, which is referred to as the *logarithmic spectral density* (since the integral with respect to $\log_e n$ is equal to the total variance —see Eq. (1.12). Following the customary assumption that one of the effects of wind speed is to increase the apparent frequencies in proportion, they also introduced the *reduced frequency*

$$f = nz/\bar{u}$$

the height z being inserted to make the quantity non-dimensional. The reduced frequency may thus be regarded as the ratio of the height to the *equivalent wavelength* of the spectral component, and to the real *wavelength* if it can be further assumed that the spatial field of turbulence is unaltered as it moves past the measuring point [see Eq. (1.4)]. From the earlier observations of turbulence (Scrase 1930) it was already to be anticipated that the energy of the mechanical turbulence would increase in proportion to the square of the wind speed, and this type of variation was found to be supported by the logarithmic spectral densities at a fixed high value of f (0.8). The results are shown in Fig. 2.4. As pointed out by Panofsky and McCormick the deviations from the linear relation did not seem to be related in any systematic way to the atmospheric stability as represented by measured values of the incoming solar radiation. On the other hand, it was found that the spectra of the vertical component contained fairly well-defined maxima, at reduced frequencies which showed a tendency to decrease with increasing radiation. These two results suggested that the

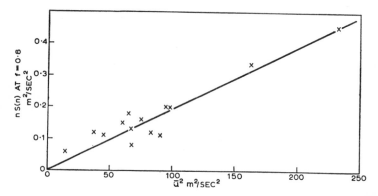

FIG. 2.4 Logarithmic spectral density of the vertical component, for a reduced frequency f of 0·8, as a function of wind speed, at a height of 91 m. (Panofsky and McCormick, 1954)

spectra could be profitably examined by grouping the individual members into radiation classes, and dividing the average spectral estimates for each class by the square of the mean wind speed for the class. The procedure was applied to the spectra of the u-component also, and the resulting composite spectra are shown in Fig. 2.5 and 2.6, for values of f between 1 and 0·05, corresponding to frequencies in the range 3 to 0·15 cycles/min. The groups (a), (b) and (c) refer to incoming radiation $\geqslant 1·0$, 0·3–0·9 and $\leqslant 0·2$ cal cm^{-2} min^{-1} respectively.

The general features which stand out in Fig. 2.5 and 2.6 are as follows:

(i) At high frequencies the spectra are approximately independent of radiation (i.e. of stability), implying that the turbulence here is purely of the mechanically-induced type.

(ii) At low frequencies the spectral density increases with increasing radiation, implying that thermally-induced modifications of the turbulence appear only at a relatively large scale.

(iii) With increasing radiation the reduced frequency for maximum logarithmic spectral density decreases, i.e. the *equivalent wavelength* increases.

A few additional results for the vertical component at heights of 23 and 46 m, in unstable conditions, suggested that the predominant reduced

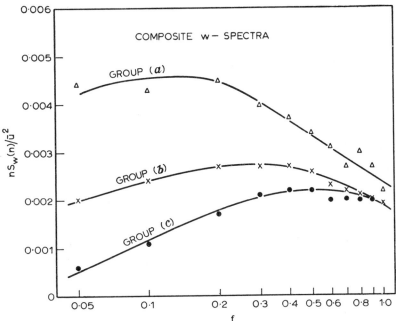

FIG. 2.5   Composite logarithmic spectra of the vertical component of eddy velocity at a height of 91 m.   Data groups correspond to incoming radiation: (a) $\geqslant 1.0$; (b) 0.3–0.9; (c) $\leqslant 0.2$ cal cm^{-2} min^{-1}.   (Panofsky and McCormick, 1954)

frequency [i.e. that with maximum $nS(n)$] was approximately independent of height, implying that the actual frequency was proportional to u/z, or that the equivalent wavelength was proportional to z.   These results have been substantially confirmed and extended by Panofsky and his co-workers, and a complete review of this work, including reference to the spectrum of the lateral (v) component, has been given by Panofsky and Deland (1959).

Panofsky and Van der Hoven (1955) have given a separate account of an extended analysis of the *u*-component, using longer samples to give a spectrum at much lower frequencies. To reduce the numerical work to reasonable proportions the spectrum was derived in sections, using increased averaging times in conjunction with increased sampling times. Details of the method are given by Griffiths, Panofsky and Van der Hoven (1956). The results suggested the existence of a 'gap' in the spectrum near periods of the order of an hour, separating a *micrometeorological* range from a *mesometeorological* range, but as the authors emphasized, the conclusion was rather tentative. A wide-range spectrum of surface wind

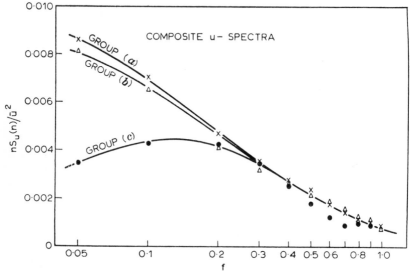

FIG. 2.6 Composite logarithmic spectra of the eddy component along the mean wind direction. Data groups as in Fig. 2.5. (Panofsky and McCormick, 1954)

speed, composed by Bushnell and Huss (1958) using an averaging technique, shows no sign of this gap.

A useful general discussion of autocorrelations and spectra at lower heights has been given by Webb (1955), using data for the along-wind and vertical components. The observations were made over a flat grassland site in Victoria, Australia, using hot-wire anemometers and critically damped galvanometers of free period 2·3 sec. The traces were recorded photographically, in samples of 5-min duration, eight being obtained at a height of 29 m and three .at 1·9 m. Autocorrelations were evaluated directly from the photographic records, using a differential analyser built specially for this kind of analysis. The Fourier-transform was then applied to give the energy spectra, by using an integral approximation formula, or by fitting a standard function (usually exponential) to the correlogram and treating any departure from this separately by a graphical process.   Apparently it was usually unnecessary to evaluate the correlograms beyond lags of 45 seconds.   It is noteworthy that the spectra reproduced in Webb's paper extended to frequencies as low as 0·1 cycles/min, which is much lower than would be permitted for a sampling time of 5 min in the procedure recommended by Tukey.   By applying the correction for finite sampling time as stated in Eq. (1.28) to one example Webb argues that the effect on the spectrum is negligible, but this does not alter the fact that by Tukey's criterion the statistical accuracy at these low frequencies is poor.

Webb's spectra have the same general shape as those of Panofsky *et al.* The characteristics listed include the frequency n_m at which the $nF(n)$ curves show major peaks, and the equivalent scale of turbulence, l, as given by the product of the integral of the autocorrelogram and the mean wind speed.   For correlograms of exponential form [Eq. (1.10) *et seq.*], n_m and l are related by

$$l = \bar{u}/2\pi n_m$$

In Webb's results this is usually satisfied within 20 per cent, and it is also evident that l is usually given within 30 per cent by the lag (times wind speed) at which the autocorrelogram falls to $1/e$.   This means that a useful estimate of spectrum characteristics might often be made merely by inspecting the correlogram for an approximate value of the area or of the time to fall to $1/e$.

Webb examined the values of the scale derived from the low-frequency peaks of the 29-m spectra (l_m in his paper) against stability as represented by the Richardson number Ri at a height of 1·5 m.   The main point to be noted is a tendency for the scale to increase at first with decreasing Ri, in agreement with Panofsky's results, but then to decrease for values of Ri less than about $-0·05$.   Webb suggested that the reversal was possibly associated with the transition from predominantly *forced convection* to predominantly *free convection*, a transition which has been discussed by Priestley (1955) in relation to observations on the vertical flux of heat. There is no indication of a similar reversal in the grouped results of Panofsky and McCormick, and a possible explanation of this lies in the fact that from such estimates as can be made from their data the corresponding negative values of $Ri_{1.5}$ were generally smaller than 0·05.   On the other hand, an analysis by F. B. Smith (1961), of data on the vertical component at a height of about 300 m, includes a case in which an increase of intensity of turbulence during the day, presumably as a result of increasing convection, was associated with a decrease of scale.   However, more data are required before this reduction in scale in very unstable conditions can be regarded as firmly established.

The examples given above serve to show that through spectrum analysis the earlier and vaguer notions about the structure of atmospheric turbulence, and its variations with height and stability, can be developed in a more coherent fashion.   More detailed consideration will now be given to a number of features of the structure which are particularly relevant to the theoretical and practical problems of diffusion dealt with later.

2.3   The relation between 'time' and 'space' properties

Although some aspects of the diffusion problem can be treated without specific reference to the spatial variations, other than that which is involved in the requirement of homogeneity in a statistical sense, there are aspects which require consideration of the *sizes* of the turbulent components as expressed in the wave-number spectrum, in contrast to the frequency

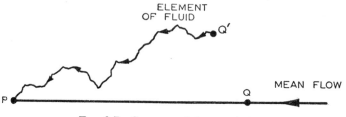

FIG. 2.7   Space- and time-variation

spectrum recently discussed.   In the first chapter it was seen that an equivalence of the variations in space (fixed time) and in time (fixed point), through the simple transformation $x = \bar{u}t$, was implied in measurements of wind tunnel turbulence.   This assumption is usually expressed in the statement that the spatial pattern of turbulence is unchanged as it is swept past the fixed measuring point at the speed of the mean wind.   Its significance can also be usefully analysed by the following elementary considerations of the variations in a two-dimensional flow (Fig. 2.7).

If the eddy velocities at points P and Q, separated by distance x in the direction of the mean flow, are u_1 and u_2, the quantity of fundamental interest in the space structure is $\overline{u_1 u_2}$.   In the statistical sense of this mean product the assumption above means that u_2 can be replaced by u_3, where the latter is measured at P at time $x/\bar{u}$ after the measurement of u_1.   This velocity u_3 will in fact refer to an element of fluid which originated at a point Q'. The statistical effect of u_3 will differ from that of u_2 in two ways, firstly owing to the separation of Q' from Q, which will have a probability distribution of magnitude dependent on $\sqrt{(\overline{u'^2})}$, and secondly owing to the *Lagrangian* variations of the fluid element in travelling from Q' to P. Obviously the difference will be less the smaller $\sqrt{(\overline{u'^2})}$ and the larger $\bar{u}$, and indeed the assumption as stated by Taylor was confined to cases of small $\sqrt{(\overline{u'^2})}/\bar{u}$, which are the normal rule in wind tunnel turbulence.

In the atmosphere the intensity of turbulence as expressed in ratios of this form is often greater than 0·1, and the validity of the space-time transformation is not obvious. A theoretical examination of the problem has been given by Ogura (1953). The starting point is the expression of the velocity fluctuation as a Fourier integral

$$u(x, t) = \frac{1}{2\pi} \int \Phi(\kappa) \exp i \left[\kappa(x - \bar{u}t) - n_{11}t \right] d\kappa \qquad (2.1)$$

$$= \frac{1}{2\pi} \int \Phi(\kappa) \exp i \left[\kappa x - (n_1 + n_{11})t \right] d\kappa \qquad (2.2)$$

where κ is wave-number, $\Phi(\kappa)$ is an amplitude function, the remaining symbols have their customary meaning, and $n_1 = \kappa \bar{u}$. This frequency n_1 thus represents the effect of translation of the field of turbulence, while n_{11} represents the Lagrangian variation, i.e. the decay and rebuilding of the turbulence with time following the motion. By assuming a general interpolation formula for the form of the wave-number spectrum, and expressing n_{11} in a hypothetical form involving the wave-number and the turbulent energy contained in all higher wave-numbers, Ogura obtains an expression for the time-correlation function in terms of the spectrum and the intensity of turbulence, $i = \sqrt{(\overline{u'^2})}/\bar{u}$. On simplifying this for extreme cases it is shown that the space and time correlation functions $R(x)$ and $R(t)$ are identical (with the transformation $x = \bar{u}t$) for $i \ll 1$, but different for $i \gg 1$. Gifford (1956) has extended Ogura's analysis to unrestricted values of the intensity of turbulence, and in the limiting case of small time-lag shows that the equivalence of the correlation functions is satisfactorily close when $i \leqslant 1$. These analyses are rather involved and, returning to the elementary considerations of Fig. 2.7, they do not obviously take into account the effect of the statistical separation between Q and Q'.

The earliest observational data on this feature in the atmosphere are contained in the wind structure observations made at Cardington (Giblett *et al.* 1932). Reference has already been made in 2.1 to the quality of these measurements, and to the indications of wind-variation patterns travelling with the speed of the mean wind. In addition the detailed correlation results provide a few examples of simultaneous autocorrelations and space-correlations from two or more instruments in line, or approximately so, with the mean wind.   The latter are not space-correlations in the strictest sense of the word, since they are based on serial values at a particular pair of points rather than on velocities measured at a large number of pairs of points, but they represent the only practicable type of space-correlation. The space-correlations $R(x)$ are compared in Table 2.I with interpolated auto-correlations $R(t)$ for $t = x/u$.   Interpolation of the value in parenthesis is rather doubtful.   The agreement is poor for the wind speed correlations. Values of $\sqrt{(\overline{u'^2})}/\bar{u}$ are not given, but from an inspection of the tabulated serial values it is clear that they were approximately 0·05.

Table 2.I

Space and time correlation from the data of Giblett *et al.* (1932) on wind speed (u) and direction (θ)

Run No.	Element	x(m)	$R(x)$	$R(t)$ $(t = x/\bar{u})$
371	u	107	0·47	0·59
	u	214	0·16	0·39
391	u	107	0·27	0·60
	θ	107	0·27	(0·32)
	θ	214	0·08	0·11

An introduction to a particularly interesting type of comparison has been reported by Gifford (1956).   This uses the spectra of the vertical component computed from simultaneous (aerovane-bivane) wind measurements at a height of 91 m at Brookhaven, and accelerometer records obtained during the flight of an aeroplane, over the Brookhaven area, at approximately the same height.   The results are shown in Fig. 2.8, reproduced from Gifford's paper.   If the space-time transformation is valid, these spectra should be identical in shape but with corresponding features occurring at respective frequencies in the ratio of the mean wind speed to the airspeed of the flight.   The correspondence in shape is obvious, and the broad peaks occurring at 360 cycles/hr (aeroplane) and 42 cycles/hr (fixed point) are remarkably consistent with the respective airspeeds of 57 and 5·5 m/sec.   The intensity of turbulence is not given.

A more extensive comparison of tower and aeroplane data has been included by Lappe, Davidson and Notess (1959) in a 'tri-tower' study based on Brookhaven (Long Island), Peekskill (New York) and Round Hill

Field Station (Massachusetts). In these cases the velocity components in the aeroplane data were based on actual airspeed measurements using a differential pressure tube arrangement, corrections being made for the motion of the aeroplane with respect to the ground. Comparative wave-number spectra of the vertical and head-on components, obtained by applying the space-time transformation to time-spectra computed using a form of Tukey's technique, were derived from experiments on two days at Brookhaven and Peekskill. Wind speeds were near 6 m/sec on one day, 11–14 m/sec on the other. The authors concluded that the tower and

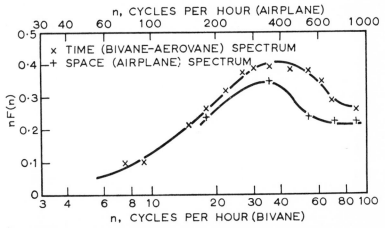

FIG. 2.8   Energy spectra of space and time vertical velocity fluctuations at 300 ft. above surface, obtained at Brookhaven National Laboratory. Note that top abscissa scale applies to airplane data only, and bottom abscissa scale to bivane-*Aerovane* date. (Gifford, 1956)

aeroplane spectra were in approximate agreement for the higher wave-numbers evaluated, i.e. 0·01 to 0·05 rad/ft. At lower wave-numbers the tower data indicated lower spectral densities than the aeroplane data; some of the differences appeared to be consistent with the difference in the precise heights at which the turbulence was sampled, but no over-all explanation was available.

It is particularly noteworthy that as a preliminary to the above compari-son Lappe *et al.* examined spectra obtained on repeated aeroplane runs on the same track and on different tracks. For the relatively homogeneous terrain in the Brookhaven area it was concluded that the turbulence was apparently homogeneous, and also isotropic with respect to rotation of the flight track about a vertical axis. Over the less homogeneous terrain near Peekskill considerable variations with the track of the flight were found.

For conditions closer to the ground the most detailed examination to be reported so far comes from Panofsky, Cramer and Rao (1958). This is based on longitudinal and lateral components measured at a height of 2 m above the ground during an extensive programme of diffusion experiments on smooth unobstructed grassland at O'Neill, Nebraska. A description of the instruments, comprising sensitive bivanes and heated thermocouple

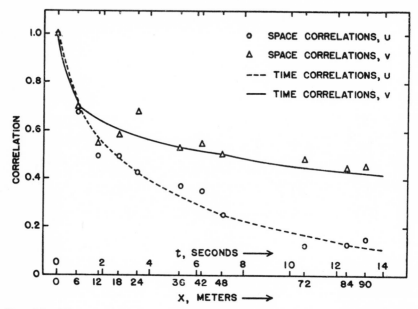

FIG. 2.9   Time- and space-correlograms at a height of 2 m.   (Panofsky *et al.*, 1958, Run 6)

anemometers, providing time-lapse traces of the speed, direction and inclination of the wind, has been given by Cramer, Record and Vaughan (1958). Five sets of instruments were set up on a fixed line, and the data considered here refer to occasions when the mean wind direction was within 10° of the line. Each record was maintained for a period of 20 min and the values were extracted at 1-sec intervals. From the time-spectra computed from simultaneous runs at the various positions it was concluded that the turbulence was sufficiently homogeneous for a test of the space-time relation.

Fig. 2.9 shows a comparison of the two correlations for one of the runs (Run 6), and the data for three other runs are given in Table 2.II, the transformation $x = \bar{u}t$ being applied.   The time-correlations are averages for the five instruments in each case, and on that account show less scatter from a smooth curve than do the space-correlations.   The mean wind speed ranged from 2·2 m/sec in Run 32 to 6·7 m/sec in Run 6, the 'level of turbulence' (presumably the intensity i as previously defined) from 0·16 (Run 6) to 0·26 (Run 32).   A convincing over-all degree of agreement is shown, and Panofsky *et al.* conclude from this that Taylor's hypothesis is valid over the range of distances studied at O'Neill, for intensities of turbulence as large as 0·26.

Table 2.II

Space-correlation, $R(x)$, and interpolated time-correlation, $R(t)$, where $t = x/\bar{u}$, from instruments set out along the wind direction.   (After Panofsky, Cramer and Rao, 1958)

	Run 17				Run 21				Run 32			
	u		v		u		v		u		v	
x, m	$R(x)$	$R(t)$	$R(x)$	$R(t)$	$R(x)$	$R(t)$	$R(x)$	$R(t)$	$R(x)$	$R(t)$	$R(x)$	$R(t)$
6	0·55	0·59	0·16	0·25	0·81	0·81	0·45	0·49	0·86	0·87	0·09	0·15
12	0·42	0·43	0·06	0·14	0·71	0·70	0·39	0·38	0·85	0·84	0·15	0·13
18	0·29	0·33	0·14	0·10	0·63	0·64	0·33	0·32	0·87	0·83	0·13	0·13
24	0·27	0·27	0·08	0·08	0·53	0·58	0·31	0·29	0·85	0·83	0·13	0·14
36	0·18	0·18	0·07	0·07	0·49	0·51	0·24	0·24	0·83	0·83	0·07	0·12
42	0·12	0·14	0·08	0·07	0·48	0·49	0·20	0·22	0·83	0·83	0·12	0·11
48	0·14	0·11	0·10	0·06	0·44	0·46	0·29	0·21	0·83	0·82	0·10	0·10
72	0·07	0·07	0·10	0·05	0·36	0·40	0·24	0·20	0·85	0·82	0·04	0·05
84	0·05	0·05	0·16	0·04	0·37	0·39	0·20	0·18	0·83	0·82	0·07	0·06
90	0·05	0·05	0·24	0·04	0·38	0·39	0·26	0·17	0·85	0·72	0·09	0·07

Other indirect evidence in support of this conclusion is provided in the studies of the small-scale structure of atmospheric turbulence discussed in the next section.   Obviously a good many more observations will be required to establish the quality and range of validity of the space-time relationship, but on the whole the data already available at least provide some justification for its use as an approximate working basis.

2.4   Specific forms of the correlogram and energy spectrum

Reference has already been made to the empirical indications of a roughly exponential shape in the autocorrelograms for atmospheric turbulence, implying an energy spectrum of the form given in Eq. (1.11).   This simple form may sometimes be convenient in the analytical treatment of diffusion, and for this reason alone its adoption as a working approximation may be justifiable.   Also, in the analysis of turbulence data from measurements made during aeroplane flights (e.g. see Lappe *et al.* 1959), a form equivalent to Eq. (1.11) has been adopted for the longitudinal spectrum. Assuming isotropic turbulence the corresponding transverse spectrum, which would be appropriate to the vertical component of turbulence as observed during level flight, is given by substituting Eq. (1.11) for $F(n)_{long}$ in Eq. (1.16).

We now consider in more detail the progress which has been made towards the establishment of functional and explicit forms, in two particular respects. The first is concerned with the high-frequency end of the spectrum, where the Kolmogoroff universal equilibrium theory might be expected to apply, the second with empirically-based generalizations about the whole spectrum of the *vertical* component near the ground. As regards the shapes of the whole spectra for the horizontal components, the generalizations which have so far been made have already been noted briefly in 2.2.

The high-frequency section of the spectrum of atmospheric turbulence

As already stated in 1.3, the universal equilibrium theory leads to predictions of the forms of the correlogram and spectrum in the *inertial sub-range* of eddies. These functional forms are given in Eq. (1.18) and (1.19). They are commonly referred to as the 'two-thirds' and 'minus five-thirds' laws respectively, and have been found to hold for the types of turbulence studied in the laboratory. As regards atmospheric turbulence, Batchelor (1950) suggested at an early stage that the inertial sub-range might be expected to exist over an important range of eddy sizes, perhaps extending to 100 m or more in wavelength in the atmosphere well away from the ground. In the lower layers, however, the physical restriction imposed by the ground will ensure that the upper limit of the range is considerably less than this.

Before considering the evidence provided by the measurements of atmospheric turbulence it should be recalled that while the 'two-thirds' law is a consequence of the condition of *local isotropy*, the observation of such a form in the correlogram, or of its counterpart in the spectrum, does not prove the existence of isotropy. It is also necessary that the intensities of the orthogonal components should be appropriately related, and that the virtual stresses associated with pairs of the components should be zero. As regards the intensities, the spectral densities are the relevant quantities here, and as pointed out in 1.3 these are only *equal* in locally isotropic turbulence where the spectrum is described in the same sense for each component, i.e. in either the longitudinal or transverse sense. However, the existence of isotropy is frequently conjectured on the grounds of spectral or correlogram shape alone, and it is then necessary to be cautious in accepting the upper wavelength limit of the 'minus five-thirds' region in the spectrum as truly an upper limit for isotropy. The limit so obtained may be an overestimate in two ways.

In the first place, if there is an input of turbulent energy at some intermediate scale, as for example in the case of convection near the ground, then the energy equilibrium conditions as postulated in the Kolmogoroff theory no longer apply in this region of the spectrum. Nevertheless, it is already at least qualitatively evident, from spectra such as those shown in Fig. 2.5 and 2.6, that convectively-induced turbulence extends the region in which energy decreases rapidly with increasing frequency, and hence possibly the range over which a 'minus five-thirds' power applies. In the second place, it has recently been argued theoretically by Gifford (1959a) that a substantial overestimation of the upper limit of isotropic wavelengths arises from the process of measurement, in that the variations in space are observed effectively one-dimensionally (e.g. along the mean direction of flow in the case of the usual observation at a single point). The essential point is most easily appreciated by considering a two-dimensional system of waves of constant wavelength with the displacements in, say, the x, z plane, and the crests parallel to the y axis. As long as the displacements are observed in the obviously correct way, i.e. in the x, z plane, they will appear to be associated with the correct wavelength λ. However, observed in any other plane through the z axis they will obviously appear to be associated with a wavelength greater than λ. It follows that, in a one-dimensional observation of a three-dimensional spectrum, part of the energy at a given *real* wave-number ($1/\lambda$) will be associated with an apparently smaller wave-number. Gifford has analysed this point in more formal terms, and ultimately considers an interpolation formula, due to Ogura, for the three-dimensional spectrum, as follows

$$E(\kappa) = \kappa/(1+\kappa^2)^{4/3} \qquad (2.3)$$

This form, shown in Fig. 2.10, follows the minus five-thirds form for large κ, and departs from it noticeably only when $\kappa < 3$ say. Using a formula due to Batchelor, Gifford then obtains the corresponding one-dimensional spectrum, also shown in Fig. 2.10, from which it is clear that a similar agreement with the five-thirds law now occurs down to $\kappa \simeq 1$.

For the atmosphere near the ground a direct test of the applicability of the 'two-thirds' correlation law, in terms of actual space variations, was reported by Obukhov in 1951, and this work has more recently been summarised by Obukhov and Yaglom (1959) in a general review of the work in the U.S.S.R. in this field since about 1942. Their discussion is in terms of a *structure function* which in the present notation may be written

$$D_{\text{trans}} = \overline{(u_1 - u_2)^2} \qquad (2.4)$$

where u_1, u_2 refer to simultaneous wind velocities at points separated by a

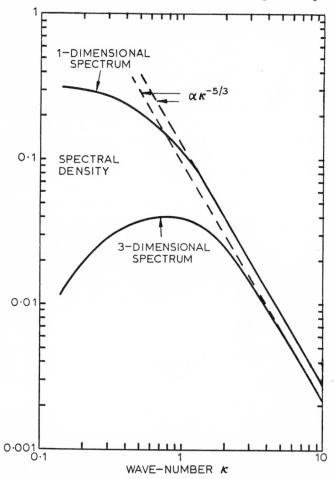

FIG. 2.10   The range of the ' $-5/3$ law' in a three-dimensional spectrum, and in its corresponding one-dimensional form.   (Gifford, 1959a)

distance y normal to the mean wind direction (hence the function is transverse.   See 1.3).   It is easily seen that

$$D_{\text{trans}} = 2\overline{u'^2}(1 - R(y))$$

where $R(y)$ is a transverse correlation coefficient defined as in Eq. (1.2), but with the longitudinal (x) separation replaced by a transverse (y) separation.   On the universal equilibrium theory the form for D_{trans} (the counterpart of Eq. (1.17)) is

$$D_{\text{trans}} = C\epsilon^{2/3}y^{2/3} \qquad (2.5)$$

where C is a non-dimensional constant of order unity.   In the steady state, and in neutral conditions of stability, the rate of dissipation of turbulent kinetic energy is taken equal to its rate of provision from the mean motion, through the horizontal shearing stress.   Therefore near the ground the rate of dissipation per unit mass of air is

$$\epsilon = u_*^2 \frac{du}{dz} = u_*^3/kz \qquad (2.6)$$

where u_* is the *friction velocity* and k is von Karman's constant (a well-known result, for which see Sutton, 1953, pp. 152 and 232).   It then follows that

$$D_{\text{trans}} = C\frac{u_*^2}{(kz)^{2/3}}y^{2/3} \qquad (2.7)$$

The measurements presented by Obukhov and Yaglom are actually in terms of the *mean deviation* $|u_1 - u_2|$, which is taken to be proportional to $(D_{\text{trans}})^{1/2}$, and is later converted 'through multiplication by a number, determined from empirical distribution functions'.   The wind velocities were measured by hot-wire anemometers, and recorded photographically with time-resolution of the order of 0·01 sec.   Results for separations up to 60 cm, at heights of 1·5, 3 and 15 m are given in support of the theoretical variation, and it is also stated that Eq. (2.7) is satisfied with $C = 1·2$.

Various other examinations of the fine-structure near the ground have been made in terms of the *time-variation* of wind velocity at a fixed point. In these cases the relation between the variations in time and space is also involved, and so it is a matter of choice whether the results are taken to demonstrate the 'two-thirds' law, or the space-time transformation, the validity of one or the other being assumed at the outset.   In a preliminary examination R. J. Taylor (1952) concluded that observations of $(u - u_t)$ (i.e. velocity differences between instants separated by t) showed a variation

$$\overline{(u - u_t)^2} \propto t \qquad (2.8)$$

for values of $\bar{u}t$ up to the order of the height of observation which ranged from 2 to 30 m.   It should be noted that this form, which corresponds to $1 - R(t) \propto t$, follows from the incorrect application of dimensional arguments to the inertial sub-range in terms of time rather than space (see 1.3).

The result apparently contradicted either the 'two-thirds' law or the 'space-time' transformation hypothesis. However, in a further consideration of this point, based on autocorrelations for all three components in unstable conditions, Taylor (1955) concluded that on average the form $D \propto t^{2/3}$ (where D is the mean square velocity difference) was supported, though in individual cases there were considerable divergences from the $\frac{2}{3}$ exponent. This result applied up to values of t such that $\bar{u}t$ was frequently several times the height of observation, which suggested that the turbulence could not really have been locally isotropic over the whole range of eddy sizes implied, and Taylor found other and more compelling support for this view in data on shearing stress and on the relation between the *longitudinal* and *transverse* autocorrelations.

MacCready (1953b) has reported measurements which are notable for the elaborate electrical techniques employed in obtaining satisfactory records and convenient analysis of the fine-structure variation of the wind components. His paper gives the correlogram analysis of five samples at heights ranging from 7·5 cm to 146 m. In each case the correlogram was evaluated for lags up to $\frac{1}{10}$ or less of the sampling time, which ranged from 13 sec to 33 min. Each of the curves has a region of small lag t which is consistent with $1 - R(t) \propto t^{2/3}$, though as MacCready points out 'the exponent could not have been derived from the shape of the curves presented'. The departure of the curves from this form occurs fairly decisively at values of $\bar{u}t$ which are equal to or greater than the height of observation z, according as the conditions are thermally slightly stable or unstable. The 5-min runs at heights of 15, 70 and 240 cm were also analysed to give spectral densities at frequencies of 2·5, 10 and 40 cycles/sec. Although there is evidently considerable scatter of the points, they tend to cluster about the $n^{-5/3}$ relation. In the same context, Webb's (1955) spectra for a height of 29 m indicated exponents in the range $-1·5$ to $-1·2$, for equivalent wavelengths up to several times the height. Also, in Businger and Suomi's (1958) report of spectra of the vertical component, derived from measurements with a sonic anemometer at various heights up to 12 m, it is stated that an exponent of $-\frac{5}{3}$ was closely followed over a more or less extended range of frequency.

Spectra of the vertical component, computed from measurements with a sonic anemometer, have also been given by Gurvic (1960) for heights (z) of 1 and 4 m. These show a close approximation to the $-\frac{5}{3}$ exponent for equivalent wavelengths up to about $2·5z$ in unstable conditions, $1·4z$ in neutral conditions, and $0·5z$ in stable conditions.

For greater heights in the atmosphere broad features of the spectrum shape have been inferred from measurements of aircraft acceleration (see,

for example, Zbrozek, 1958), but the transformation from aircraft acceleration to air motion presents difficulties, and direct measurements of air
flow are preferable. An impressive wide-range spectrum, covering
equivalent wavelengths from 3 to 20,000 m, has been obtained by Crane
and Chilton (1956) from such measurements, made from an aircraft
flying at 1700 ft over a track of 170 air-miles.   Three overlapping sections
of spectra were calculated separately, the low-frequency portion from
measurements of the variation in aircraft altitude, and the middle and high-
frequency portion from the records of angle-of-attack vanes, of suitable
response, mounted on a nose-boom projecting ahead of the aircraft.   For
the high-frequency portion, over wavelengths of 3–200 m, the power-law
variation of spectral density with frequency evidently had an exponent
somewhere between $-\frac{5}{3}$ and 2.   From the tower and aeroplane study
referred to in 2.3 Lappe *et al.* find, for wavelengths less than 200 to 300 m,
exponents approaching -2 (aeroplane) and $-\frac{5}{3}$ to -2 (tower).   The
measurements were not accurate enough to verify the theoretical ratios of
the spectral densities of the u, v and w components.

For heights of 500, 1000 and 2000 ft, Smith (1961) has evaluated spectra
of the vertical component from measurements made with instruments
mounted on the cable of a captive balloon (Jones and Butler, 1958).
Estimates of the index in the power law variation of spectral density with
frequency, over the range 0·5 to 15 cycles/min, are given for about twenty
cases.   Over the highest part of this frequency range the values are mainly
between $-1·3$ and $-1·9$, and it is concluded that there is a tendency for
the index to be nearer $-\frac{5}{3}$ the larger the scale and intensity of turbulence.

Hutchings (1955) has analysed data on the large-scale horizontal motion
in the free atmosphere in the light of the 'inertial sub-range' considerations
and the space-time relationship.   Obtaining the longitudinal and transverse autocorrelations from the westerly and southerly components at the
500 mb level at Larkhill, Hutchings concluded that there was fair agreement with the form $1-R \propto t^{2/3}$.   However, a similar analysis of winds at
30,000 ft at Auckland, New Zealand, gave an exponent of 0·88.   On
Ogura's (1953) theoretical treatment of the space-time relationship this was
interpreted as a result of a greater intensity of turbulence at the higher level,
the implication being that in terms of actual space variations the 'two-
thirds' law would hold.   Gifford (1956) has questioned this on the grounds
of the evidence available on the intensities of turbulence.   Other conflicting results have been provided by Ogura's (1958) examination of Benton
and Kahn's (1958) data on the large-scale spatial structure of the horizontal
flow at the 300 mb level, for the northern hemisphere between latitudes of
20 and 70 deg.   Values of the exponents in the power-law variation of

spectral density with wave-number were found to be considerably greater than $\frac{5}{3}$. Moreover, the relation between the u (zonal) and v (meridional) spectral densities conformed to the relation for two-dimensional isotropy only at the extreme latitudes of 20 and 70 deg.

To sum up, the rather complex mass of data now available on the high-frequency properties of the spectrum of atmospheric turbulence is con-clusive only to the extent that a range is always evident over which spectral density decreases rapidly with increasing frequency. For the lower troposphere the variation of spectral density with n^{-p} is followed with p in the range 1–2 and most frequently in the range 1·5–2. However, the precise 'minus five-thirds' law, or what is more to the point, the precise range over which this applies, is not yet firmly established. Furthermore, where such a law is supported it does not follow that the turbulence is actually isotropic, and in some cases it may be demonstrably anisotropic. The only simple rule yet to emerge even tentatively is that near the ground in neutral or unstable conditions the *isotropic limit* occurs at a wavelength roughly the same as the height above ground (see Priestley, 1959a, for a brief review of this last point.)

The form of the w-spectrum near the ground

For many diffusion problems interest extends well into the low-frequency region of the spectrum, and some further discussion of the form of the whole spectrum is relevant at this point. The most important generaliza-tions to be made so far concern the spectrum of the vertical component, especially near the ground.

Charnock and Robinson (1957) have presented a semi-empirical treat-ment which provides a useful representation of a range of spectra, though the full implications have yet to be clarified and exploited. They consider the properties of a finite time-series of consecutive values, each averaged effectively over some elementary time interval, and derive an analytical result equivalent to Eq. (1.34). From this the correlogram may be obtained by computing the variance as a function of sampling time, which is more convenient than computing the correlation coefficient directly, apart from the practical difficulty of actually obtaining the double differential in Eq. (1.34). This difficulty they avoid by appeal to a tractable empirical relation for the variance properties, which they find to be approximately supported by a number of observed series of the u and v components near the ground. The substitution of this relation in Eq. (1.34), followed by application of the Fourier-transform in Eq. (1.9), leads to a spectrum relation in terms of sine and cosine integrals which has to be evaluated numerically. Expressed in the form $nF(n)$ versus $\log n$ this spectrum has a near-symmetrical form, and at high frequencies $F(n)$ tends to a variation with n^{-2}. Charnock and Robinson draw attention to the point that the n^{-2} variation is to be expected over a range of eddies smaller than the inertial sub-range. They also draw attention to the fact that their form of spectrum, though based empirically on observations very close to the ground, may be fitted remarkably well to the wide-range spectrum of the w-component at 1700 ft determined by Crane and Chilton (1956).

Panofsky and McCormick (1960) have put forward a generalized form of the w-spectrum near the ground. This is based in the first instance on the

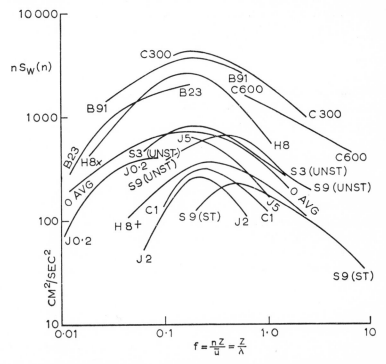

FIG. 2.11   Various spectra of the vertical component.   B Brookhaven, C Cardington, H Hancock, J Japan, O O'Neill, S Silver Hill, × large u, + small u.
The numbers are heights in metres.   (Panofsky and McCormick, 1960)

observation that many spectra, plotted in the form of *logarithmic spectral density* $nS(n)$ against reduced frequency f $(=nz/\bar{u},$ see 2.2), show an approximately similar shape under all conditions in the first few metres above ground, and up to greater heights in unstable air. This feature is demonstrated in Fig. 2.11. They suggest that these data can all be fitted best by the simple analytical function

$$nS(n) = \frac{4f\overline{w'^2}}{(1+4f)^2} \qquad (2.09)$$

where $\overline{w'^2}$ is the *total* variance. This form implies that the equivalent scale of turbulence [as defined in Eq. (1.3), and given by the value of $uF(n)/4$, or of $uS(n)/4\overline{w'^2}$, when $n=0$] is equal to the height z. The maximum value of $nS(n)$ occurs when $f=\frac{1}{4}$, i.e. at an equivalent wavelength equal to $4z$.

In contrast with Panofsky and McCormick's generalization that the w-spectrum near the ground is a universal function of f, irrespective of stability, Gurvic's (1960) data show a systematic variation with stability as represented by the Richardson number. From these data the equivalent wavelength for maximum $nS(n)$ ranges from z in stable conditions to about $5z$ in unstable conditions.

The simple expression suggested by Panofsky and McCormick is not very different in shape from the more complex form derived by Charnock and Robinson. Both forms, and also that appropriate to an exponential correlogram, i.e. Eq. (1.11), have symmetrical or near-symmetrical *cocked-hat* shapes when $nF(n)$ is plotted against log n (see, for example Fig. 1.1). Also all three give $F(n)$ tending to a variation with n^{-2} at large values of n.

Panofsky and McCormick have given Eq. (2.09) a more comprehensive form by relating the variance $\overline{w'^2}$ to wind speed, height, surface roughness and thermal stability. Their treatment is based on the assumption that this variance is determined completely by the height z and the rates (ϵ_1, ϵ_2) at which turbulent energy is added to the system by mechanical energy and convection respectively. Dimensional arguments give

$$\sigma_w = (\overline{w'^2})^{1/2} = A[z(\epsilon_1 + \delta\epsilon_2)]^{1/3} \qquad (2.10)$$

where A and δ are dimensionless constants to be determined. The quantity ϵ_1 is the same as ϵ in Eq. (2.6). The quantity ϵ_2 follows from the expression for the work done by buoyancy forces (for a statement of which see Sutton, 1953, p. 152), and amounts to $gH/c_p\rho T$, where H is the vertical flux of heat, T is absolute temperature, and g, ρ, c_p have their customary meanings. With these values, and introducing a length-scale stability parameter L [see 3.1 and Eq. (3.13)], and a universal function $\phi(z/L)$ for (kz/u_*) $(d\bar{u}/dz)$, both due to Monin and Obukhov (1954), Eq. (2.10) is developed to

$$\sigma_w = Bu_* \left[\phi\left(\frac{z}{L}\right) + \frac{\delta z}{L} \right]^{1/3} \qquad (2.11)$$

where B is another dimensionless constant which is to be determined.

For convenience the heat flux as such is eliminated by writing $L = L'/P$, where P is the ratio of the eddy diffusivities for heat and momentum (for a discussion of this ratio see Priestley 1959). The quantity L' is accordingly given by

$$L' = \frac{Tu_*(d\bar{u}/dz)}{kg(d\theta/dz)} \tag{2.12}$$

where θ is the potential temperature of the air, and Eq. (2.11) becomes

$$\sigma_w = Bu_*\left[\phi'\left(\frac{z}{L'}\right) + \frac{\delta Pz}{L'}\right]^{1/3} \tag{2.13}$$

In neutral conditions of stability $\phi'(z/L') = 1$, $L' = \infty$, and Eq. (2.13) necessarily reduces to the simple form

$$\sigma_w = Bu_* \tag{2.14}$$

When z_1 is small, so that the logarithmic wind profile relation can be assumed to be valid (see 3.1), this becomes

$$\sigma_w = B\,\frac{k\bar{u}_1}{\ln\,(z_1/z_0)} \tag{2.15}$$

The agreement between these relations and observations of σ_w is discussed in 2.8.

2.5 Lagrangian properties

The preceding discussions have been concerned with the turbulence indicated by variations of velocity with time, as measured by an instrument which is usually fixed, but which may also be carried on a moving platform. For both cases the measurements will refer to a continually changing sample of air. In general this is the only type of measurement which is feasible, and it is in such terms that the effects of diffusion must be described in practice. However, in a qualitative way, it is obvious that the diffusion of a cloud of airborne material will depend on the *development* of the turbulence affecting particular elements of the cloud as they are carried along. In other words interest centres on the variations of velocity (with time) which would be observed in following the motion of the elements—the system described as Lagrangian—and it will be seen later that formal expressions of diffusion all involve the Lagrangian correlogram or spectrum. Because of the continuity of diffusion processes, down the scale of motion to the ultimate molecular agitation, the view is sometimes expressed that the term *Lagrangian velocity* has no obvious meaning in the case of a fluid, except presumably when referred to a single molecule. In practice this difficulty is evaded by thinking either in terms of an element of fluid so small that its own diffusive spread is negligible compared with its translation under the action of the larger-scale turbulence, or in terms of a solid particle of negligible buoyancy. Whatever formal view is taken, it is evident that the observation of such velocities presents considerable difficulties.

Various workers have tried to approach a satisfactory measurement by observing the trajectories of *markers* floating more or less truly in the air. An early published account by Edinger (1952) contains an example of the form of the Lagrangian correlation coefficient associated with small-scale turbulence. The technique used here was to release soap bubbles from a generator carried aloft by a captive balloon, and to record their motion by a high magnification cine-camera vertically below on the ground, the bubbles being identifiable in sunny conditions by the reflection of the sun from their surfaces. However, the techniques which have been most productive so far are those using horizontal balloon flights on a medium or large scale, and air trajectories computed from the synoptic charts used in meteorological practice.

Following a preliminary study (1953) with balloons, Gifford (1955) has reported further experiments which are particularly noteworthy in that they were accompanied by fixed-point measurements on a tower (at Brookhaven National Laboratory, Long Island, New York), so as to provide a direct comparison between Lagrangian and Eulerian time-spectra. The principle of using so-called *neutral* balloons, i.e. balloons adjusted in weight so that they truly float, is well known, as is also the difficulty of achieving this condition in practice. In this case the balloons were first inflated to an approximately neutral state, and brought to final equilibrium by a length of string tied to the neck. This adjustment was carried out in the tower elevator, from which the balloons were then released, synchronous readings being taken at 10-second intervals and used to compute average vertical velocities over such intervals. The resulting serial values of average vertical component were then used to compute spectra by the technique advocated by Tukey, over frequencies from about 5 to just over 100 cycles per hour.

Despite the usual scatter in the spectral estimates, Gifford's results contain the general impression that the Lagrangian spectra are broadly similar in shape to the Eulerian spectra, but displaced from them toward lower frequencies. Gifford estimated the frequencies corresponding to the maximum values of $nF(n)$, say n'_E for the Eulerian time spectra and n'_L for the Lagrangian spectra, and argued that these values were related in a way which was consistent with Ogura's (1953) model of the space- and time-variation of turbulent velocity, which implies that $n'_E - n'_L$ should be proportional to mean wind speed and that n'_E/n'_L should depend linearly on the reciprocal of the intensity of turbulence. It is noteworthy that the values of n'_E/n'_L were within the range 1·7 to 4·0, and averaged approximately 3.

Durst *et al.* (1957) have analysed computed air trajectories derived on the usual working assumption that the horizontal flow in the atmosphere is *geostrophic* [see Brunt (1941) p. 189]. In practice the geostrophic wind was computed on charts of isobars, or of height-contours of a given pressure level, starting at a chosen point of origin. The position which the air at that point would reach after half the time interval to the next chart was plotted on the next chart. This second chart was then used in 'moving on' the air up to the mid-time between the second and the third charts, and so on. Charts at intervals of three or six hours were employed, and trajectories started at the same fixed point were followed for periods up to 72 hours in some cases. These trajectories were used in a study of the spread of the trajectory ends (see 4.6), and the serial values of wind velocities used in constructing them were also analysed to give auto-correlation coefficients in the Lagrangian sense. About 290 trajectories were computed from 700 or 500 mb charts, corresponding to levels in the atmosphere of approximately 10,000 and 20,000 ft, and 140 from surface charts. Correlation coefficients of similar type were also computed from the trajectories of constant-level balloon flights at the 300 mb level (approximately 30,000 ft), over America and the Atlantic Ocean north of 40° N.

On average the correlation coefficients showed a close fit to an exponential form $R(t) = \exp(-\alpha t)$, with values of $1/\alpha$ (i.e. the time-scale given by $\int_0^\infty R(t)\,dt$) as follows:

Constant level balloons at 300 mb	8 hr
Trajectories from 700 and 500 mb charts	22 hr
Trajectories from surface charts	5 hr

It is doubtful whether any significance can be attached to the relative magnitudes at the various heights, especially as the data do not refer to the same periods, and the main interest here is the indication of exponential form with a time scale in the region of 10 hr. This is especially interesting in view of the previous demonstrations that the turbulence observed at a fixed point, though on a much smaller scale in the lower atmosphere, can also often be approximately represented by an exponential correlogram.

The balloon data used by Durst *et al.* were derived from U.S. Navy long-range constant-level balloon flights, so-called *transosondes* (trans-oceanic-sondes), in 1953.   This series of five flights, and a further seven flights launched from Japan in 1956, have since been discussed by Angell (1958).   In the period September 1957–June 1958 many more transosondes were launched from Japan, and the results of these have also been presented by Angell (1960).   The balloons were maintained at the 300 mb level by means of a ballast system operated by a barograph, and were tracked over the Pacific Ocean and North American continent by networks of radio direction-finders.   To eliminate errors in the positions, which were fixed at 2-hr intervals, averages were taken of three successive positions and assigned to the middle time.   From the resulting smoothed trajectory consecutive 6-hr averages of the zonal and meridional wind velocities were obtained.   The deviations of these individual values from the mean values as determined from all flights were used in computing mean autocorrelation coefficients at 6-hr intervals.

Average autocorrelograms were obtained from 93 flights which were tracked for one day or more during the autumn, winter and spring of 1957–1958.   For the zonal component the correlation coefficient was found to be well represented up to a lag of four days by

$$R_u(\xi) = \exp\left[-(7\xi+1)/6\right] \tag{2.18}$$

where ξ is in days.   This is not very different from the simple exponential form found by Durst *et al.*   The meridional component, on the other hand, is represented by a combination of a simple exponential form and a sinusoidal component of 2-day period, in the form

$$R_v(\xi) = \exp\left(-\xi\right)\cos\pi\xi \tag{2.19}$$

The serial values of the velocity components for each flight of more than four days' duration were also analysed to give energy spectra, following the numerical technique recommended by Tukey.   The average spectral densities showed a peak in the meridional case at an equivalent period of slightly more than two days.   This was obviously to be compared with the 2-day periodicity in the correlogram, the slight difference being possibly a result of the exclusion from the spectrum analysis of flights lasting less than four days.   Angell associates this periodicity with the average transit time of the transosondes through the long waves in the average pattern of the westerly flow at the 300 mb level.

These Lagrangian analyses by Durst *et al.* and Angell are directly relevant to the problem of large-scale horizontal dispersion in the free atmosphere, indeed the raw data can alternatively be analysed specifically from this point of view, and further reference to the results will be found in Chapter 4.   Unfortunately the data as they stand do not give any direct comparison of the Lagrangian and Eulerian properties as in Gifford's experiment, though a rough assessment reported by Hay and Pasquill (1959), on the basis of Durst *et al.*'s data, indicates that the Lagrangian and Eulerian correlograms have approximately the same time-scale, implying that the corresponding spectra are also approximately the same.   Further indirect support of this conclusion is provided by Solot and Darling's (1958) estimates of a Lagrangian time-scale of about 1 day, and an Eulerian time-scale of about 2 days, based on trajectory and wind data in the upper atmosphere.

Two recent developments in balloon technique are noteworthy.   Lucas, Spurr and Williams (1957) have investigated the suitability of various types of balloon, primarily for indicating the rise of hot plumes from chimneys, but their findings are relevant to the carrying out of basic Lagrangian studies.   They recommend the use of a laminate of terylene and polythene, which has a high resistance to gas leakage, and is easily formed into suitable envelopes by heat-sealing.   Angell and Pack (1960) have reported preliminary experience with balloons made of a polyester film called *mylar*. In this case the balloons were filled with helium to an excess pressure of about 100 mb, with the object of maintaining constant volume even after some leakage or cooling, and so ensuring approximately constant-level flight.   From radar-tracking of flights over tens of miles, at levels a few thousand feet above ground, positions were fixed at 1-min intervals and used to derive velocities averaged over 5-min periods.   From the first results the technique appears to be particularly suitable for Lagrangian studies on a medium scale.

2.6   The probability distribution of the magnitudes of wind fluctuations

Although within the context of this discussion interest centres mainly on the intensity of turbulence, and the contributions made to it by the different parts of the spectrum, there is both theoretical and practical interest in the distribution of the magnitudes of fluctuations.   From the time of the *mixing length theories*, with their implied analogy with the kinetic theory of gases, it has been customary to assume eddy velocities to be distributed in a Gaussian form.   The first demonstration of the approximation to this form in the wind fluctuations in the atmosphere was presented by Hesselberg and Bjorkdal (1929).   They argued theoretically that the distribution of eddy velocity in space should follow the classical Maxwellian law.   Data on

5—A.D.

the distribution of time-variations of wind velocity reported by Robitzsh were shown to agree fairly closely with such a form, the actual deviations from it being ascribed to the fact that the *mean* velocity varied with time (i.e. the variations contained a marked low frequency component). However, the implication in the paper that the complication would not have arisen had the distribution been obtained from space-variations is unlikely to be valid, for it is evident that corresponding components of large

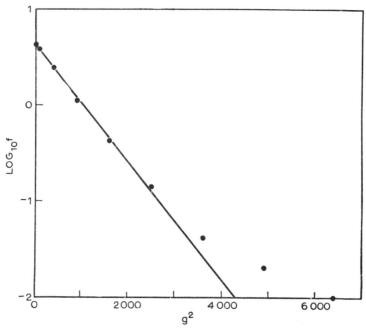

FIG. 2.12   Distribution of fluctuations of wind speed. f is percentage occurrence of unit ranges of g ($=100|u'|/\bar{u}$), from 174 3-min samples at heights of 200, 50 and 10 cm, comprising spot readings at 10-sec intervals. (Best, 1935) (from *Meteorological Office Geophysical Memoirs No. 65 H.M.S.O.* Crown Copyright Reserved)

wavelengths could also occur. The real point is that a random variation superimposed on some systematic (say sinusoidal) trend will necessarily show some departure from the Gaussian form, to an extent dependent on the amplitude of the systematic variation.

Best (1935) examined his fine-structure measurements of wind speed from the point of view of their distribution in magnitude, and the overall result is shown in Fig. 2.12. The quantity g is $100u'/\bar{u}$ and f is the percentage number of observations per unit range of g.   It is seen that a law of the form

$$f = f_0 \exp\left(-kg^2\right) \tag{2.20}$$

is well supported except at the extreme values of g, but Best points out that the three points which deviate from this relation represent less than one per cent of the observations.   The values of g were obtained from 3-min samples comprising readings at 10-sec intervals, and the data plotted are a composition of 174 such samples obtained at heights of 2, 0·5 and 0·1 m. A similar examination has been reported by Cramer (1952) for samples of both wind speed and direction.   The average length of the samples was 8 min, and the readings were taken at 1-sec intervals with a hot wire

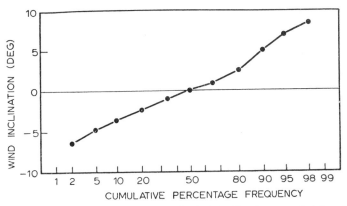

Fig. 2.13   Distribution of fluctuations of wind inclination at a height of 150 m. Average of ten samples, each of about 30-min duration, comprising 'spot' readings at $2\frac{1}{2}$-sec intervals.   (Hay and Pasquill, 1957)

anemometer and a suitably responsive vane.   In Cramer's results the individual samples show points which are slightly scattered, but the general trend is in good agreement with the Gaussian form, for both wind speed and direction.

More recently Hay and Pasquill have given distributions from 3-min samples of wind direction at a height of 2 m (1959), which again confirm the earlier results, and from 30-min samples of wind inclination at a height of 150 m (1957), both sets of observations being made with sensitive vanes.   Although the individual samples of wind inclination show appreciable departures from a Gaussian form it is clear that these departures do not all recur in a systematic way.   However, as can be seen from Fig. 2.13, the average of the ten available distributions still contains an obvious asymmetry, the negative inclinations (i.e. downward-moving air) being somewhat less in magnitude than those on the positive side. Qualitatively, this is entirely consistent with the normal downward transport of momentum, in the lower atmosphere, which is brought about by a statistical tendency for the downward-moving air to have a higher horizontal velocity than the upward-moving air. Indeed, with the assumption that $\bar{w}$ is zero, and that on average the durations of the upward and downward flow are equal, a rough estimate of the net vertical transport of momentum may easily be made. Expressing this in terms of the so-called *friction velocity*, which is $\sqrt{(\overline{u'w'})}$ the value obtained is about 1 m/sec, which is in reasonable agreement with other estimates of this quantity (see Sutton, 1953, p. 233). This suggests that if the distributions of wind inclination were converted to true vertical velocities the skewness observed would be modified in the right direction, but it is not possible to test this point in the present case, since the necessary data on the fluctuation of wind speed was not provided.

However, distributions of the actual vertical component have been obtained by Crane and Chilton (1956) using the measurements made from an aircraft at 1700 ft. The spectrum derived from these has already been referred to in 2.4. Three separate distributions, corresponding to the samples used in obtaining the three portions of this spectrum, all showed a good approximation to Gaussian form, except at the extreme values, and there was no sign of asymmetry.

If the distribution of wind fluctuations may be assumed Gaussian then this has useful practical consequences, both in the application of standard statistical techniques for estimating the reliability of the data from individual samples (as for example in the spectral analysis procedure advocated by Tukey, see 1.5), and in the task of obtaining comprehensive estimates of the intensity of turbulence. In the latter respect good use can be made of the simple relations which then exist between the standard deviation and other characteristics of the distribution which are more easily measured or computed. A case in point is the *mean deviation*, which avoids the squaring procedure involved in obtaining the standard deviation, and is related to the latter by the equation

$$\sqrt{(\overline{x^2})} = \sqrt{(\pi/2)} \times \overline{|x|}$$

where x represents departure from a mean value. A direct test of the latter, for short samples of wind direction fluctuations, has been reported by Jones and Pasquill (1959). The data consisted of over a hundred overlapping 3-min samples, extending over a total period of 90 min, for each of which the standard deviation and mean deviation of consecutive 5-sec averages was obtained. The *form factor*, i.e. the standard deviation divided by the mean deviation, was obtained for the individual values and from values averaged over various periods up to an hour, and the results are shown in Table 2.III. For the individual samples the extreme variation from the theoretical form factor was about 20 per cent but this was greatly reduced in the case of the averaged data, becoming negligible for most practical purposes when the total period was 15 min or more.

Table 2.III

Form factors (i.e., standard deviation/mean deviation) for fluctuations of wind direction analysed with sampling duration (τ) 180 sec and averaging time(s) 5 sec. (Jones and Pasquill, 1959)

Data used	No. of values of form factor	Range of form factor
Individual values	117	1·06–1·54
15-min means	99	1·18–1·28
30-min means	78	1·21–1·26
60-min means	38	1·23–1·24

In general conclusion, while the data available at present are far from embracing all the wide variations of the properties of atmospheric turbulence, there is some evidence to support the adoption of a Gaussian distribution of eddy velocities as an approximate working basis.

2.7   The accumulation of statistics of the intensity of turbulence

The growing emphasis on the representation of diffusion directly in terms of the structural properties of turbulence, in preference to bulk properties such as the lapse-rate of temperature, has greatly increased the demand for the rather specialized measurements of turbulence in the atmosphere. In connection with actual diffusion experiments, or in the assessment of diffusion effects for a specific release of airborne material, it may sometimes be enough to make a limited number of these special observations on the particular site. Techniques using responsive vanes (see Cramer, Gill and Record, 1957, and Jones and Butler, 1958) or hot-wire anemometers (e.g. Swinbank, 1951) are now fairly well established. In these methods the final record is in the form of time-lapse traces of the variable on photographic paper, or on the charts of suitable pen-recording galvanometers or milliammeters.

When there is interest in acquiring representative statistics, it is necessary not only to cover the wide range of atmospheric conditions, but also to provide a reliable average of the random variations which occur in apparently similar conditions.   An example of the magnitude of this variability is contained in some data on wind direction fluctuations quoted by Hay and Pasquill (1959).   These were measured over a level unobstructed site, in thoroughly overcast conditions with wind speed in the region of 5 m/sec and wind direction steady in the broad sense of the term.   Such conditions would be expected to yield a minimum variation in the statistical properties of turbulence.   However, values of $\sigma_{\tau,s}$, i.e. the standard deviation for an averaging time (s) of 5 sec and sampling duration (τ) of 4 min, varied between 4·1 and 7·5° during a total period of 30 min.   With this sort of variability in normal steady conditions, it is obvious that in general large numbers of observations will be required to give a complete statistical description, and the practical problem of extraction and reduction of the observations then becomes important.

The labour of computing can be reduced by transcribing the conventional traces, either manually or semi-automatically, into digital form on punched cards or tape, and analysing the latter on an electronic computer. This procedure was followed in the analysis of the data obtained at O'Neill in Nebraska, U.S.A. during the *Great Plains Turbulence Field Programme* (see Lettau and Davidson, 1957) and the *Project Prairie Grass* diffusion studies (see Haugen, 1959).   Direct transcription into digital form at the recording stage would be even better, but although this may be technically possible, no substantial recordings of atmospheric turbulence in this way have yet been reported.   Undoubtedly the position can be expected to develop in this direction, and there would be the definite advantage of having permanent records which can be analysed in various ways at will. Alternatively, the original continuous variation, recorded either as a conventional trace or on magnetic tape can be analysed by some suitable form of *analogue* computer as in investigations by Webb (1955), Businger and Suomi (1958) and others.

For many purposes it will be seen later that the requirement may be simply the variance, or standard deviation, considered in relation to the sampling duration and averaging time.   In these cases, processes which include a permanent time-lapse record of the variable are of questionable value where a large mass of observations is involved, and a technique of directly recording the standard deviation deserves serious consideration.

A simple development in this direction, which seems likely to be profitable in amassing broad statistics of atmospheric turbulence, has been reported by Jones and Pasquill (1959).   The first essential stage of this method is the passage of a continuous electrical signal representing the turbulent fluctuation through electrical filters which are appropriate to

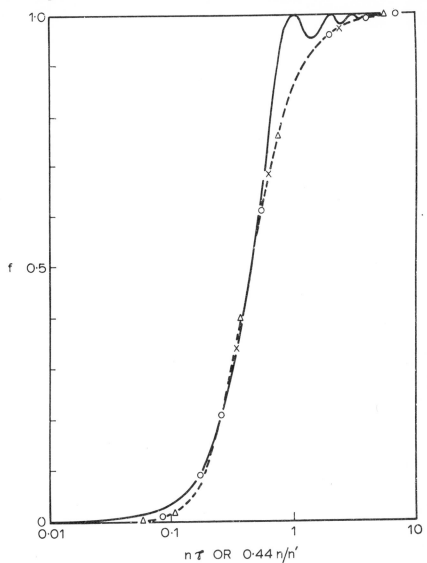

Fɪɢ. 2.14   Electrical filter corresponding approximately to a finite duration of sampling

———— $f = 1 - \sin^2 \pi n \tau / (\pi n \tau)^2$ where n is frequency (cycles/sec) and τ is sampling-duration (sec)

– – – – $f = \left(1 + \dfrac{1}{\omega^2 C^2 R^2}\right)^{-2}$ where $\omega = 2\pi n$, C and R are the capacity (farads) and resistance (ohms) of a two-stage high-pass filter, for which the frequency for 50 per cent power transmission is $n' = 0.247/CR$.   The points are measured values for CR 101 (⊙), 16·9 (×) and 2·8 (△) sec.   (Jones and Pasquill, 1959) specific sampling and averaging times or, alternatively, to definable 'windows' in the spectrum (e.g. see Fig. 1.6).   In practice this follows from the fact (Fig. 2.14) that the 'filtering' effect of sampling for a specified duration can be reproduced to a good approximation by a simple two-stage capacitor-resistor filter.   Since in Eq. (1.28) $\sigma^2_{\tau,0}/\sigma^2_{\infty,0}$ falls to 0·5 for $n\tau = 0·44$, it follows that a high-pass electrical filter of adequately similar shape will give an output corresponding to a sampling duration of $0·44/n'$, where n' is the frequency for 50 per cent power transmission, or in the present case $1·78CR$ sec, where C is the capacity in microfarads and R the resistance in megohms.   The second stage is the conversion of this filtered output (which automatically has zero mean value), by rectification and then by smoothing with a low-pass filter, into an output which represents a smoothed mean deviation, and which can be recorded at a relatively slow chart speed.   With the assumption of a Gaussian distribution of the component fluctuations, which is approximately supported by evidence already discussed in 2.6, the scale can be adjusted to give readings of standard deviation directly.   This system of recording can of course be adopted for any variable which can be arranged to give a linear electrical output.

Practical details and discussion of possible corrections for the small difference in 'mathematical' and 'electrical' filter characteristics are given in the paper.   Also, some tests against a conventional numerical determination of the standard deviation of wind direction are presented.   In practice the records of standard deviation correspond to an effective averaging time, s', which is determined by the response characteristics of the instrument.   For the wind vane used in the present case the value of s' was about 0·2 sec at wind speeds near 5 m/sec.   When sampling durations τ_1 and τ_2 are used such that $\tau_1 > \tau_2 \gg s'$, the standard deviation for a sampling duration τ_1 and averaging time τ_2 is given by

$$\sigma_{\tau_1,\tau_2} = (\sigma^2_{\tau_1,s'} - \sigma^2_{\tau_2,s'})^{1/2} \qquad (2.21)$$

where the quantities in the brackets are the squares of the recorded standard deviations.   Values for $\tau_1 = 180$ sec and $\tau_2 = 5$ sec, obtained from averages of the records over periods of one hour, were found to agree to within a few per cent with values obtained by the conventional and much more laborious analysis, using component 3-min samples of the basic time-lapse variation of wind direction.

Two samples of 24-hr recordings (with a chart speed of $\frac{1}{2}$ in/hr) of wind direction fluctuations at a height of 16 m over open downland are shown in Fig. 2.15, the three traces in each case referring to sampling durations (τ) of 5, 30 and 180 sec.   These records (when converted to radians) may

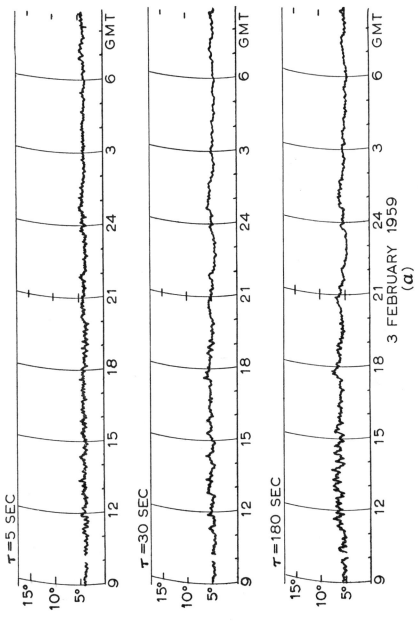

FIG. 2.15.   Diurnal records of the standard deviation of wind direction at a height of 16 m over open downland at Porton, England.   Sampling-durations (τ) 5, 30 and 180 sec.

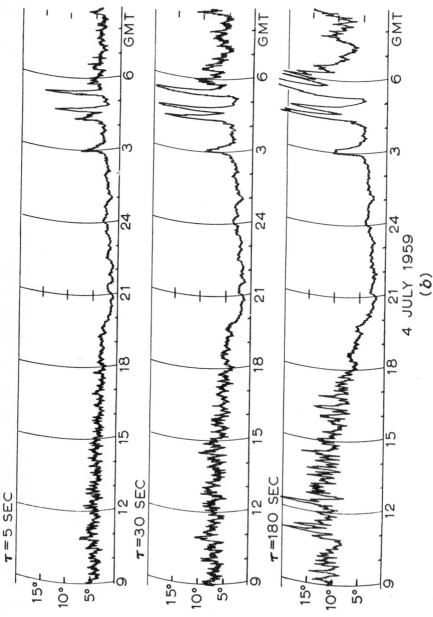

Fig. 2.15   Diurnal records of the standard deviation of wind direction at a height of 16 m over open downland at Porton, England.   Sampling-durations (τ) 5, 30 and 180 sec.

be taken as an approximation to $\sqrt{(\overline{v'^2})}/\bar{u}$ which will be satisfactory for values up to about 10°. The first example (a) is typical of high wind speeds (about 10 m/sec), and displays a remarkable steadiness in the *statistical* value of the standard deviation (spot values actually correspond to an average over about 25 min). The second example (b) shows typical features of the diurnal variation in lighter winds, with larger and more variable values of the standard deviation in the middle of the day, followed by smaller values in the evening as a consequence of the onset of stability. The very large values between 4 a.m. and 6 a.m. are associated with temporary falls in wind speed to values near 1 m/sec.

2.8   Recent analyses of the intensity of atmospheric turbulence

The vertical component

Panofsky and McCormick (1960) have examined various data on the standard deviation, σ_w, of the vertical component of turbulence near the ground, as a function of wind speed and atmospheric stability. These data were derived from measurements in Australia by Swinbank (at heights of 1·5, 1·9, 2·0, 23 and 29 m), at O'Neill, Nebraska (12 m) and at Brookhaven, New York (91 m). It is implied that the duration of sampling was always sufficient to include virtually all the low-frequency contributions to the spectrum. In all cases σ_w in near-neutral conditions was approximately proportional to wind speed at a fixed low height, such that Eq. (2.15) held with $B = 1·25$ (k being taken as 0·41). As an example, the O'Neill results (those obtained during the *Great Plains Turbulence Programme*) are reproduced in Fig. 2.16, in which the straight line corresponds to Eq. (2.15) with $B = 1·25$.

The only systematic departure from the straight line, at low wind speed, is implied to be due to inadequate response of the bidirectional vanes at these low speeds, but it may be relevant that the points concerned were all obtained at night, presumably with somewhat stable conditions. At the higher wind speeds there is no systematic separation of the day-time and night-time results, implying absence of any significant degree of instability or stability. Both the Australian and Brookhaven data contain values in unstable conditions which are systematically greater than those in neutral conditions for similar wind speed. The Australian data for a height of 29 m, in the most unstable conditions, are stated to be consistent with Eq. (2.13) with $\delta \times P = 2·4$.

According to Gurvic's (1960) data the value of B (i.e. the ratio of σ_w to the friction velocity, in neutral conditions) is approximately 0·7. The appreciable difference between this and the value obtained by Panofsky and McCormick from several sources of data has yet to be explained. However, both sets of data are in agreement on the point that near the ground σ_w is approximately proportional to wind speed, so that the intensity of this component of the turbulence $(\sigma_w/\bar{u})$ is virtually independent of wind

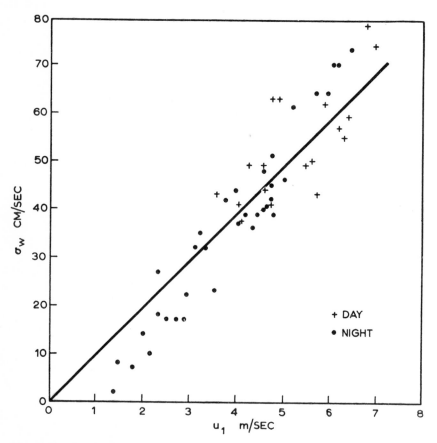

FIG. 2.16   Standard deviation of vertical velocity at 12 m, as a function of wind speed at 1 m, at O'Neill, Nebraska.   Solid line gives theoretical relation for neutral conditions.   (Panofsky and McCormick, 1960)

speed.   The early indications of this feature in Scrase's results, noted in 2.1, are thus confirmed in a fairly comprehensive way.   In the data summarized by Panofsky and McCormick there is no evidence for an important departure from the simple relation with wind speed when conditions are stable or unstable, but at greater heights and with somewhat greater wind speeds observations analysed by F. B. Smith display a different relation.

Smith's analysis (1961) contains estimates of the intensity (effectively of the whole spectrum) from over seventy samples of wind inclination, of duration usually one hour or more, obtained from remote-recording vanes mounted on the cable of a tethered balloon at Cardington, Bedfordshire (see Jones and Butler, 1958).   The variance of wind inclination was evaluated by adding the variance for a sampling duration of 30 sec, as recorded directly by the technique described in 2.7, to the variance estimated from a relatively slow time-lapse trace representing the wind inclination averaged over 30-sec intervals.   This effect was achieved by passing the output of the instruments through a low-pass electrical filter of shape approximating to Fig. 1.5.   The relation between the standard deviation of wind inclination (effectively σ_w/u in Panofsky and McCormick's presentation) and wind speed is displayed in Fig. 2.17.   Different symbols are used according as the original variation of wind inclination was symmetrical or not about zero-inclination, this being judged to be characteristic of non-convective or convective conditions respectively.   The observations are also separated into broad stability bands based on routine temperature data for the range of heights involved.   No systematic variation with height was evident in these observations, which were mainly in the range 150–1500 m.

Fig. 2.17 displays an overall decrease of intensity of turbulence with increase of wind speed, which is in striking contrast with the lack of dependence on wind speed found nearer the ground.   When the data are separated into stability bands the decrease is less obvious, but is still evident especially at the higher wind speeds.   Conversion of the results to the standard deviation of the vertical component w, shows that this quantity increases roughly in proportion to wind speed up to about 5 m/sec, but that beyond this speed it tends to be independent of wind speed or even to decrease slightly.

Smith emphasizes that there may be some bias in the results in Fig. 2.17 because the observations were restricted to fair weather.   Furthermore, it is clear that more observations and critical analysis will be required to establish and explain the full variation with wind speed.   A simple linear relation between σ_w and u is a rational expectation when the turbulence is primarily of dynamical origin, but it is at least qualitatively evident that a different relation is to be expected when convective motion is the dominant supplier of turbulent energy, as it would appear to be at greater heights. Referring to Eq. (2.10) the linear relation is merely a consequence of the dominance of the ϵ_1 term, which is itself approximately proportional to u^3. The other term, ϵ_2, is proportional to the heat flux, H, which in conditions of *free* convection (see Priestley, 1959) has been argued to be independent of shearing stress and hence of wind speed. This suggests that in conditions of vigorous convection, with ϵ_2 the more important term, a lack of dependence of σ_w on u may likewise be expected.

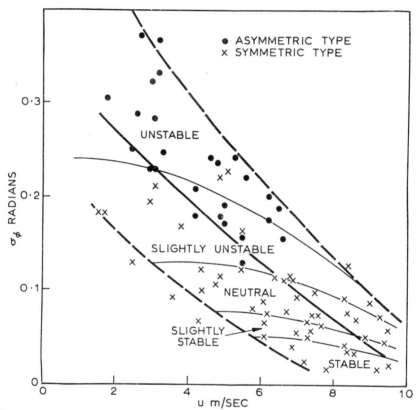

Fɪɢ. 2.17   Variation of the intensity of the vertical component (actually the standard deviation σ_ϕ of the inclination of the wind) with wind speed, at heights in the range 100 to 1500 m. (Smith, 1961)

The lateral component

A summary based on the measurements at low heights at O'Neill, and at the Round Hill Field Station, of the Massachusetts Institute of Technology, has been set out by Cramer (1957). This is in the form of rounded values of the standard deviations of the wind direction variation over a period of 10 min, for conditions of stability which are indicated qualitatively. These results are also particularly noteworthy in specifying the change in intensity

of the lateral component associated with a substantial difference in the
aerodynamic roughness of the two sites (see 6.4 for a brief summary).

A very detailed examination of the properties of the lateral component
near the ground is now made feasible by records of the type shown in
Fig. 2.15.   An analysis of about 1000 hr of such records, for a height of
16 m over open downland at Porton, England, has been made by Smith and
Abbott (1961).   The basic data consisted of hourly averages of the standard
deviations of wind direction for the standard sampling durations of 5, 30
and 180 sec.   For near-neutral conditions, as specified by

$$-0.01 \leqslant \Delta T_{7 \cdot 1 - 1 \cdot 2}/\bar{u}^2 \leqslant +0.01$$

where the numerator is the temperature in °F at a height of 7·1 m minus

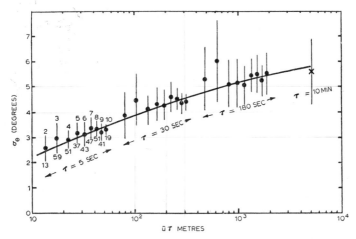

FIG. 2.18   The standard deviation σ_θ of wind direction at a height of 16 m over
open grassland, in neutral conditions of stability, as a function of sampling-
duration τ and wind speed $\bar{u}$.   ● Porton, England.   × O'Neill, Nebraska.

that at 1·2 m, and $\bar{u}$ is the mean wind speed (at 15·5 m) in m/sec, the
variation of standard deviation σ_θ with wind speed and sampling duration,
τ, is displayed in terms of the product $\bar{u}\tau$ in Fig. 2.18.   The points are
mean values for 1 m/sec ranges of wind speed, the lower limits of the
ranges being entered above the points, while the figures below the points
represent the numbers of hourly averages included.   In each case the
standard deviation of the hourly averages is represented by the vertical line
extending above or below the point.   For wind speeds greater than 4 m/sec
the groups of points for different sampling durations appear to follow a

simple curvilinear relation with the length $\bar{u}\tau$.　Such a relation would be consistent with a field of turbulence in which (a) the shape of the wavenumber spectrum is invariant with wind speed, (b) the total intensity of turbulence, $\sqrt{(\overline{v'^2})}/\bar{u}$, is independent of wind speed, and (c) the time-variation at a fixed point is statistically equivalent to the space-variation, with the transformation $x = \bar{u}t$.

The single point for a sampling duration of 10 min was obtained from the observations at a height of 12 m at O'Neill (Lettau and Davidson, 1957, Vol. 2, Tables 5.2a), and is an average of eighteen individual values for similar near-neutral conditions.　This value conforms reasonably closely to the trend of the Porton data, suggesting that the curve drawn in can be regarded as an approach to a universal empirical relation between σ_θ and $u\tau$ for an open grassland site, for wind speeds between 4 and 10 m/sec and sampling durations up to 10 min.

Variation with height

The important matter of the variation of intensity of turbulence with height has yet to be fully investigated.　For the vertical component it is implied in Panofsky and McCormick's (1960) analysis that the total intensity in neutral conditions is independent of height in the first 100 m.　In their general review of the data Panofsky and Deland (1959) state that there is considerable evidence for a slow increase with height in unstable air, and a decrease in stable air, over the same height range.　They also make the broad generalization that the intensities of both the lateral and longitudinal components are virtually independent of height, in convective conditions, in the first 30 m at least.　On the other hand, in stable conditions, the intensities of these components are said to decrease rapidly upwards.

3

Theoretical Treatment of Diffusion

The theoretical analysis of the dispersion of material released into the atmosphere has followed two main lines, which may be termed the *transfer theory* approach and the *statistical* approach respectively. In the former approach a physical model is implied, basically relying on the assumption that in the presence of a gradient of concentration of diffusing substance the local rate of transport of material by turbulence will be proportional to the local gradient, the proportionality factor being referred to variously as *exchange coefficient, austausch coefficient,* or *eddy diffusivity.* Effective application of the idea entails two problems, namely the assignment of suitable explicit forms to the eddy diffusivity, in terms of measurable properties of the flow, and the solution, with the appropriate boundary conditions, of the differential equations which follow from the principle of continuity. The classical background and advances up to about 1950 have been completely surveyed by Sutton (1953), and the references to these in the present discussion will be limited to summaries and comments which are essential to coherence.

In much of its development the alternative approach does not rest on any particular physical model of diffusion, and is essentially an analytical technique for representing the history of marked elements of the fluid in terms of given statistical properties of the turbulent motion. Although the history of this treatment goes back almost as far as that of the transfer theories, the full emergence of its application, together with that of the understanding of the structure of atmospheric turbulence, has proceeded rapidly only over the last ten years or so.

3.1 Eddy diffusivity

The eddy diffusivity K, or austausch coefficient A, is effectively defined by writing the following simple linear relation between the flux, F, across a fixed surface, and the gradient, measured normal to the surface, of the concentration of the property undergoing diffusion.

$$F = -A \frac{\partial \bar{s}}{\partial n} \simeq -\bar{\rho} K \frac{\partial \bar{s}}{\partial n} \qquad (3.1)$$

6—A.D.

In this equation s is the quantity per unit mass of air, and the negative sign denotes that the gradient is being measured in the direction of the flux. The simplest possible basis for the relation is the assumption of analogy between the process of turbulent transport, and that of molecular transport, such as the conduction of heat in a non-turbulent fluid, the usual molecular coefficient of transport, such as thermal conductivity, being replaced by a much larger *eddy* coefficient. The earliest and simplest treatment of the vertical transport of momentum and heat in the atmosphere did indeed immediately show that with the flux represented as in Eq. (3.1) the quantities K and A had to be assigned values several orders of magnitudes greater than their molecular counterparts. These early treatments, developed especially by Taylor (1915) and Schmidt (1925), were given more definite form by expressing the eddy flux as

$$F = \overline{(\rho w')s'} \qquad (3.2)$$

where w' is the velocity of the air (normal to the surface) and the primes denote departures from mean values measured at a fixed point in space. It was then argued on simple lines that s' should be proportional to the average local gradient of s, the constant of proportionality being a length, l, and substitution of this in (3.2) gave, with (3.1), the familiar form

$$K = \overline{w'l} \qquad (3.3)$$

In Prandtl and von Kármán's subsequent developments for momentum transport, w' is the vertical component of eddy velocity and s' is u', the horizontal component. Similar proportionality between w' or u' and the mean gradient $\partial u/\partial z$ was assumed, the proportionality constant l being regarded as a 'mixing length' analogous to the mean free path of molecular motion. Intuitive assumptions about the form of l led to the well known logarithmic profile of velocity (see below) in the boundary layer over a rigid surface. This provided the link between the eddy diffusivity for momentum and the velocity profile, and together with the assumption of equality with the eddy diffusivity for other diffusible properties, such as suspended matter, formed the basis of one of the most effective treatments of diffusion in the lower atmosphere.

It is now generally agreed that the classical arguments briefly noted above are of no real value in the physical sense. The justification of Eq. (3.1), together with the expression of K in suitable terms, are features which at the present stage must be decided on empirical grounds.

Eddy diffusivity for vertical transport in the lower atmosphere in adiabatic conditions

Classical laboratory studies by Nikuradse and Schlichting established the laws relating the drag of a surface on the motion of a fluid adjacent to it, and the velocity profile set up in the fluid in a direction normal to the surface. These laws recognized two distinct regimes of flow: an *aerodynamically smooth* flow, when the drag appears as a purely viscous stress at the surface, and its relation with the velocity profile depends on the kinematic viscosity ν: an *aerodynamically rough* flow, which applies (at higher velocities and over rougher surfaces) when the drag is predominantly due to pressure forces exerted normally on the projecting roughnesses of the surface, and is therefore virtually independent of viscosity (see Sutton, 1953, p. 77 *et seq.*, for further details). Taking the surface to be horizontal the laws and their limits of application may be written as follows,

Aerodynamically smooth flow $(u_* z_0/\nu < 0\cdot 13)$

$$\frac{u}{u_*} = \frac{1}{k} \ln \frac{u_* z}{\nu} + 5\cdot 5 \tag{3.4}$$

Fully rough flow $(u_* z_0/\nu > 2\cdot 5)$

$$\frac{u}{u_*} = \frac{1}{k} \ln \frac{z}{z_0} \tag{3.5}$$

where τ_0 is the shearing stress or drag per unit area of the boundary, $u_* = \sqrt{(\tau_0/\rho)}$ is the so-called friction velocity, ρ the density of the fluid, k is von Karman's constant ($\simeq 0\cdot 4$) and z_0 is a *roughness length* characterizing the effect of the surface roughness.

For intermediate magnitudes of $u_* z_0/\nu$ the flow is described as transitional. It is noteworthy that the quantity $u_* z_0$ has the dimensions of kinematic viscosity, and has been termed the macroviscosity N by Sutton. With this relation it follows that Eq. (3.5) is of essentially the same form as (3.4) with ν replaced by N, and on this basis an interpolation formula applicable both to rough and smooth surfaces has been given by Sutton (*loc. cit*).

For the lower atmosphere, over the first few metres at least, numerous wind profile studies have shown a linear relation between u and $\log z$ in effectively *adiabatic* conditions, i.e. in the absence of buoyancy effects, though in the case of surfaces of appreciable roughness (e.g. long grass) it is necessary to introduce a *zero-plane displacement*, d, allowing for the virtually stationary layer of air trapped within the roughness element, and to replace z by $z - d$. In the following presentations the simple form of Eq. (3.5) will be retained, it being implied that z is actually measured from the effective zero-plane. Indirect evaluation of u_* from the profile measurements, assuming the profile forms of Eq. (3.4) and (3.5), indicated that the flow was aerodynamically rough even for the smoothest of natural surfaces (snow fields and mud flats), except when the wind was light. However, the first step in the explicit verification of Eq. (3.5) in the atmosphere, with the same value of k as in the laboratory, was provided by Sheppard (1947), using a drag-plate technique for the measurement of the drag on a metal surface. Extension of the technique to a natural grass-covered surface by Pasquill (1950) and subsequent measurements by Rider (1954) consolidated the result.

Both Eq. (3.4) and (3.5) give

$$\frac{du}{dz} = \frac{u_*}{kz} \qquad (3.6)$$

and from this and Eq. (3.1), with F now the upward flux of momentum at height z (i.e. $= \overline{\rho u' w'} = -\tau_z$), the eddy diffusivity for momentum is

$$K_M = \frac{\tau_z}{\rho} \frac{kz}{u_*} \qquad (3.7)$$

Neglecting the variation of shearing stress τ with height, i.e. taking $\tau_z/\rho = \tau_0/\rho = u_*^2$, this reduces to the simple linear form

$$K_M = ku_* z = k^2 z^2 \, du/dz \qquad (3.8)$$

The constancy of shearing stress with height in the lower atmosphere (as also of the vertical flux of water vapour) is now accepted as a general principle [see Sutton (1953) and Priestley (1959)]. Typical values of K_M at $z = 1$ m, using the typical values of u_* listed by Sutton (1949), and taking $k = 0.4$, are given in Table 3.I. With the further assumption that

Table 3.I

Typical values of the eddy diffusivity, $K = ku_* z$, in adiabatic conditions (for mean wind speed 500 cm/sec at $z = 200$ cm, and assuming $k = 0.4$)

Type of surface	Roughness parameter z_0 (cm)	K at 200 cm (10^3 cm^2/sec)
Mud flats, ice	1×10^{-3}	1·3
Smooth sea	2×10^{-2}	1·7
Level desert	3×10^{-2}	1·8
Lawn (grass *c.* 1 cm)	0·1	2·2
Lawn (grass *c.* 5 cm)	1–2	3·4
Long grass (*c.* 60 cm)	4–9	4·8
Fully grown root crops	14	5·6

the eddy diffusivity for matter is identical with K_M, the former is now completely determinable, in adiabatic conditions, from observations of the wind profile alone. Measurements at a minimum of two heights, or three if a zero-plane displacement is necessary, are required to prescribe u_* and hence K.

The effect of thermal stratification on the eddy diffusivity for vertical transport in the lower atmosphere

The simplicity of the foregoing relations is immediately lost when the temperature gradient in the vertical departs from the adiabatic value and, in consequence, the vertical motions are affected by buoyancy forces. Qualitatively, it is obvious that these forces will enhance or suppress the vertical mixing according as the thermal stratification is unstable or stable, but a satisfactory quantitative expression of the effect on K, in terms of the obviously determining parameters (the shearing stress and the heat flux) has yet to be given. The problem amounts to generalizing Eq. (3.5), in accordance with wind profile observations which clearly show a departure from this logarithmic form, in the sense that $du/d(\log z)$ decreases with height in unstable conditions and increases with height in stable conditions. In terms of K this corresponds to an increase with height which is respectively more rapid and less rapid than the linear variation of Eq. (3.8).

Of the purely empirical extensions of the wind profile law the most attractive and applicable is that due independently to Laikhtman (1944) and Deacon (1949) who proposed the form

$$\frac{du}{dz} = az^{-\beta} \tag{3.9}$$

where a is independent of z, and β is greater or less than unity in unstable or stable conditions respectively. The integral form of Eq. (3.9), with a equated to $u_*/kz_0^{1-\beta}$ to provide transition to the adiabatic form as $\beta \to 1$, is

$$\frac{u}{u_*} = \frac{1}{k(1-\beta)} \left[\left(\frac{z}{z_0}\right)^{\beta-1} - 1 \right] \tag{3.10}$$

Deacon's observations showed that the magnitude of β determined from mean profiles was systematically related to the conditions of stability as represented by the Richardson number Ri, defined as

$$Ri = \frac{g}{T} \frac{(\partial T/\partial z) + \Gamma}{(\partial u/\partial z)^2} \tag{3.11}$$

where T is the absolute temperature and Γ the dry adaibatic lapse-rate of temperature. From the same arguments as led to Eq. (3.8)

$$K_M = ku_* z \left(\frac{z}{z_0}\right)^{\beta-1} = k^2 z^2 \frac{du}{dz} \left(\frac{z}{z_0}\right)^{2\beta-2} \tag{3.12}$$

Eq. (3.10) and (3.12) prescribe u_* and K_M entirely in terms of von Karman's constant and the shape of the wind profile. Explicit test of these relations, indirectly by Pasquill (1949) from measurements of natural evaporation and hence of K for vapour, directly by Rider (1954) from drag plate measurements of τ_0 and hence of K_M, showed clearly that the relations held to an adequate degree over grassland in unstable conditions, but were in considerable error in stable conditions, K_M being seriously underestimated. Deacon (1957) has attributed this discrepancy to the fact that in stable stratifications of the air flow, with consequent steepening of the wind profile, the wind speed at the level of the grass blades may become low enough for the viscous component of the drag to be important, in which case the condition of fully rough flow would not be satisfied. Apart from this fundamental difficulty, for which no satisfactory solution has yet been offered, there are other qualifications to be made. As Deacon pointed out, β is not truly constant with height, but converges on unity as the surface is approached, i.e. even in non-adiabatic conditions the flow close to the surface tends to the adiabatic regime represented by Eq. (3.5), a feature which is also reflected in the near-linear increase of Ri with height. Although a difficulty in principle, this can be turned to advantage in practice, in that if wind profile observations are practicable close to the surface (as for example over a relatively uniform area of short grass) K may be obtained with useful accuracy from Eq. (3.8) over a range of stability. Another complication is that the determination of β implies a knowledge of d^2u/dz^2, which is difficult to achieve with sufficient accuracy, and this is reflected in the fact that the statistics of β as derived from individual samples of wind profile measurement (say over a period of ten minutes or so) are commonly found to display considerable irregularity.

Early attempts by Rossby and Montgomery (1935) and Holzman (1943), the former on the basis of the mixing-length ideas, the latter on intuitive and empirical grounds, provided relations between K_M and Ri, containing in each case a 'constant' to be determined by observation. It suffices here to note that neither gives a comprehensive fit, the former failing in unstable conditions, the latter in stable conditions. More recently, the problem has been attacked on purely dimensional grounds, by several workers, with results that have raised considerable hopes for the attainment of a satisfactory universal wind profile. The lead was given by Monin and Obukhov

(1954) in a treatment which is usually described as one of 'similarity', and which gives wind profiles similarly shaped in relation to the parameter z/L, where L is a length-scale representing the stability, defined on dimensional grounds by

$$L = -\frac{u^3_* c_p \, \rho T}{kgH}$$ (3.13)

H being the upward turbulent flux of heat.   The parameter L is positive or negative in stable or unstable stratifications respectively, and becomes infinite in adiabatic conditions.   The constant value of $(kz/u_*)(du/dz)$ in neutral conditions [Eq. (3.6)] is now replaced by an undetermined function of the non-dimensional variable z/L, and retaining only the first term in a power-series representation of this function, i.e. restricting to small values of z/L, Eq. (3.6) is generalized to

$$\frac{du}{dz} = \frac{u_*}{kz}\left(1 + \alpha\frac{z}{L}\right)$$ (3.14)

Furthermore, in this case, if also the eddy diffusivities for heat (K_H) and momentum (K_M) are equal, it may be shown that z/L is equivalent to Ri, hence from (3.14) it follows that

$$K_M = ku_*z(1 - \alpha Ri)$$ (3.15)

Thus, in principle at least, and for small departures from adiabatic conditions, K_M may be prescribed completely in terms of the wind and temperature profiles, once the parameter α is specified.

From the earlier evaluations of α, carried out entirely on the basis of the shapes of the wind and temperature profiles, conflicting data were reported, including a value of 0·6 by Monin and Obukhov.   The acceptability of the values of α must ultimately be judged on the accuracy with which the explicit form (3.15) is satisfied, and it has been pointed out by Pasquill (see the discussion of the paper by Deacon (1959)) that Rider's (1954) data on $u_*/(zdu/dz)$ ($= K_M/u_*z$), when smoothed over a range of Ri from about $-0·1$ to $+0·1$, require $\alpha \simeq 2·5$ in stable conditions and $\alpha \simeq 9$ in unstable conditions.   Analysis of this feature has been discussed further by Taylor (1960) in terms both of Rider's data and Swinbank's (1955) direct measurements of eddy flux, and the conclusion reached that, for small values of Ri, α takes on a value of about 6.   Such a value has also been deduced theoretically by Priestley (1960) by applying an interpolation procedure to the expressions for the limiting cases of forced convection [i.e. Eq. (3.8)] and free convection.

Panofsky, Blackadar and McVehil (1960) have shown that collected data on the horizontal shearing stress in the lower atmosphere, in unstable conditions, can be closely fitted by a relation which is equivalent to

$$K_M = ku_*z(1 - \gamma' Ri)^{1/4}$$

with $\gamma' = 18$. This relation was attributed to Ellison (1957), but in Ellison's derivation γ' is explicitly a function of Ri (γ' is proportional to K_H/K_M, where K_H is the eddy diffusivity for heat). Panofsky (1961) has since given an independent derivation on dimensional grounds, assuming $K_M \propto \overline{(w'^2)}^{1/2}z$, and expressing $\overline{(w'^2)}^{1/2}$ as in Eq. (2.10). For small Ri the expression reduces to Eq. (3.15), with $\alpha = \gamma'/4 = 4.5$, which is to be compared with the value of about 6 derived by Taylor. In stable conditions $\gamma' = 18$ leads to values of K_M appreciably smaller than those observed.

An alternative method for determining τ (and hence K_M) from practicable observations has been suggested by Deacon (1959). This follows from equating the magnitudes of the rate of dissipation (ϵ) of turbulent energy, as expressed in terms of the so-called *structure function* introduced by Obukhov [see Eq. (2.4)], and in terms of the shearing stress. For neutral conditions the point is contained in Eq. (2.5), (2.6) and (2.7), from which it follows that K_M is determined by measurements of D_{trans} and the wind profile, once the non-dimensional constant C has been found. Deacon suggests that an empirical extension to conditions other than neutral should be possible, but the method has yet to be established and exploited.

Eddy diffusivity at greater heights

At heights above about 100 m or less, according to the conditions of surface heating or cooling, the variation with height of the horizontal shearing stress may not be neglected as a matter of course, and in view of this the convenience of taking K inversely proportional to the vertical gradient of wind velocity (as follows from Eq. (3.1) with F constant) can no longer be adopted. The treatment of the transport of momentum over these deeper layers has been generally reviewed by Sutton (1953) and Priestley (1959). In the present context it is especially relevant to note that the classical concept of a boundary layer of effectively infinite depth, with K either constant or increasing indefinitely with height, cannot be retained as a general rule. Rejection of the old concept was first advocated in treatments by Rossby (1932) and Rossby and Montgomery (1935), in the latter of which Eq. (3.8) was considered to apply up to a height of 50–100 m, with thereafter a decrease of K to a zero or small residual value at a height in the region of 500 m.

Rossby and Montgomery's model was broadly supported by determinations of K made by Mildner from detailed observations of the wind profile at Leipzig.   Later, from considerations of the shapes of the vertical profiles of temperature and humidity in stable air over the sea, up to heights of about 500 m, Booker (1948) concluded that here also the eddy diffusivity must decrease above some small height.   More recently the acquisition of data on the vertical component of turbulence (see 2.8) has strengthened the reasonable expectation that rapid vertical mixing will normally be confined to a limited depth of the atmosphere, according to the vertical extent of thermal convection.   The adoption of a form for K containing a more or less rapid decrease with height to small or zero value would therefore appear to be at least qualitatively acceptable.   However, for the quantitative detail of the variation of K over greater heights there is as yet no general framework of analysis equivalent to that developed for the surface layer.

3.2   Solutions of the parabolic equation of diffusion

The differential equation which has been the starting point of most mathematical treatments of diffusion from sources is a generalization of the classical equation for conduction of heat in a solid.   In the case of a turbulent fluid, with the concentration of suspended matter (mass per unit volume) at any point x, y, z denoted by χ, it is written as follows:

$$\frac{d\chi}{dt} = \frac{\partial}{\partial x}\left(K_x\,\frac{\partial\chi}{\partial x}\right) + \frac{\partial}{\partial y}\left(K_y\,\frac{\partial\chi}{\partial y}\right) + \frac{\partial}{\partial z}\left(K_z\,\frac{\partial\chi}{\partial z}\right) \qquad (3.16)$$

It will be noted that this equation allows for differences in the eddy diffusivities in the component directions, i.e. for anisotropic diffusion, and also for spatial variations of these diffusivities.   Sutton (1953) defines a *simple diffusion process* as one which is expressed completely by the above equation [i.e. one in which the rate of transfer across a reference plane is defined by Eq. (3.1)].   If the K's are constant, independent of x, y or z, the simplified equation and the type of diffusion implied are usually referred to as Fickian.   For a full discussion of the solutions of the Fickian equation, and a statement of the resulting expressions for the distribution downwind of sources of matter generated at a point or along a line, see Sutton (1953), Chapters 4 and 8).   The essential feature of these expressions is that the distribution of the suspended material, with respect to distance from the centre of the 'puff' in the case of instantaneous generation at a point, or from the line or plane through the point or line source, is of Gaussian form with variances (defined as at the end of 4.1)

$$\sigma_x{}^2 = 2K_x t = 2K_x x/u \text{ etc.} \qquad (3.17)$$

Comparison of the expressions with experimental data on diffusion in the atmosphere has from the beginning consistently shown that the equivalent values of K vary systematically with the time of travel, with position, and with the *scale* of the diffusion process (see later, in this section, in 3.4 and in 3.6). This has led to much preoccupation with the solving of Eq. (3.16) with the K's variable.

The two-dimensional form of the equation

As the most satisfactory progress has been made for the two-dimensional case, corresponding to the infinite cross-wind line source of material, emitting continuously at a constant rate, the development of this case will be treated first. With the usual coordinate system, and with the source along the y axis, $d\chi/dt$ reduces to $u(\partial\chi/\partial x)$ ($\bar{v}$ and $\bar{w}$ being zero, and a steady state, i.e. $\partial\chi/\partial t = 0$, being assumed). The second term on the right-hand side of Eq. (3.16) is zero, and neglecting the first term the equation finally becomes

$$\bar{u}\frac{\partial\chi}{\partial x} = \frac{\partial}{\partial z}\left(K_z\frac{\partial\chi}{\partial z}\right) \tag{3.18}$$

For the lower atmosphere, in adiabatic conditions, it has been seen that the wind velocity varies with the logarithm of the height, but such a variation proves intractable in the manipulation of Eq. (3.18), and progress has been made only by adopting a power-law form of wind profile. The significant mathematical step was provided by Roberts [unpublished, see Sutton (1953)] for the case when

$$K_z(z) = K_1\left(\frac{z}{z_1}\right)^n, \quad \bar{u}(z) = \bar{u}_1\left(\frac{z}{z_1}\right)^m \tag{3.19}$$

where $\bar{u}_1$ and K_1 are the values of $\bar{u}$ and K_z at a fixed reference height z_1. The boundary conditions are

$$\chi \to 0 \text{ as } x, z \to \infty$$
$$\chi \to \infty \text{ at } x = z = 0$$
$$K_z\frac{\partial\chi}{\partial z} \to 0 \text{ as } z \to 0, \ x > 0$$

and with Q the rate of emission per unit cross-wind length

$$\int_0^\infty u\chi(x, z)\, dz = Q \quad \text{for all } x > 0$$

The solution of Eq. (3.18), valid for $r = m - n + 2 > 0$, is

$$\chi(x, z) = \frac{Qr}{\bar{u}_1 \Gamma(s)} \left[\frac{\bar{u}_1}{(m-n+2)^2 K_1 x} \right]^s \exp \left[-\frac{\bar{u}_1 z^{m-n+2}}{(m-n+2)^2 K_1 x} \right] \qquad (3.20)$$

where $s = (m+1)/(m-n+2)$ and z_1 is taken to be unity.

When the horizontal shearing stress [i.e. $\rho K (du/dz)$] is assumed constant with height, it follows that $n = 1 - m$ (this is usually referred to as Schmidt's conjugate-power-law theorem). Note also that when $m = n = 0$ the solution reduces to the Fickian form.

An attractive composition of this mathematical solution with the physical laws for the wind profile and the shearing stress in the lower atmosphere in adiabatic conditions has been developed by Calder (1949), using power forms approximating to the logarithmic forms, viz.

$$u/u_* = q(u_* z/v)^\alpha \qquad (3.21)$$

and

$$u/u_* = q'(z/z_0)^\alpha \qquad (3.22)$$

respectively for smooth and rough flow. For a unified mathematical treatment Calder represents these in the general forms

$$\tau_0 = \epsilon \rho u^{2\beta} (\delta/z)^{2\alpha\beta} \qquad (3.23)$$

$$K(z) = (\epsilon/\alpha) \delta^{2\alpha\beta} u_1^{2\beta-1} z_1^{\alpha(1-2\beta)} z^{(1-\alpha)} \qquad (3.24)$$

where, for smooth flow

$$\beta = 1/(1+\alpha), \quad \delta = v, \quad \epsilon = (1/q)^{2/(1+\alpha)}$$

for rough flow

$$\beta = 1, \quad \delta = z_0, \quad \epsilon = 1/q'^2 \qquad (3.25)$$

In practice the basic parameters are determined from wind profile observations over the anticipated height-range of diffusion, the appropriate fitting to the power forms being accomplished by first obtaining the effective value of α [u varies as z^α in Eq. (3.23)], and evaluating u_* and z_0 from the logarithmic forms Eq. (3.4) and (3.5). Substitution of α, u_* and z_0 in Eq. (3.21) and (3.22) then gives q and q'. The full solution is given by substituting in (3.20) $m = \alpha$, $n = 1 - \alpha$ and K_1 as in Eq. (3.24) with z equal to unity.

A solution of Eq. (3.18), for wind constant with height ($m = 0$), and K varying linearly with height ($n = 1$), was stated by Bosanquet and Pearson

(1936), and an explicit version of this, with K as in Eq. (3.8), has been put forward by Calder (1952) as a useful approximation. The result is

$$\chi = \frac{Q}{ku_*x} \exp \left(\frac{-uz}{ku_*x}\right) \qquad (3.26)$$

and as Calder has demonstrated this gives an agreement with observations almost as good as that obtained with the more elaborate solution in his 1949 paper. In conditions other than adiabatic Deacon (1949) has applied Robert's solution with the form of K in Eq. (3.12), together with a simple power-law wind profile as in Eq. (3.22), and has obtained reasonable agreement with data on short range diffusion in conditions of moderate instability. However, the little data in very unstable conditions did not support the derivation and in stable conditions, as discussed previously, the wind-profile law in Eq. (3.10) is unacceptable.

It may be noted that a detailed analysis of the two-dimensional equation of diffusion, though in the different context of the problem of evaporation from a plane, free-liquid surface, has been given by W. G. L. Sutton (1943), again for the conjugate-power-law condition, i.e. with $n = 1 - m$ in Eq. (3.19). Rounds (1955) has given further discussion, adopting forms for K and u as used by Deacon above, and so includes the condition $n \geqslant 1$ not included in Sutton's work. Solutions are given by Rounds for an arbitary initial distribution of material, and these are then applied to several types of source. In particular, solutions are given in graphical form for the concentration at ground-level from a cross-wind line source at arbitrary height, both for the previous condition when the increase of K with height is supposed to continue indefinitely, and also for the case when upward diffusion is suddenly halted by an overhead stable layer, by imposing the condition that the flux $K(\partial\chi/\mathrm{d}z)$ is zero at this level (see also reference to Rounds' solution in 6.2).

In the more general context of the point-source problem (see later) F. B. Smith (1957a) has also treated the two-dimensional equation, for the case of an elevated line source, with the conjugate-power-laws for wind and diffusivity. Smith's analysis includes a proof of the so-called reciprocal theorem, namely that the concentration distribution at ground level due to a source at height H is identical with the horizontal distribution at height H due to a source at ground level. Later work by Smith (1957b and c) has dealt further with the vertical diffusion in a layer of finite depth h bounded by the ground and the base of a stable region in the atmosphere, using forms of K as follows, and assuming constant $\bar{u}$:

(i) $K = $ constant

(ii) $K \propto z^\alpha$ $0 \leqslant z \leqslant h$

(iii) $K \propto (h-z)^\alpha$ $0 \leqslant z \leqslant h$ (3.27)

(iv) $K \propto z(h-z)$ $0 \leqslant z \leqslant h$

(v) $K \propto z$ $0 \leqslant z \leqslant h/2$

$\propto (h-z)$ $h/2 \leqslant z \leqslant h$

Note that in (v) the maximum of K occurs at the mid-height of the finite layer. The solutions are in the form of rapidly convergent series which can usually be evaluated adequately with a small number of terms.

Smith's treatment is also particularly notable in containing the first attempt to incorporate an additional transport mechanism specifically representing the effect of thermally-driven convection. An idealized model was assumed, in which bubbles or streams of air rise from the ground to the top of the layer, and are replaced by a uniform subsidence throughout the layer. In the first attempt (1957b) the 'thermals' were considered to be completely isolated from the surrounding atmosphere, but later (1957c) entrainment from the environment into the ascending currents was introduced.

The distribution of material by the convection process was represented mathematically by a series of sources which subside from the top of the layer, and by an appropriate reduction in the source strength assigned to the cloud spreading upward from ground-level in the usual way. For the diffusion from the sources K was assumed to have the forms

$$K = a(h-z) \quad (1957b)$$
$$K = bz^{-\alpha} \quad (1957c) \qquad \Big\} \, 0 \leqslant z \leqslant h \qquad (3.28)$$

where a and b are constants.

For further details of Smith's solutions reference should be made to the original papers. The treatments are so far purely formal in that the magnitudes of K, and of the convective circulations, have yet to be suitably assigned in relation to the dynamical conditions of atmospheric convection. They do however provide a mathematical framework in readiness for this step, and it is of interest to note, for example, the general concentration distribution for a cross-wind line source at the ground, with $K = a(h-z)$ and λ, the compensating velocity of subsidence (generally assumed to be βa) taken to be $0.5a$. The distributions in non-convective and convective conditions are shown graphically in Fig. 3.1, in the form of isopleths of $\chi \bar{u} h / Q$ against height and distance in the non-dimensional terms z/h and $ax/\bar{u}h$ ($Q/\bar{u}h$ is the final uniform concentration). The second graph shows a more rapid attainment of uniform concentration, and a vertical profile of concentration with maxima at the ground and the top of the finite layer, both of which features are a consequence of the particular convective model assumed.

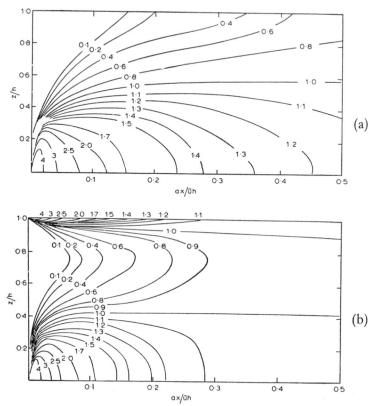

FIG. 3.1   Isopleths of the concentration parameter $\chi uh/Q$ for a cross-wind line source at ground-level, in an atmosphere with $K = a(h - z)$, for $0 \leqslant z \leqslant h$ and wind constant with height. (a) without convection; (b) with convection, $\lambda = 0.5a$. (Smith, 1957b)

The continuous point source

For a source which is continuously generating material at a fixed point, the appropriate form of (3.16) (again with w and v zero, and neglecting the first term on the right-hand side) is

$$\bar{u} \frac{d\chi}{dx} = \frac{\partial}{\partial y}\left(K_y \frac{\partial \chi}{\partial y}\right) + \frac{\partial}{\partial z}\left(K_z \frac{\partial \chi}{\partial z}\right) \tag{3.29}$$

As noted previously, it was evident at an early stage that observations of diffusion implied a dependence of K_y on the distance of travel.   On the grounds that it is physically irrational to regard K_y as a function of *horizontal position* in this particular sense, one approach has been to seek solutions with K_y, as well as K_z, a function of height above the ground.

Davies (1950) has given a solution of Eq. (3.29) for the special case when K_z and $\bar{u}$ are as in Eq. (3.19), with $n = 1 - m$, and $K_y \propto z^m$.   The solution is known to be unacceptable in that it gives an axial concentration which varies as $x^{-1\cdot40}$, whereas the empirical value of the exponent, for short distances downwind of a continuous point source at ground level, is about 1·75.   Indeed Davies shows that in order to satisfy this variation it is necessary for K_y to vary with z raised to a power $1 + m(1 - 3m)/(1 + m)$, and with values of $m \simeq \frac{1}{7}$ as normally assumed this power is slightly greater than unity.

A complete solution of Eq. (3.29) for unrestricted values of the exponent in the variation of K_y has yet to be given, but progress has been made by Smith (1957a) in the sense that an exact solution has been obtained for the standard deviation of the cross-wind distribution, for a ground level source, and for K_y varying as $z^{n+\mu}$ and K_z varying as z^n.   The general solution is given in the form of a series, which converges rapidly enough for adequate evaluation with usually no more than eight terms.   For special values of n and μ the solution can be simplified.   The solution is also generalized to give the *ground* distribution from an elevated source, and the *whole* distribution from such a source on the assumption that the cross-wind distribution always has a Gaussian form.

In an attempt to generalize Calder's explicit treatment of the two-dimensional case, Davies (1954) has treated Eq. (3.29) with K_y as a function of both z and y.   A y-variation with reference to the cross-wind distance measured from the *centre-line* of the cloud, rather than to position in the atmosphere, is not physically unreasonable and is in keeping with the variation with scale which is deemed necessary in the case of a diffusing cluster (see 3.6).   A solution is given with u and K_z as in (3.19), with $n = 1 - m$, and with $K_y \propto z^m y^\alpha$, and is evaluated for comparison with observation when $\alpha = 1 - 2m$.   Although reasonable agreement is obtained with the observed properties of a point-source cloud at a fixed distance, the variation with distance is in error.

It may be noted that the difficulties which have arisen in connection with lateral diffusion will presumably also apply in a similar way to vertical diffusion from a source well clear of the ground.

3.3   The limited velocity of propagation of material

The preceding discussions have all been in terms of a differential equation which is of parabolic form.   This has the disadvantage of not taking into account the fact that the rate of movement of matter outward from a source must have a finite limit.   A review of the point, and some discussion and use of an alternative *hyperbolic* form has been presented by Monin (1959).

Considering the case of vertical diffusion, and postulating a maximum vertical velocity of the diffusing smoke, w^*, Monin expresses the equation of the upper boundary of the plume simply as

$$\frac{dz}{dx} = \frac{w^*}{u} \tag{3.30}$$

Writing for u the integral form of Eq. (3.14)

$$\frac{dz}{dx} = \frac{kw^*}{u_*} \bigg/ \left[\ln \frac{z}{z_0} + \phi\left(\frac{z}{L}\right) \right] \tag{3.31}$$

for small z/L, i.e. for small departures from adiabatic conditions, k being von Karman's constant.   Monin evaluates w^*/u_* by appeal to the turbulent energy balance equation, and again for small values of z/L obtains

$$\frac{w^*}{u_*} \simeq \lambda\left(1 - \frac{z}{4L}\right) \tag{3.32}$$

λ being the value of the ratio when $z/L = 0$, i.e. in adiabatic conditions. From Eq. (3.32) and (3.31) it is clear that in adiabatic conditions the slope of the upper boundary of a plume varies inversely as $\ln z/z_0$, i.e. as the wind velocity at the upper boundary.   On the other hand in unstable conditions (z/L negative) this decrease in slope with distance will tend to be compensated, and may even be changed to an increase.   Using a more general empirical form of relation between $\bar{u}$ and u_* (attributed to Monin and Obukhov), in which the restriction to small values of z/L is not imposed, and integrating numerically, Monin has obtained the shapes of the upper boundary of a smoke plume and has presented these graphically.   The curve shows a vertical growth of the smoke plume which is more rapid than linear with distance in unstable conditions, and less rapid than linear in stable conditions.

For the determination of the distribution of material with height, Monin proposes the use of a hyperbolic equation, which is stated to be consistent with the principle of limited propagation velocity, in the form

$$\frac{\partial \chi}{\partial t} + \frac{\partial F}{\partial z} = 0, \quad \frac{\partial F}{\partial t} + 2aF = -w^* \frac{\partial w^* \chi}{\partial z} \tag{3.33}$$

where F is the vertical flux, and a is described as a 'typical frequency' of the turbulence, which is given the form

$$a = \frac{u_*}{z}\,\psi\!\left(\frac{z}{L}\right)$$

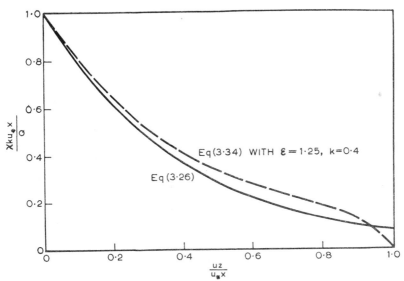

FIG. 3.2   Vertical profiles of concentration according to certain solutions of the parabolic and hyperbolic equations of diffusion

In general, i.e. for any stratification, Eq. (3.33) can be solved numerically, but solution into a usable closed form is possible only for adiabatic conditions and then, neglecting horizontal mixing and the variation of wind with height, Monin obtains

$$\chi(x,z) = \frac{Q}{ku_*x}\,\frac{\left(1-\dfrac{\bar{u}z}{\lambda u_*x}\right)^{\epsilon-1}}{\left(1+\dfrac{\bar{u}z}{\lambda u_*z}\right)^{\epsilon+1}},\quad 0 \leqslant z \leqslant \frac{\lambda u_*x}{\bar{u}} \qquad (3.34)$$

where $\epsilon = \lambda/2k \geqslant 1$. For $z=0$ the expression is identical with that obtained by Calder, Eq. (3.26), and a comparison of the vertical profiles is shown in Fig. 3.2 for $\epsilon = 1\cdot25$, an empirical value deduced by Monin from examination of data on smoke plumes, and $k=0\cdot4$. As would be expected the discrepancy between the two becomes large only near the 'top' of the cloud, where Monin's profile, in accordance with the concept of finite propagation velocity suddenly falls to zero concentration. Eq. (3.34)

7—A.D.

means that the concentration profiles are of similar shape at different distances, i.e. they can be expressed universally in terms of z/x, and Monin concludes that this is also approximately true for any stratification and for wind velocity varying with height.

3.4 Statistical analyses of the diffusion from a continuous source at a fixed position

Much of the difficulty which has been seen to arise in the transfer-theory approach to the diffusion from a continuous source may be resolved by the purely statistical treatment introduced by G. I. Taylor in his 1921 paper.

Taylor's analysis

The starting point of the treatment is the essentially mathematical (statistical) analysis of the properties of a continuously varying quantity. Taylor's discussion is at first in terms of fluctuations of barometric pressure, though the same argument could be immediately stated for the random fluctuations of *particle* velocity which were the ultimate subject of application, and this discussion includes a demonstration that the usual laws of differentiation may be applied to the mean values of fluctuating variables and their products. Then, if X is the deviation of a typical particle, due to the eddy velocity u', after a time t, and $\overline{X^2}$ the mean square of a large number of values of X,

$$\frac{d\overline{X^2}}{dt} = 2\overline{X\frac{dX}{dt}}$$

$$= 2\overline{Xu'}$$

$$= 2\int_0^t \overline{u'(t)u'(t+\xi)}d\xi \qquad (3.35)$$

If the turbulence is homogeneous and stationary, i.e. if the average properties are uniform in space and steady in time, the velocity product may be replaced by $\overline{u'^2}R(\xi)$, where $R(\xi)=\overline{u'(t)u'(t+\xi)}/\overline{u'^2}$ is a correlation coefficient of Lagrangian type. With $R(\xi)$ and $\overline{u'^2}$ both independent of the time origin the familiar results then follow,

$$\frac{d\overline{X^2}}{dt} = 2\overline{u'^2}\int_0^t R(\xi)d\xi \qquad (3.36)$$

and

$$\overline{X^2} = 2\overline{u'^2}\int_0^T \int_0^t R(\xi)d\xi\,dt \qquad (3.37)$$

where X is now the deviation of the particle in time T.

The mean square of the deviations undergone by a single particle in a succession of equal time intervals was thus completely expressed in terms of the mean square eddy velocity of the particle, and the so-called Lagrangian correlation coefficient, $R(\xi)$, between the velocity of the particle at time t and that at time $t+\xi$. Two simple deductions from this result followed immediately, without any assumptions regarding $R(\xi)$, other than the obvious ones that it should be unity when $\xi=0$ and is effectively zero for large ξ, say $\xi > t_1$. Hence, for small T

$$\overline{X^2} = \overline{u'^2}T^2 \tag{3.38}$$

for large T

$$\overline{X^2} = 2\left(\int_0^{t_1} R(\xi)d\xi \right)\overline{u'^2}T \tag{3.39}$$

the integral in the bracket being a constant *time-scale* of turbulence analogous to the *length-scale* of turbulence defined in Eq. (1.3).

The meaning of the result in relation to the dispersion of material emitted continuously from a source at a fixed point in the flow may now be considered, with the necessary assumptions that the material particles introduced do not affect the flow, and that they assume the fluid velocity completely. In effect we are now considering a large number of particles as they pass a given *fixed* point in succession. The statistics of the displacements of these separate particles, from the position they would otherwise occupy as a result of the mean flow alone, are clearly identical with those of the displacements of a single particle observed a large number of times. This follows merely by virtue of the original assumption that $\overline{u'^2}$ for the single particle is a constant, independent of time and representative of the whole field of turbulence. Hence, with the usual system of co-ordinates and eddy velocities, and with the source at $(0, 0, 0)$, the component variances of the particle displacements from the appropriate centre of gravity, i.e. $(x, 0, 0)$, after a time of travel $T=x/\bar{u}$, are

$$\overline{X^2} = 2\overline{u'^2} \int_0^{x/\bar{u}} \int_0^{t} R_x(\xi)d\xi\; dt$$

$$\overline{Y^2} = 2\overline{v'^2} \int_0^{x/\bar{u}} \int_0^{t} R_y(\xi)d\xi\; dt \tag{3.40}$$

$$\overline{Z^2} = 2\overline{w'^2} \int_0^{x/\bar{u}} \int_0^{t} R_z(\xi)d\xi\; dt$$

different values of $R(\xi)$ for the component motions of the particles being recognized. Expressions corresponding to the limiting conditions of

Eq. (3.38) and (3.39) apply with $T = x/\bar{u}$, so that at very short distances the variances are proportional to x^2, and at very long distances to x. Thus the spread of the plume, as represented by the standard deviation in the cross-wind and vertical directions, starts off with a linear form (proportional to x) and ultimately tends to a parabolic form (proportional to $\sqrt{x}$).

Development and generalization of Taylor's analysis

The results stated above have been the subject of much restatement and elaboration, notably by Kampé de Fériet and Batchelor. Kampé de Fériet (1939) has expressed the equation for $\overline{X^2}$ also in the form

$$\overline{X^2} = 2\overline{u'^2} \int_0^T (T - \xi)R(\xi)d\xi \tag{3.41}$$

and by applying the Fourier-transform relation between $R(\xi)$ and the corresponding Lagrangian spectrum function $F_L(n)$, as in Eq. (1.8), this becomes

$$\overline{X^2} = \overline{u'^2} \int_0^\infty F_L(n) \left(\frac{1 - \cos 2\pi n T}{2(\pi n)^2} \right) dn \tag{3.42}$$

which with further simple transformation may be written

$$\overline{X^2} = \overline{u'^2} T^2 \int_0^\infty F_L(n) \frac{\sin^2 (\pi n T)}{(\pi n T)^2} dn \tag{3.43}$$

Similar expressions may be written for other components. A statement of this spectral representation, in tensor notation, has been set out by Batchelor (1949) in an extended discussion of diffusion in homogeneous turbulence. The result means that at short time (T), when the integral becomes unity (and $\overline{X^2} = \overline{u'^2} T^2$), the oscillations (of particle velocity) of all frequency contribute to the dispersion exactly as they do to the turbulent energy. At larger value of T the slower oscillations progressively dominate the dispersion; in effect the high-frequency components merely oscillate the position of the particle, whereas the low-frequency components tend to displace it in a more sustained way.

Batchelor's discussion contains an important recognition regarding the applicability of the theory of universal equilibrium outlined in 1.3. Since the dispersion is at no time dominated by the high-frequency oscillations, i.e. by the small-scale structure, it follows that it is not possible to apply the theory to the dispersion of material from a *continuous source at a fixed position*. The relation between the properties of dispersion, and those implied by transfer theory, is also discussed. On the basis of experimental evidence, from studies in effectively homogeneous turbulence in wind tunnels, that the probability distribution of the fluid particle displacement is normal, it follows that the diffusion may be represented by a differential equation of the Fickian type, with the effective K defined by

$$K = \frac{1}{2}\frac{\overline{dX^2}}{dt} \qquad (3.44)$$

From Eq. (3.36) this effective K is at first zero, increases with time at first linearly and then more slowly, and then finally tends to the constant value

$$K = \overline{u'^2}\int_0^{t_1} R(\xi)d\xi \qquad (3.45)$$

where t_1 is the value of ξ beyond which $R(\xi)$ remains zero. It was recognized at an early stage in the study of the spread of smoke plumes in the atmosphere over short distances that an increase of Fickian K with distance of travel was implied. In terms of the foregoing analysis this result is due to the slower oscillations of the eddy velocities, i.e. the larger eddies. This is not, as is sometimes implied however, a matter of the progressively more important effect of the larger eddies as dispersion increases, for all frequencies of oscillation are effective from the beginning *when the source is continuous*. The real reason is that slower oscillations of dominating amplitude tend to maintain $R(\xi)$ at its initially high value, whereas, true Fickian diffusion implies $R(\xi)$ falling to zero in a time very small compared with the time of travel involved.

Understanding of the various features of dispersion in homogeneous turbulence is often helped by more detailed reference to the spectrum representation in Eq. (3.43). The spectrum weighting function, which imposes the combined influence of eddy frequency (n) and of time of travel (T), is the same as that already discussed in 1.4 in relation to measurements of turbulent velocities at a fixed point in the flow, and the shape is that given in Fig. 1.5. The effect on the variation of dispersion with time of travel is represented in Fig. 3.3. Here, the outer curve represents the shape of the full spectrum of turbulent velocity (of a particle), a form equivalent to Eq. (1.11) being adopted for convenience, i.e. corresponding to

$$R(\xi) = \exp\left(-t/t_L\right)$$

where

$$t_L = \int_0^{\infty} R(\xi)d\xi$$

For generality and simplicity (as in Fig. 1.1) the ordinates are $\pi n F(n)$, the maximum value of which is unity, and the abscissae are $2\pi t_L n$ on a logarithmic scale. The integral in Eq. (3.43) is proportional to the area under this curve when it is weighted by the expression $\sin^2(\pi n T)/(\pi n T)^2$, and the inner curves show the effect of this weighting function for various values of T/t_L. When $T/t_L = 0$ the original spectrum curve applies, the integrand is unity, and $\overline{X^2} = \overline{u'^2} T^2$. In general $\overline{X^2}/T^2$ is proportional to the areas under the curves, and thus diminishes systematically with T as the high-frequency side of the spectrum is effectively cut off.

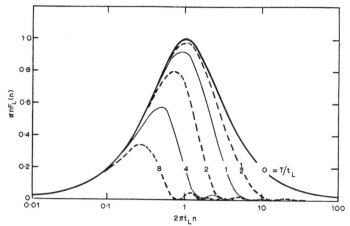

F<small>IG</small>. 3.3   Spectrum representation of the effect of time of travel on the dispersion of particles from a continuous point source in homogeneous turbulence. T is the time of travel, t_L the Lagrangian time-scale defined by $\int_0^\infty R(\xi)\,d\xi$, and $F_L(n)$ is the corresponding Lagrangian spectrum function, with $R(\xi)$ assumed to be of exponential form

Referring to the derivation of the appropriate weighting function in 1.4 it will be seen that this function represents the effect of averaging the fluctuating velocity over a specified time interval before determining the variance. Thus, the quantity

$$\overline{u'^2} \int_0^\infty F_L(n) \frac{\sin^2(\pi n T)}{(\pi n T)^2}\, dn$$

is simply the variance of the turbulent velocity when the latter has been averaged over a time T, and following the subscript nomenclature of 1.4, Eq. (3.43) may be written in the simple form

$$\overline{X^2} = \overline{u'^2}_{\infty,T}\, T^2 \tag{3.46}$$

This is merely the definition of X as the product of the time of travel and the velocity of the particle *averaged over the time of travel*. The result is of course implicit in the usual form of Taylor's relation, Eq. (3.37), though this is not obvious immediately. In the form Eq. (3.46) it seems first to have been recognized by Ogura (1952 and later papers), although no discussion was given of the attractively simple interpretation which it provides, in that the dispersion relation in Eq. (3.43) may be obtained directly, by writing the definition of $\overline{X^2}$ as in Eq. (3.46), and inserting the form of the weighting function (for averaging) as simply derived in 1.4 and stated in Eq. (1.25).

So far it has been assumed that the time over which the history of the single particle is observed and, correspondingly, the time over which a continuous source is maintained, are both long enough for all the turbulent velocity fluctuations, however low in frequency, to exert their effect statistically. It is immediately clear from experience, however, that this will often not be so in the case of diffusion in the atmosphere. Very close to the source it is physically obvious that the linear law, say $\overline{Y^2} = \overline{v'^2} T^2$, must apply for release of particles over any arbitrary time τ, with $\overline{v'^2}$ now representing the velocities *at the position of the source* over the time τ. The magnitude of $\overline{v'^2}$ is known to be a function of sampling time, τ, and in many cases of atmospheric turbulence will still be increasing with τ for times which may be of practical interest as regards release of airborne material.

A formal expression in entirely Lagrangian terms follows directly from the relations in 1.4. Using the subscript notation of 1.4 for sampling duration and averaging time, if the spectrum of particle velocity is represented by a total variance $\overline{v'^2_{\infty,0}}$, with spectrum shape $F_L(n)$, then the dispersion $\overline{Y^2}$, observed by measuring particle displacements in a time T from initial positions which are uniformly distributed in a period τ in the trajectory of a typical particle, is given by

$$\overline{Y^2} = \overline{v'^2_{\tau,T}}\, T^2$$

and writing $\overline{v_\tau^2}_{,T}$ from Eq. (1.30)

$$\overline{Y^2} = \overline{v'^2_{\infty,0}} T^2 \int_0^\infty F_L(n)\left(1 - \frac{\sin^2 \pi n\tau}{(\pi n\tau)^2}\right) \frac{\sin^2 \pi nT}{(\pi nT)^2}\, dn \qquad (3.47)$$

The practical expression of the dispersion of particles released serially from a fixed point, over a finite time (or the equivalent case of the dispersion from a permanent continuous source when the dispersion is observed or sampled for a finite time), requires that Eq. (3.47) should be transformed into Eulerian terms, and this feature is considered later.

The effect of shear

The preceding analysis is strictly valid only for homogeneous turbulence, and the extension to sheared flow is very difficult, because the Lagrangian properties then depend on the initial position and subsequent trajectory of the particle.   An extension limited to small times of diffusion has been provided by Batchelor and Townsend (1956) in connection with the interpretation of wind tunnel experiments on the spread of heat from a line source.   For a line source parallel to the y axis the vertical displacement Z of particles at a short distance x downwind has the following properties:

$$\frac{\overline{Z}}{x} = \frac{-\overline{u'w'}}{\bar{u}^2} + \frac{\overline{u'^2w'}}{\bar{u}^3} - \cdots$$

$$\frac{\overline{Z^2}}{x^2} = \frac{\overline{w'^2}}{\bar{u}^2} - \frac{2\overline{u'w'^2}}{\bar{u}^3} + \cdots \tag{3.48}$$

In the special case of homogeneous turbulence, when the intercorrelations involving u' and w' are zero, $\overline{Z}=0$ and $\overline{Z^2}/x^2$ reduces to $\overline{w'^2}/\bar{u}^2$ [Equivalent to Eq. (3.38)].   In general, however, the equations show that to the approximation given by the first two terms, the cloud is initially inclined upward at an angle $-\overline{u'w'}/\bar{u}^2$ and has an initial angle of spread $[\sqrt{(\overline{Z^2})}/x]$ differing from that in homogeneous turbulence by a fraction of order $(\overline{u'^2})^{1/2}/\bar{u}$.

3.5   The form of the Lagrangian correlogram and spectrum

Although the foregoing treatment of diffusion from a continuous point source in homogeneous turbulence requires, for its full exploitation, an explicit formulation of the Lagrangian correlogram or spectrum, a good deal of clarification may be achieved merely by examining the consequences of assuming various possible functional forms.   The exponential form

$$R(\xi) = \exp\left(-\xi/t_L\right) \tag{3.49}$$

was used by Taylor in his original discussion of the results in Eq. (3.37). Frenkiel (1952a) has considered this and other forms including

$$R(\xi) = \exp\left(-\frac{\pi\xi^2}{4t_L^2}\right) \tag{3.50}$$

where t_L, as before, is the time-scale as defined by

$$t_L = \int_0^\infty R(\xi) d\xi \tag{3.51}$$

For simplified considerations of the diffusion law Inoue (1950) has applied a form

$$R(\xi) = 1, \quad \xi \leqslant t_L \tag{3.52}$$
$$= 0, \quad \xi \geqslant t_L$$

and in further discussion (1951) has used a relation equivalent to

$$R(\xi) = 1 - \xi/2t_L, \quad \xi \leqslant 2t_L \tag{3.53}$$

Substitution of the above forms in the y-component equation corresponding to Eq. (3.37) leads to the following relations for dispersion, expressed in a common non-dimensional form, following Frenkiel (loc. cit.), in which $D^2 = Y^2/t_L^2 \overline{v'^2}$ and $T' = T/t_L$

From Eq. (3.49)

$$D^2 = 2[\exp(-T') + T' - 1] \tag{3.54}$$

From Eq. (3.53) and assuming $R(\xi) = 0$ for $\xi \geqslant 2t_L$

$$D^2 = T'^2\left(1 - \frac{T'}{6}\right), \quad T \leqslant 2t_L$$

$$= 2T' - \frac{4}{3}, \quad T \geqslant 2t_L \tag{3.55}$$

From Eq. (3.50)

$$D^2 = 2T' \operatorname{erf}\left(\frac{\pi^{1/2}T'}{2}\right) + \frac{4}{\pi}\exp\left(-\frac{\pi T'^2}{4}\right) - \frac{4}{\pi} \tag{3.56}$$

From Eq. (3.52)

$$D^2 = T'^2 \quad T \leqslant t_L$$
$$= 2T' - 1 \quad T \geqslant t_L \tag{3.57}$$

Values of D (i.e. $(\overline{Y^2}/\overline{v'^2}T^2)^{1/2}$) are shown in Table 3.II for a suitable range of T/t_L, and graphs for the two extreme shapes of correlograms, i.e. the 'square form' Eq. (3.52) and the exponential form Eq. (3.49), are shown in Fig. 3.4. As can be seen from the table, the dispersion curves for the other two forms of correlogram, i.e. the 'Gaussian form' Eq. (3.50) and the 'triangular form' Eq. (3.53), would lie between the curves in

Fig. 3.4. Lines corresponding to the asymptotic limits applicable for any form of correlogram i.e.

$$D = T' \text{ as } T' \to 0$$

$$D = \sqrt{(2T')} \text{ as } T' \to \infty$$

are also shown.

Table 3.II

Values of the dispersion parameter, $D = (\overline{Y^2}/t_L{}^2\,\overline{v'^2})^{1/2}$, for a continuous point source in homogeneous turbulence, computed from Eq (3.37) with various forms of Lagrangian correlation coefficient $R(\xi)$

$T' = T/t_L$		0·1	0·2	0·4	1·0	2·0	4·0	10·0
$R(\xi)$ according to	Eq (3.49)	0·098	0·193	0·375	0·86	1·51	2·46	4·24
	Eq (3.53)	0·099	0·197	0·386	0·91	1·63	2·58	4·32
	Eq (3.50)	0·100	0·199	0·396	0·94	1·65	2·59	4·33
	Eq (3.52)	0·100	0·200	0·400	1·00	1·73	2·65	4·36

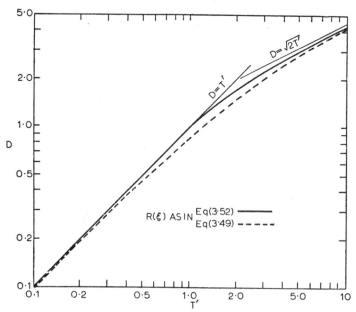

Fig. 3.4   Relation between dispersion and time of travel in homogeneous turbulence for assumed forms of $R(\xi)$. $D^2 = \overline{Y^2}/t_L{}^2\,\overline{v'^2}$ and $T' = T/t_L$

These results show certain useful properties.   In the first place it is clear that the form of the D, T' curve is insensitive to wide variations in the shape of the Lagrangian correlogram.   The variation imposed on D by the present range of shapes is a maximum when T' is near unity, and there has an overall range of about 20 per cent.   With this as an approximate upper limit of uncertainty the dispersion can be expressed entirely in terms of the intensity and scale of turbulence by adopting say the simple square form of correlogram.   Furthermore, within a similar magnitude of error the curves can be represented by the linear asymptotic form for $T' < 1$ and by the parabolic asymptotic form for $T' > 4$, and indeed at $T' = 10$ [i.e. when $\sqrt{(2T')} = 4\cdot47$] it can be seen from Table 3.II that in all cases D is within 5 per cent of this asymptotic value.   Finally, a good approach to the complete curves of Fig. 3.4 would be represented by adopting the linear and parabolic laws respectively below and above $T' = 1$ and 4, and interpolating linearly (on a log-log basis) for the intermediate range of T'.   For the virtually linear range $\sqrt{(\overline{Y^2})}$ is independent of the scale as well as the shape of the correlogram, and is determined by the intensity of turbulence alone, while in the virtually parabolic range the scale of turbulence is effective only as the square root.   This brings out the point that a good first approximation to the dispersion from a continuous point source in a field of homogeneous turbulence will be obtainable from a good estimate of the intensity of turbulence and a rough estimate of the Lagrangian scale of turbulence.

Explicit forms of $R(\xi)$

The difficulties of measuring Lagrangian properties except in very special experimental studies (see 2.5) have already been noted, and on the purely theoretical side no progress has yet been made which is effective in the present context.   The final step in the application of Eq. (3.37) and its developments thus rests entirely on some form of indirect empirical argument.

Power-law forms of $R(\xi)$ which are tractable when substituted in Taylor's expression, leading to diffusion formulae which have been used extensively, were put forward by O. G. Sutton (1932, 1934).   The form first conjectured

$$R(\xi) = \left(\frac{a}{\bar{u}\xi}\right)^n \qquad (3.58)$$

where n is a positive constant, gives with Eq. (3.37),

$$\overline{X^2} = \frac{2a^n}{(1-n)(2-n)}\,\bar{u}T^{2-n} \quad n \neq 1 \text{ or } 2 \qquad (3.59)$$

the values of n and a being left to be determined by comparison with experimental data. At this stage the value of the approach lay in the feature that it enabled a number of observations to be represented without large variations in the parameters a and n, whereas interpretation through the Fickian law required an enormous range of values of K. In the later analysis (1934) this form for $R(\xi)$ was replaced by

$$R(\xi) = \left(\frac{\nu}{\nu + \overline{w'^2}\xi}\right)^n \qquad (3.60)$$

where ν was subsequently identified as the kinematic viscosity of the air.

Justification of this form was provided by appeal to an aerodynamic result. By writing the eddy diffusivity as in Eq. (3.45), though necessarily with a different meaning attached to t_1, and invoking mixing length relations due to Prandtl and von Karman, a form for K was obtained. On substitution in 3.1, and assuming F constant with height, this gave the following result for the horizontal shearing stress

$$\tau_z = \tau_0 = f(n)\rho\nu^n\bar{u}_1{}^{2-n}z_1{}^{-n} \qquad (3.61)$$

with $f(n)$ an explicit function of n. From comparison with the experimental law for the resistance of a smooth pipe to turbulent flow, it was found that agreement in functional form would be given by $n = \frac{1}{4}$, and substitution of this in $f(n)$ gave a value of $0 \cdot 020$, compared with an observed coefficient of $0 \cdot 023$. Sutton later generalized this result to the case of aerodynamically rough flow by replacing ν in Eq. (3.60) by the macroviscosity $u_* z_0$.

Substitution of Eq. (3.60) in Eq. (3.37) gave

$$\overline{X^2} = \frac{2\nu^n}{(1-n)(2-n)\overline{u'^2}}\overline{(u'^2}T)^{2-n} \qquad (3.62)$$

$$= \tfrac{1}{2}C_x{}^2(\bar{u}T)^{2-n} \qquad (3.63)$$

where

$$C_x{}^2 = \frac{4\nu^n}{(1-n)(2-n)\bar{u}^n}\left(\frac{\overline{u'^2}}{\bar{u}^2}\right)^{1-n} \qquad (3.64)$$

with similar expressions for $\overline{Y^2}$ and $\overline{Z^2}$ involving v', C_y and w', C_z respectively. With the assumptions of Gaussian distribution in the diffusing cloud and of wind constant with height, these expressions immediately give the well-known formulae for point and line sources (see Chapter 5).

There are various approximations involved in the above analysis, for details of which the full discussion by Sutton (1953) should be consulted. The main point to be noted here is that the analysis led to simple power forms for the spread of a plume, the exponent being derivable from the implied power-law variation of wind with height [since in accordance with Eq. (3.61) $u \propto z^{n/(2-n)}$]. It should be recalled, however, that from Taylor's analysis, on which the derivation is directly based, the relation between spread and distance is not strictly expressible in power-law form, and could only be so represented by accepting an exponent varying with distance, from unity at short distance to $\frac{1}{2}$ at long distance. The difference is partly concerned with the fact that the integral of Eq. (3.60) is not convergent, and this together with the point that the analysis is used to derive the stress in sheared flow, for which condition Taylor's theorem does not apply, introduces certain theoretical difficulties.

An alternative approach is contained in the idea of relating the Lagrangian correlogram or spectrum, if only empirically, to the corresponding Eulerian properties defined by the velocity fluctuations at a fixed point. This approach is especially attractive in view of the rapid developments in the techniques of sensing and recording these fluctuations. The general idea was present in latent form for some time, in discussions by Sutton (1953, p. 263) and unpublished analyses by Calder, though in these cases with the special implication that the Lagrangian and Eulerian correlograms were identical. The next step came with attempts to exploit the Taylor expression in reverse, namely to use it with carefully designed diffusion observations in order to deduce the essential properties of $R(\xi)$ for comparison with Eulerian measurements. From wind tunnel experiments on the cross-stream diffusion of a plume of gas Mickelsen (1955) demonstrated the following simple scale relation (in the present nomenclature, different from Mickelsen's)

$$\int_0^{x_2} \int_0^{x_1} R(x)\, dx\, dx_1 = \overline{v'^2} \int_0^{\xi_2} \int_0^{\xi_1} R(\xi) d\xi\, d\xi_1$$

when

$$\xi = \frac{x}{B\sqrt{(\overline{v'^2})}}$$

The right-hand side of this equation [see Eq. (3.37)] is one-half of the measured dispersion of the gas, while $R(x)$ is the Eulerian space-correlation coefficient, actually obtained from measurements at a fixed point by applying the familiar space-time transformation stated in 1.2. The implied relation in the Eulerian and Lagrangian correlograms is

$$R(x) = \frac{1}{B^2} R(\xi) \quad \text{when} \quad \xi = \frac{x}{B\sqrt{(\overline{v'^2})}} \tag{3.65}$$

With the observed value of B, approximately 0·65, it is clear that the above relation cannot hold near ξ or $x=0$, but aside from this complication the result means that the Lagrangian correlogram fell off much more slowly than the corresponding Eulerian value.

On the basis of preliminary observations in the atmosphere Hay and Pasquill (1957) concluded that here also the Lagrangian correlation fell off much more slowly than did the autocorrelation of the velocity component measured at a fixed point, a result which had already been indicated by Gifford's neutral-balloon measurements (see 2.5). In a later study (1959) Hay and Pasquill adopted the simple hypothesis

$$R_L(\xi) = R_E(t) \quad \text{when} \quad \xi = \beta t \tag{3.66}$$

the subscript L referring to the true Lagrangian autocorrelation, the subscript E to the autocorrelation from measurements at a fixed point. This corresponds to Mickelsen's relation only when $B=1$, $u/\sqrt{(\overline{v'^2})}=\beta$. Making this time-scale transformation in the Fourier-transform expression for the spectrum function [Eq. (1.9)], it is easily shown that

$$nF_L(n) = \beta n F_E(\beta n)$$

where by definition $\int_0^\infty F(n)\, dn = \int_0^\infty nF(n)\mathrm{d}\log_e n = 1$. The correlogram and spectrum relations are displayed diagrammatically in Fig. 3.5. Substituting $F_L(n)$ from above in Eq. (3.43), written now in the form appropriate to the y-component of diffusion,

$$\overline{Y^2} = \overline{v'^2}T^2 \int_0^\infty \beta F_E(\beta n) \left[\frac{\sin \pi n T}{\pi n T}\right]^2 \mathrm{d}n$$

which reduces to

$$\overline{Y^2} = \overline{v'^2}T^2 \int_0^\infty F_E(n) \left[\frac{\sin \pi n T/\beta}{\pi n T/\beta}\right]^2 \mathrm{d}n \tag{3.67}$$

When the duration τ of the release of particles from a fixed point source is long enough to include the effect of the whole spectrum of turbulence, Eq. (3.67) is valid with $\overline{v'^2}$ and $F_E(n)$ prescribed for a sampling duration τ at a fixed point. For shorter durations of release, however, the application of the equation requires further qualification. In the treatment developed by Hay and Pasquill it is assumed that $\overline{v'^2}$ [and implicitly $F_E(n)$] can still be identified with a sampling duration equal to τ, provided the time of travel T is not substantially larger than τ.   This restriction is based simply on the idea that, with the Lagrangian correlation coefficient expected to fall only slowly, the effective variation of v' is dominated by the fluctuations occurring at the point of release and during the period of release.

The influence of a finite duration of sampling on the diffusion of particles has also been discussed by Ogura (1959) in terms of Eq. (3.47).   Ogura applies this equation with an assumed specific form of the Lagrangian

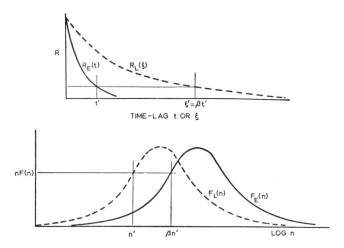

FIG. 3.5   Hypothetical scale relation between Lagrangian and Eulerian (fixed point) correlograms and spectra.   (Hay and Pasquill, 1959)

correlation coefficient, and with $T \leqslant \tau$ (in the present notation, which is different from that used by Ogura).   The precise meaning of this restriction is not clear, however, for in Eq. (3.47) τ is implicitly a time in a Lagrangian sense, whereas in the practical case of a fixed point source it is necessary to consider τ in an Eulerian sense.   On the other hand Ogura's discussion contains the important physical implication that the restriction is necessary because at greater values of T the diffusion would be occurring relative to a moving origin instead of relative to the fixed position of release.

An approximate argument for the restriction on T in applying Eq. (3.67) is as follows.   When τ is the *finite duration of release*, and $T \ll \tau$ it is clear that the dispersion of the particles is determined by their relative velocities as they leave the source, i.e. by the variations of velocity over a duration τ at a fixed point or, approximately, the variations occurring instantaneously over a length $\bar{u}\tau$.   When $T = \tau$ the plume of particles is detached from the source, and thereafter travels and grows as an elongated cluster. The spread of the particles will then be determined by relative velocities over a progressively increasing length, and this is a particular aspect of diffusion which is analysed in more detail in the next section. In the present context the important point is that as T increases the effective sampling duration determining $\overline{v'^2}$ is thereby increased beyond the value τ initially set by the duration of release. Similarly, when τ is the finite duration over which an indefinitely maintained plume is *observed*, particles with a separation greater than $\bar{u}\tau$ will be involved, and again the sampling duration determining $\overline{v'^2}$ will be greater than τ. Application of Eq. (3.67) with v' observed over the time τ should therefore be restricted to values of T such that the effective separation of the particles does not exceed $\bar{u}\tau$ by more than a small fraction, say one-tenth, of $\bar{u}\tau$. As a first approximation the additional separation is given by $\sqrt{(\overline{v'^2})}T$, and therefore the required restriction is

$$\sqrt{(\overline{v'^2})}T < \bar{u}\tau/10$$

or

$$T < \tau$$

since $\sqrt{(\overline{v'^2})}/\bar{u}$ in the atmosphere is about 0·1.

The application of Eq. (3.67) does not necessarily require the evaluation of the spectrum function $F_E(n)$, for recalling again the significance of the weighting function applied to $F_E(n)$, the equation may be written shortly as

$$\overline{Y^2}/T^2 = \overline{v'^2}_{\tau,T/\beta} \tag{3.68}$$

where the subscripts refer respectively to the sampling duration and averaging time with which v' is observed. This is simply a statement to the effect that if the magnitudes of the Lagrangian variations of particle velocity are identical (statistically) with the variations shown by separate particles as they pass through the point of release, but are on a time-scale longer by a factor β, then the variance of Lagrangian velocity averaged over time-interval T (i.e. $\overline{Y^2}/T^2$) is identical with the variance of velocity at a fixed point averaged over a time-interval T/β. The treatment thus leads to the exceedingly simple result that the dispersion of particles over a useful range of distance down-wind of a maintained source is determined completely by appropriately smoothing (averaging) the eddy velocity at the point of release, and then evaluating the variance over the period of release.

From the arguments set out previously concerning the effect of the shape of the Lagrangian correlogram, it is clear that if the Lagrangian and Eulerian correlograms are in fact of very different shapes the assumption of similar shape as above cannot introduce any important error.   The crucial feature of the relation assumed in Eq. (3.66) is that

$$\int_0^\infty R_L(\xi)\,\mathrm{d}\xi = \beta \int_0^\infty R_E(t)\mathrm{d}t$$

i.e. that the time-scales of turbulence are in the ratio $\beta:1$, but even in this respect it follows, again from the previous analysis of the dispersion law, that error in the estimation of β (i.e. the error in the estimation of the Lagrangian time-scale) will often not be serious.   If the true value is β, and the value assumed is β', it is easily seen that the value of $\sqrt{(\overline{Y^2})}$ derived will be $(\beta'/\beta)^p$ times the true value, where p will vary from zero when T is small to a maximum of 0.5 when T is large.

3.6   The expanding cluster and the instantaneous properties of a plume

Although it is only recently that proper attention has been given to the differences between the diffusion from a continuous source, in which particles are released in sequence at a fixed position, and that of a single puff or cluster of particles, the particular nature of the latter type of diffusion was recognized by L. F. Richardson at a very early stage (1926). Richardson's analysis was concerned with reconciling the enormous range of Fickian K's which was apparently required to explain the whole range of diffusion processes which could be experienced in the atmosphere.   In this analysis he introduced the fundamental notion that the rate of separation of a pair of particles at any instant is dependent on the separation itself, and that as separation increases so also does the rate of separation. This meant that the spread of a large cloud of particles could not be built up by superimposing the growths of component elements of the cloud treated separately.

In Fickian diffusion the distribution of particles is described in terms of concentration as a function of distance from a chosen origin and, in the simple case of diffusion of particles along a line, the development of the distribution is determined by the one-dimensional form of Eq. (3.16), with K constant, i.e.

$$\frac{\partial\chi}{\partial t}+\bar{u}\,\frac{\partial\chi}{\partial x} = \frac{\partial}{\partial x}\left(K\,\frac{\partial\chi}{\partial x}\right) = K\,\frac{\partial^2\chi}{\partial x^2} \tag{3.69}$$

where χ is now a number of particles per unit length of the line.   So as to bring in the effect of the separation of the particles in a rational way

8—A.D.

Richardson described the distribution in terms of a *distance-neighbour* function

$$q(l) = \frac{1}{Q} \int_{-\infty}^{+\infty} \chi(x)\chi(x+l)\mathrm{d}x \qquad (3.70)$$

where Q is the total number of particles, and proved that if Eq. (3.69) held q and l were related by the differential equation

$$\frac{\partial q}{\partial t} = 2K \frac{\partial^2 q}{\partial l^2} \qquad (3.71)$$

For non-Fickian conditions Richardson then argued that while Eq. (3.69) could not be generalized, as K could not rationally be regarded a function of position in the atmosphere, Eq. (3.71) could be generalized by replacing $2K$ by $F(l)$ and regarding $F(l)$ as an increasing function of l, so that

$$\frac{\partial q}{\partial t} = \frac{\partial}{\partial l}\left(F(l) \frac{\partial q}{\partial l}\right) \qquad (3.72)$$

The only observations available to Richardson were in the form of effective values of K, and so the only way to estimate the relation between $F(l)$ and l was to assume that Fickian diffusion applied in these cases, i.e. that $F(l)=2K$. Richardson then took l equal to the standard deviation of the particles from their mean position, or where this was not applicable, in the case of estimates of K from wind profile observations, to a length characteristic of the system of observation. For further details reference should be made to the original paper, the main point to be noted here is that three types of data were involved, giving in all seven values of l as follows:

Molecular diffusion	$l = 5 \times 10^{-2}$
Wind profiles at heights up to 800 m	$l = 1 \cdot 5 \times 10^3, 1 \cdot 4 \times 10^4, 5 \times 10^4$
Scattering of balloons, volcanic ash or cyclonic depressions	$l = 2 \times 10^6, 5 \times 10^6, 10^8$

The logarithms of K and l were found to lie on a line of slight curvature in the sense that $\mathrm{d}(\log K)/\mathrm{d}(\log l)$ increased with l, but all except the extreme points could be represented with good approximation by the relation

$$K = 0 \cdot 2 l^{4/3} \qquad (3.73)$$

This simple law obtained by Richardson is especially remarkable in the light of later deductions [see Eq. (3.84)], though the mixed quality of the observations which provided it should not be forgotten.   Indeed it may be noted that if attention had been confined to those observations which were directly representative of scattering of particles on a large scale, so involving only the last of the above groups of l, then the exponent in the power law would have been almost exactly $\frac{5}{3}$.   However the really important feature which had been introduced in this and other discussions by Richardson was the idea of a virtually continuous range of eddy sizes, with turbulent energy being handed down from larger to smaller eddies and ultimately dissipated in viscous action.   Specific expression of the concept came considerably later in the parallel developments by Kolmogoroff (1941), on the basis of his similarity theory, and by Obukhov (1941), on the basis of the equation of energy balance in the spectrum.   The relevance to Richardson's relation, as reviewed recently by G. I. Taylor (1959), is clearly seen on dimensional grounds.   If the dimensions length and time are expressed in terms of kinematic viscosity and rate of energy dissipation, as the only two physical quantities relevant to the regulation of energy transfer in the spectrum, then length has dimensions $\nu^{3/4} \epsilon^{-1/4}$ and time has dimensions $\nu^{1/2} \epsilon^{-1/2}$.   Richardson's differential equation may be written

$$\frac{\partial q}{\partial t} = A \frac{\partial}{\partial l} \left(l^m \frac{\partial q}{\partial l} \right)$$

in which A has dimensions $l^{2-m} t^{-1}$ or $\nu^{-1+(3/4)m}$, so that if the law of diffusion does not depend on ν it follows that $m = \frac{4}{3}$.   This is identical with the empirical result obtained by Richardson, though fortuitously so, partly because of the nature of the data, and partly because in the dimensional argument it is implicitly assumed that the magnitude of l is small compared with the size of the energy-containing eddies, an assumption which is not obviously justified for the largest scale of diffusion considered by Richardson.

The detailed analysis of the separation of particles in homogeneous turbulence

The elaboration and development of the formal mathematical analysis of the relative diffusion of particles was carried further by Batchelor and Brier independently.   Batchelor's full discussion, an exposition of the fundamental principles involved in three-dimensional relative diffusion in a field of homogeneous turbulence, is contained in his 1952 paper, but the main achievement as regards application to atmospheric diffusion had been set out earlier (1950).   A review of this work on relative diffusion is also contained in the article by Batchelor and Townsend (1956).   Brier's (1950) analysis was specifically aimed at a generalization of Taylor's analysis, so as to allow for initial separation of the particles, and as such has stimulated an application by Gifford (1959b) to the important problem of the *fluctuating properties* (as distinct from the mean properties) of the plume formed by the continuous release of material at a fixed position. In the discussion here the intricate details of the analyses will be avoided, and only the essential principles and final results will be stated.

Batchelor treats the case of the separation of a pair of marked particles (or volume elements of fluid) as the simplest representation of the diffusion of a group of such particles, and defines a distribution function which is equivalent to Richardson's distance-neighbour function generalized to three dimensions. Attention is then concentrated on the most important parameter specifying this distribution function, namely the variance of the separation of the pair of particles, and its dependence on the velocities of the particles. Batchelor obtains an equation which may be written in the form

$$\overline{y^2} = \overline{y_0^2} + 2 \int_0^T \int_0^{t'} \overline{\delta v(t)\delta v(t+\xi)} d\xi \, dt' \tag{3.74}$$

where y is the (vector) separation of the pair of particles at time T after an initial separation y_0, and $\delta v(t)$ the relative velocity of the particles at time t. Apart from the $\overline{y_0^2}$ term Eq. (3.74) will be recognized as formally identical with Taylor's equation (3.40) when the latter is expressed in terms of a covariance instead of a correlation coefficient. In the present case, however, the relative velocity is not a random function of time, as is the absolute velocity in Taylor's analysis, since as the two particles separate the range of eddy sizes contributing to δv will increase. Two specific predictions follow immediately for the simple cases of extreme values of T. At very small values of T, when the velocities of the two particles have not had time to change appreciably, the particle trajectories will be approximately straight lines and

$$\overline{y^2} = \overline{y_0^2} + \overline{(\delta v)^2} T^2 \quad (T \text{ small}) \tag{3.75}$$

where δv is simply the initial relative velocity, at separation y_0. At very large values of T, when the particles have separated so widely that their velocities are uncorrelated

$$\overline{\delta v(t)\delta v(t+\xi)} = \overline{2v'(t)v'(t+\xi)}$$

where v' is now the corresponding absolute velocity of either particle, and

$$\overline{y^2} = \overline{y_0^2} + 4 \int_0^T \int_0^{t'} \overline{v'(t)v'(t+\xi)} d\xi \, dt \quad (T \text{ large}) \tag{3.76}$$

The second term on the right-hand side of Eq. (3.76) is identical with twice the quantity in Eq. (3.40), i.e. the dispersion $\overline{Y^2}$ of a single particle, and as $T \to \infty$ this term becomes dominant and

$$\overline{y^2}_{T \to \infty} \to 2\overline{Y^2} \tag{3.77}$$

Thus after a very long time or distance of travel the mean square separation of a pair of particles tends to a value which is exactly twice the mean square displacement of particles released serially from a fixed position.

For small and intermediate times further predictions are made possible by appeal to dimensional arguments, and to the universal equilibrium theory of the small-scale structure of turbulence (see 1.3). When the scalar separation of the two particles is small compared with the size of the energy-containing eddies, i.e. with the scale of turbulence, the development of this separation will depend only on the initial separation and the parameters ν and ϵ. Then, following Batchelor and Townsend's (1956) presentation, from dimensional arguments it is possible to write

$$\frac{d\overline{y^2}}{dt} = \epsilon T^2 f(y_0/\epsilon^{1/2} T^{3/2},\ T\epsilon^{1/2}/\nu^{1/2}) \tag{3.78}$$

If the diffusion is independent of molecular processes ν must disappear from the expression, and Eq. (3.78) simplifies to

$$\frac{d\overline{y^2}}{dt} = \epsilon T^2 f(y_0/\epsilon^{1/2} T^{3/2}) \tag{3.79}$$

At small values of T Eq. (3.79) must be linear in T [conforming to Eq.' (3.75)] and

$$\frac{d\overline{y^2}}{dt} \propto T(\epsilon y_0)^{2/3} \quad (T \text{ small}) \tag{3.80}$$

Then when T is of intermediate magnitude, i.e. large enough for y to have become independent of its initial value y_0, but not too large in relation to the scale of turbulence, the parameter y_0 must also disappear from Eq. (3.79) and

$$\frac{d\overline{y^2}}{dt} \propto \epsilon T^2 \quad (T \text{ intermediate}) \tag{3.81}$$

Integration of Eq. (3.80) and (3.81) gives

$$\overline{y^2} \propto [\text{const.} + T^2(\epsilon y_0)^{2/3}] \quad (T \text{ small}) \tag{3.82}$$

$$\overline{y^2} \propto \epsilon T^3 \quad (T \text{ intermediate}) \tag{3.83}$$

the constant in Eq. (3.83) being omitted as negligible in view of the already assumed lack of dependence on y_0. These results bring out the essentially accelerative nature of the relative diffusion, which occurs as long as the separations involved are small compared with the scale of turbulence, and which is in contrast to the case of serial release of particles from a fixed point (see 3.4), when the exponent of T in the expression for the variance of particle spread is initially 2, as in Eq. (3.82), but thereafter *decreases*. This situation is a direct consequence of the fact that as the separation of the particles increases the variance of their relative velocity also increases, in a manner analogous to the more familiar increase of intensity of turbulence with sampling time.

Batchelor (1952) also re-examines the question of describing relative diffusion by a differential equation, and suggests that it is more reasonable to regard the equivalent diffusivity as a function of $\sqrt{(\overline{y^2})}$, as representing the *statistical* value of the separation of particles, rather than of the value of y (or l in Richardson's analysis), and takes

$$K \propto (\overline{y^2})^{2/3} \qquad\qquad (3.84)$$

as consistent with Eq. (3.83) and (3.17). Solution of the differential equation then gives a probability distribution for the separation, y, of a pair of particles, of the form $\exp(-y^2/2\overline{y^2})$. On the other hand Richardson's analysis leads to a form $\exp(-l^{2/3}/\alpha T)$, where T is the time of travel and α is a constant, i.e. one which is much more sharply peaked than the Gaussian form in Batchelor's solution. Yet another form has been suggested by Monin (1957), and observational evidence for the relative adequacy of these distributions has yet to be provided.

Explicit formulation for a diffusing cluster

The relative-velocity covariance inside the integral of Eq. (3.74) involves three kinds of correlation between the absolute velocities of particles, the purely Lagrangian correlation for a single particle, the Eulerian correlation referring to two particles at a given instant, and a mixed correlation referring to two particles at different instants. One of the chief problems is to express this latter type of correlation in more manageable terms. Brier (1950) has attempted this by some speculation about the relation between the various correlations, and expresses the mixed correlation in terms of the Lagrangian and Eulerian forms. Batchelor (1952) has drawn attention to a related and complementary suggestion made earlier in an unpublished note by G. I. Taylor, but suggests that neither of these approximations is likely to be good except at small values of the time interval (of diffusion) involved.   Brier carries his analysis further, to the extent of also eliminating the Lagrangian type of correlation, and expressing the relative dispersion entirely in terms of the correlation between particle velocities at the same instant.   However, it is not obviously valid to assume that this type of correlation (as a function of particle separation y) is identical with the correlation between velocities measured at *fixed* points y apart, and this is a difficulty which has not yet been satisfactorily resolved in any treatment.

An attempt to make progress in an empirical way, by adopting a simple scale relationship between the Lagrangian and Eulerian variations, on the lines introduced by Hay and Pasquill (1959) for a continuous source, has been presented by Smith [see Smith and Hay (1961)].   Smith starts with the equation for a pair of particles, equivalent to Eq. (3.74).   Taking averages over all pairs of particles in a three-dimensional Gaussian cluster (of standard deviation σ about the centre), and replacing the relative velocity of a *pair* of particles by the velocity (v'') of a particle relative to the mean velocity of all the particles in the cluster, the equation becomes

$$\frac{d\sigma^2}{dt} = \frac{2}{3} \int_0^{t'} \overline{v''(t)v''(t+\xi)}d\xi \qquad (3.85)$$

Apart from the numerical factor arising from the three-dimensional Gaussian distribution, and the fact that v'' is a (vector) velocity relative to the movement of the clusters as a whole, the equation is identical with Taylor's Eq. (3.36).   The assumption is then made that the Lagrangian covariance and the Eulerian covariance, *both appropriate to the finite cluster of particles*, are similar in shape, the ratio of the respective time-scales being β.   Development of Eq. (3.85) then leads to

$$\frac{d\sigma}{dt} = \frac{2}{3}\frac{\beta}{\bar{u}} \int_0^\infty \int_0^{\bar{u}t/\beta} E(\kappa) \frac{\sin \kappa s}{\kappa s} \cdot \frac{1-e^{-\sigma^2\kappa^2}}{\sigma} ds \, d\kappa \qquad (3.86)$$

where $E(\kappa)$ is the complete Eulerian three-dimensional spectrum function in terms of wave-number κ.   For $x/\beta = \bar{u}t/\beta > \sigma$ this simplifies to

$$\frac{d\sigma}{dt} = \frac{\pi}{3}\frac{\beta}{\bar{u}} \int_0^\infty E(\kappa) \frac{1-e^{-\sigma^2\kappa^2}}{\sigma\kappa} \, d\kappa \qquad (3.87)$$

so that $d\sigma/dt$ can now be evaluated, given β, from a knowledge of the Eulerian energy spectrum.   For practical use Eq. (3.87) is expressed in terms of the measurable one-dimensional spectrum function.   The development is carried further for the particular case when the Eulerian correlogram (actually the so-called trace-correlogram, for an explanation of which see the original paper) is of exponential form with length-scale l. With the function $E(\kappa)$ expressible in terms of l and κ, Eq. (3.87) becomes

$$\frac{d\sigma}{dx} = 2\beta i^2 \int_0^\infty \frac{n^2}{(1+n^2)^2} \cdot \frac{1-e^{-r^2 n^2}}{nr} \, dn \tag{3.88}$$

where $i^2 = \overline{u'^2}/\bar{u}^2$ (u being the vector component of eddy velocity), $r = \sigma/l$ and $n = \kappa l$ (the latter not to be confused with the use of n to denote frequency).

The weighting function $(1-e^{-\sigma^2 \kappa^2})/\sigma \kappa$ in Eq. (3.87) [and the corresponding term in Eq. (3.88)] is in effect a 'band-pass filter' which modifies the

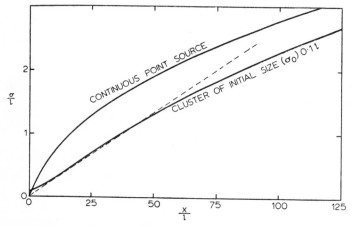

FIG. 3.6   Dispersion as function of distance of travel for a continuous point source and a small cluster.   Correlograms of exponential form are assumed. l is the Eulerian length-scale of turbulence, and the curves are for an intensity of turbulence (i) of 0·1, and a Lagrangian-Eulerian time-scale ratio (β) of 4.

whole three-dimensional spectrum (and the corresponding correlogram) to the form which is effective in determining the rate of growth of a cluster. Finite size of the cluster is taken into account by the cut-off on the low-frequency side, while the cut-off on the high-frequency side represents the diminishing contribution to the dispersion as eddy size decreases to a magnitude small with respect to the cluster.

For clusters which are initially small (say $\sigma_0 < 0·1 l$), the first part of the growth, i.e. that which is dependent on σ_0, is a relatively insignificant contribution to the ultimate growth, and this means that numerical integration of Eq. (3.88) yields a virtually universal curve valid for initially small clusters.   An example, for $\sigma_0/l = 0·1$, $i = 0·1$ (a common value in the atmosphere) and $\beta = 4$ (a value near this is found to satisfy the observations —see Chapter 4) is shown in Fig. 3.6 with the corresponding curve for a continuous point source. At first, say over a distance up to about ten times the length scale of the turbulence, the rate of spread of the cloud from the continuous source is substantially greater than that of the cluster, because the whole spectrum of turbulence is operative in the former case, while in the latter only those eddies of a size similar to or less than that of the cluster are effective. Thereafter the rate of spread of the continuous cloud falls off noticeably, while that of the cluster is maintained (and even accelerated for a time) by the progressive action of larger and larger eddies. The percentage difference between the two values of σ/l is then reduced, and when $x = 100l$ is less than 20 per cent.

From Eq. (3.88) it may be shown that

$$\left(\frac{d\sigma}{dx}\right)_{\max} = \frac{2}{3}\beta i^2 \qquad (3.89)$$

and since, as can be seen from Fig. 3.6, the rate of expansion is almost constant and equal to the maximum value over a wide range of σ/l, this constitutes a simple practical formula for evaluating σ, given β and an estimate or measurement of i. The broken line drawn through the origin in Fig. 3.6 has a slope equal to this maximum value, and is seen to give a good approximation to the cluster curve for values of x/l between say 10 and 80, while at larger values of x/l the values for the continuous source may be adopted as a good approximation for the cluster. It is to be noted that application of the approximation based on Eq. (3.89) does not require any accurate knowledge of the length-scale l, whereas in the application of the true curve (as also of the continuous-source curve), at high values of x/l, the value of σ tends to a dependence on $l^{1/2}$.

The dependence of $(d\sigma/dx)_{\max}$ on i^2 is particularly noteworthy in view of the fact that the rate of spread of cloud from a continuous source is always proportional to i. Qualitatively it can be seen that this extra sensitiveness, to an increase (say) in i, is a consequence of the shape of the energy spectrum. The first effect is that in a given time the cluster attains larger size, but then larger eddies are effective and on that account the rate of growth is larger still. For a general mathematical analysis of the point see the original paper.

The instantaneous properties of a plume

So far the mean dispersion of particles released serially from a fixed point, and the relative dispersion of particles supposed to spring into existence simultaneously, have been regarded as distinct and separate modes of diffusion. In the classical mathematical treatments of the continuous source (see Sutton, 1953) one of the essential simplifications was to consider the plume from a point source as composed of a succession of overlapping clusters. Physically, it is evident that if this model is to be realistic the 'clusters', or elementary sections of the plume, cannot be regarded as travelling consistently along a single line in the direction of the mean wind (see 5.1 for further qualitative discussion of this feature). In general, referring to a vertical plane normal to the mean wind at a fixed distance down-wind it is to be expected that the centres of mass of the successive clusters will pass through this plane at different positions, and that the mean distribution of particles at this plane will be determined by a combination of the spread within the cluster and the scattering of the clusters themselves. A relation between the separate and total effects on dispersion is implicit in Brier's (1950) 2-particle analysis, and may be expressed as follows. If $\overline{y^2}$ is the mean square separation of pairs of particles released simultaneously from fixed points y_0 apart, and $\overline{D^2}$ is the mean square deviation of the centres of mass of the pairs, then at any given time

$$\overline{y^2} + \overline{2D^2} = \overline{y_0{}^2} + 2\overline{Y^2} \qquad (3.90)$$

where $\overline{Y^2}$ is the mean dispersion of particles serially-released from a single fixed point, as in Eq. (3.40). In principle the generalization of this to successive clusters is applicable either to a finite-size continuous source or to a theoretical point source, where in the latter case the elementary cluster may be regarded as formed by the series of particles which pass through the source-point in some arbitrary small interval of time.

Gifford (1959b) has developed a formal treatment of the *fluctuating plume*, using a model in which, for mathematical convenience, the clusters are represented as discs in the plane normal to the mean wind direction. For further simplification he assumes that the distribution of concentration in the discs is a definite physical function (rather than a probability distribution), so that the mean distribution of concentration is determined by the scattering of the discs. It is also assumed that both this mean distribution and the distribution of the disc centres are of Gaussian form, which implies that the distribution within the disc is also Gaussian. Taking $\overline{Y^2}$ as the variance of the mean distribution, σ^2 the variance with respect to the disc-centre of the distribution in the disc, and $\overline{D^2}$ as the mean square displacement of the disc-centres from a fixed axis through the source,

$$\overline{Y^2} = \sigma^2 + \overline{D^2} \qquad (3.91)$$

The instantaneous and mean concentration distribution from a source of strength Q per sec may then be written as

$$\frac{\bar{u}\chi}{Q} = \frac{1}{2\pi\sigma^2} \exp\left[-\frac{(y-D_y)^2+(z-D_z)^2}{2\sigma^2}\right] \tag{3.92}$$

$$\frac{\bar{u}\bar{\chi}}{Q} = \frac{1}{2\pi(\sigma^2+\overline{D^2})} \exp\left[-\frac{(y^2+z^2)}{2(\sigma^2+\overline{D^2})}\right] \tag{3.93}$$

These equations refer to isotropic diffusion, but they can be generalized for the anisotropic case merely by introducing different values for σ^2 and $\overline{D^2}$ in the two component directions. The variance of the point concentration frequency distribution corresponding to Eq. (3.92), defined as

$$V = \overline{\chi^2} - \bar{\chi}^2$$

is given by

$$V = \frac{Q}{(2\pi\bar{u})^2} \left[\frac{\exp\left(-\dfrac{y^2+z^2}{\sigma^2+2\overline{D^2}}\right)}{\sigma^2(\sigma^2+2\overline{D^2})} - \frac{\exp\left(-\dfrac{y^2+z^2}{\sigma^2+\overline{D^2}}\right)}{(\sigma^2+\overline{D^2})^2}\right] \tag{3.94}$$

Relations are also derived for the frequency distribution f of the quantity χ/Q, and the simplest form of this, for positions on the mean plume axis, is the power law relation

$$f\left(\frac{\chi}{Q}\right) = \frac{\sigma^2}{\overline{D^2}} (2\pi\sigma^2\bar{u})^{\sigma^2/\overline{D^2}} \left(\frac{\chi}{Q}\right)^{(\sigma^2/\overline{D^2})-1} \tag{3.95}$$

From Eq. (3.92) and (3.93) it follows that the ratio of the peak concentration in the instantaneous plume to the average concentration on the mean plume axis is

$$\frac{\text{Peak}}{\text{Average}} = \frac{\sigma^2+\overline{D^2}}{\sigma^2} \tag{3.96}$$

As Gifford points out, since both σ^2 and $\sigma^2+\overline{D^2}$ $(=\overline{Y^2})$ tend to a variation with T (time of travel) for large values of T, the peak/average ratio should tend to a constant value. The argument can be carried further, for as shown by F. B. Smith in an unpublished analysis

$$\frac{d\overline{D^2}}{dt} \to 0$$

for large clusters each of many particles. This means that at large T, $\overline{D^2}$ tends to a constant value, which eventually implies

$$\sigma^2 \gg D^2$$

and

$$\frac{\text{Peak}}{\text{Average}} \to 1$$

3.7 The diffusion of falling particles

All the foregoing discussions are concerned with hypothetical elementary particles of the fluid, or alternatively with real foreign particles of the same density as the fluid, whose motions are in effect completely responsive to the whole spectrum of turbulent motion above some wavelength limit of similar size to the particles. When the particles are dense enough and large enough to have terminal velocities v_s which are not obviously negligible, say in relation to the eddy velocities, the distribution of the particles will be affected in various ways. The immediately obvious effect is the settling of the plume or cluster of particles as a whole, and this is usually accounted for in the differential equations of diffusion by introducing a convective term $v_s \chi$, i.e. the two-dimensional equation of diffusion becomes

$$\bar{u}\frac{\partial \chi}{\partial x} = \frac{\partial}{\partial z}\left(K_z \frac{\partial \chi}{\partial z} + v_s \chi\right) \tag{3.97}$$

Solutions of a special case of this equation have been given by Rounds (1955, see also 6.2 and Eq. (6.14) *et seq.*).

Inasmuch as the treatments through the equations of diffusion incorporate the normal eddy diffusivity of the fluid they are obviously suspect, except for very small terminal velocities, because they ignore two other important effects, namely that the particle is continually falling out of the sample of eddies affecting it at any instant, and that its response to eddy motion is reduced by its inertia. Attempts to allow for the former have been made by Yudine (1959) and F. B. Smith (1959) [see also Smith and Hay, 1961], in terms of the statistical treatments of dispersion.

Yudine applies Taylor's single-particle analysis for large T, with $R(\xi)$ in effect replaced by an $R(\xi, v_s\xi)$ incorporating the effects of time and vertical displacement $v_s\xi$. Then

$$K = \overline{w'^2} \int_0^\infty R(\xi, v_s\xi)\,d\xi \tag{3.98}$$

According as the effects of time or vertical displacement are dominant the function reduces to either the ordinary Lagrangian or Eulerian correlation coefficients.   For these Yudine takes functions in accordance with the universal equilibrium theory (1.3) i.e. $1 - R \propto \xi$ for the Lagrangian and $1 - R \propto (v_s \xi)^{2/3}$ for the Eulerian form, and assumes these relations to extend to values of ξ and $v_s \xi$ at which R becomes zero.   Functions approximately representing the upper and lower limits of the function $R(\xi, v_s \xi)$ are then constructed and corresponding limits to the integral in Eq. (3.98) obtained. The results show that K decreases with increase of v_s as would be expected on physical grounds, and at large v_s tends to vary with v_s^{-1}.   The general variation is displayed graphically in terms of v_s and the parameters defining the assumed Lagrangian and Eulerian correlation functions.   Since the treatment is only concerned with large values of the diffusion time T, at which the process is dominated by the low-frequency components of turbulence, this means that the error arising from neglect of the inertia of the particle will be at a minimum.

Smith's treatment is concerned with the diffusion of a cluster, which is a problem identical with the single particle (i.e. continuous source) case, treated by Yudine, only in the limit of large time of travel.   The development falls into two main parts, firstly the determination of the cluster expansion for rapidly falling particles (inertia effects being neglected), and secondly the construction of an interpolation formula for intermediate and small terminal velocities.   For the first part (1959) the general nature of the argument is as follows: the loss of correlation in particle velocity due to its vertical fall is the controlling feature when it is substantially more rapid than that associated with the normal Lagrangian decay of correlation for a floating particle.   This condition obtains when

$$l/v_s \ll t_L$$

where l is the Eulerian length-scale and t_L the Lagrangian time-scale, i.e.

$$v_s \gg \bar{u} t_E / t_L \qquad (3.99)$$

where t_E is the equivalent Eulerian time-scale defined by $l = \bar{u} t_E$ and t_L/t_E is the Lagrangian–Eulerian scale ratio β introduced in Eq. (3.66). In this case the statistics of the velocity fluctuations experienced by a particle will be equivalent to those which would be measured by an instrument moving at speed v_s through the field of turbulence.   The correlation coefficient $R(\xi)$ for the particle can accordingly by replaced by $R_E(t')$, the autocorrelation coefficient obtained from measurements at a fixed point, when $ut' = v_s \xi$.   Then, for example Eq. (3.36) becomes

$$\frac{\mathrm{d}\overline{\chi^2}}{\mathrm{d}t} = 2\overline{u'^2} \frac{\bar{u}}{v_s} \int_0^{v_s t/\bar{u}} R_E(t')\, \mathrm{d}t' \qquad (3.100)$$

In Smith's (1959) analysis of the spread of a cluster Eq. (3.100) is replaced by

$$\frac{d\sigma^2}{dt} = \frac{2}{3v_s} \int_0^{v_s t} (R_{ii}) \, ds \qquad (3.101)$$

where σ is the standard deviation of the particles from the centre of the cluster, and (R_{ii}) is the Eulerian vector covariance for distance separation s, appropriately modified for the size σ of the cluster as in the floating cluster problem previously treated. For the floating cluster (see Smith and Hay, 1961), the corresponding equation is

$$\frac{d\sigma^2}{dt} = \frac{2}{3} \frac{\beta}{\bar{u}} \int_0^{\bar{u}t/\beta} (R_{ii}) \, ds \qquad (3.102)$$

which transforms into Eq. (3.101) when $v_s = \bar{u}/\beta$. Remembering that Eq. (3.101) holds only for $v_s \gg \bar{u}/\beta$ this equivalence in the equations means that it does not matter whether the cluster moves purely horizontally at speed $\bar{u}$, or purely vertically at $v_s = \bar{u}/\beta$, statistically it experiences the same conditions. In other words, if the horizontal scale is compressed by a factor β, then in these transformed coordinates the direction of motion of the cluster is irrelevant. In the general case, therefore, when neither v_s nor $\bar{u}/\beta$ can be neglected, the appropriate result is given by replacing v_s or $\bar{u}/\beta$ by $\sqrt{(v_s^2 + \bar{u}^2/\beta^2)}$, so that

$$\frac{d\sigma^2}{dt} = \frac{2}{3} \frac{1}{\sqrt{(v_s^2 + \bar{u}^2/\beta^2)}} \int_0^{t\sqrt{(v_s^2 + \bar{u}^2/\beta^2)}} (R_{ii}) ds \qquad (3.103)$$

and the solutions for $d\sigma/dt$ and $d\sigma/dx$ are as in Eq. (3.87), (3.88) and (3.89), with $\bar{u}/\beta$ replaced by $\sqrt{(v_s^2 + \bar{u}^2/\beta^2)}$. Numerical evaluation of σ for typical values of the parameters gives the curves in Fig. 3.7, taken from Smith and Hay's paper. For particles with terminal velocities less than say 0·5 m/sec the reduction in σ due to the fall of the particles is less than 10 per cent at a time of travel of one minute. On the other hand the effect of terminal velocity is obviously nil at the beginning [since for small t the integral in Eq. (3.103) is proportional to $t\sqrt{(v_s^2 + \bar{u}^2/\beta^2)}$]. Then at large values of t, when this integral is a constant,

$$\frac{d\sigma^2}{dt} \propto \frac{1}{\sqrt{(v_s^2 + \bar{u}^2/\beta^2)}} \quad (t \text{ large}) \qquad (3.104)$$

in which case

$$\frac{\sigma}{\sigma_{(v_s = 0)}} = \frac{1}{(1 + v_s^2 \beta^2/\bar{u}^2)^{1/4}} \quad (t \text{ large}) \qquad (3.105)$$

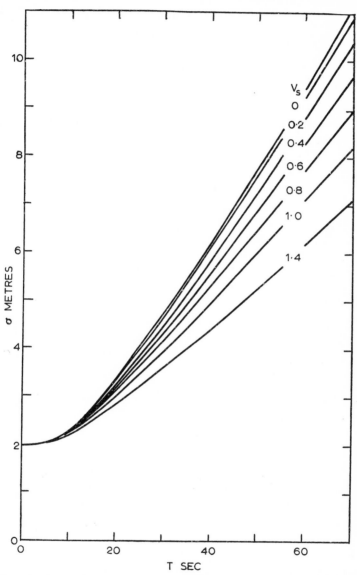

FIG. 3.7   Dispersion of a falling cluster of particles as a function of time of travel T and terminal velocity v_s. A correlogram of exponential form is assumed. Eulerian length-scale $(l) = 20$ m, $\bar{u} = 5$ m/sec, $i = 0\cdot1$, $\beta = 5$, initial standard deviation $\sigma(0) = 2$ m.   (Smith and Hay, 1961)

and for the parameters in Fig. 3.7, and $v_s = 0.5$ m/sec, the magnitude of this ratio is 0.95. Since Eq. (3.103) applies to a serial release of particles when R_{ii} is the covariance for the whole spectrum of turbulence these generalizations concerning the effect of terminal velocity at limiting times are also applicable to a continuous point source. When $v_s \gg \bar{u}/\beta$ Eq. (3.104) shows that at large times of diffusion σ varies as $v_s^{-1/2}$ and hence K varies as v_s^{-1}, in accordance with Yudine's result.

For the continuous source, with R_{ii} in Eq. (3.103) independent of σ, it is clear that the dependence of the integral on $\sqrt{(v_s^2 + \bar{u}^2/\beta^2)}$ will decrease systematically with increasing t, between linear dependence at small t and independence at large t. Thus it can be said that the dependence of σ on v_s will at all times be between the limits of independence at small t and dependence as in Eq. (3.104) at large t. Hence for $v_s = 0.5$ m/sec and the parameters in Fig. 3.7 the value of 0.95, obtained for $\sigma/\sigma_{(v_s=0)}$ at limitingly large time, may be regarded as a lower limit for all times in practice. This generalization cannot however be applied to the case of the cluster, because R_{ii} in Eq. (3.103) then depends on σ, and hence on v_s. Further examination of the results in Fig. 3.7 indicates that the ratio $\sigma/\sigma_{(v_s=0)}$ decreases with increase in t throughout the range of t covered, though at $t = 60$ sec the rate of change of the ratio is slow, suggesting that the value there is near the minimum.

These estimates of the effect of terminal velocity still require some qualification on account of the effect of inertia, which will be further to reduce the amount of turbulent spread. Theoretical estimates by Smith (1959) suggest that for terminal velocities of 2 m/sec the response of the particles will be virtually complete for eddies of wavelength of the order of 1 m and greater. Hence for most practical diffusion problems, and for particles with $v_s < 2$ m/sec, the indication is that the effects of inertia may be neglected.

3.8   The effects of buoyant motion

Although the influence of thermal stratification of the atmosphere has been considered in the sense of the modifications which are thereby impressed on the turbulent motion, no reference has yet been made to the direct effects of the more organized ascending motions which are induced by the heating of the ground. Furthermore, buoyancy is important in the present context in an additional sense, for many sources of practical interest emit their gaseous or other material at a temperature in excess of the surrounding air. For details of the various aspects of free convective motion reference should be made to general discussions by Scorer (1958) and Priestley (1959). The discussion here will be confined to brief comments on features which are particularly relevant to the special interests under review.

The classical considerations of convection (see Sutton, 1953) dealt with the relatively slow motions set up in a horizontal layer of stationary viscous fluid by imposing an unstable density gradient in the vertical. It had been observed by Bénard that in such circumstances a circulating vertical motion could be set up in a well-defined pattern of polygonal cells, and the theoretical analysis of this cellular motion followed in well-known papers by Rayleigh and others. Extension of these analyses to the case of a fluid already in turbulent motion, simply by replacing the viscosity and conductivity of the fluid by 'eddy' counterparts, was always regarded as of doubtful validity and, as Priestley (*loc. cit.*) has pointed out, actually leads to a criterion, for the onset of free convection near the ground, which is in considerable disparity with observation. Moreover, although it has been argued that the geometrical patterns of certain cloud formations provide support for the idea that cellular motions exist on a large scale in the atmosphere, there is no convincing evidence for its existence in the well-stirred layers of the lower atmosphere. For these reasons attention has long been turned from the classical concept, and significant progress in the rationalizing of ideas on the structure of convection has followed mainly from studies, by several workers, of the behaviour of an individual buoyant element in the form of either an isolated volume or a continuous stream of buoyant fluid. Development has proceeded along two lines. On the one hand there are the formal analyses in terms of the equations of motion, notably those given by Priestley (1953) for the 'ascending parcel' in a turbulent atmosphere, and by Priestley and Ball, (1955), and Morton, Taylor and Turner (1956), for convection in a calm atmosphere. There are several earlier continuous plume treatments but only those of the last two references have so far provided results for unrestricted thermal stratification of the environment. On the other hand there are the idealized laboratory studies by Scorer and his co-workers which have led to the idea that the basic element in penetrative convection is a detached volume of buoyant fluid with a characteristic development of internal circulation and growth.

The 'parcel' treatment due to Priestley assumes a mixing with the environment entirely as a result of the existing environmental turbulence, whereas in the treatments of ascent in a calm atmosphere the sharing of excess momentum and buoyancy with the surrounding fluid is usually assumed to be induced by the actual relative motion of the buoyant element. In all problems of the latter type the central problems still remaining are

9—A.D.

those of properly representing the process by which this sharing process occurs, and of accurately specifying the resulting shapes of the distributions or profiles of vertical velocity and temperature within the element.   Assuming that for each property the profile shape is *similar* at all stages in a continuous plume (i.e. can be represented by a unique function of position across the plume expressed in terms of a characteristic radius), the equations of motion and conservation can be solved to yield expressions for the expansion of the plume, its excess temperature and its upward velocity, by admitting certain further simplifying assumptions concerning the *constants* in the profile shapes.   For Gaussian shapes with equal variance for both temperature and velocity (in any thermal stratification), Priestley and Ball (1955) give solutions which include a simple linear increase of plume radius with height above the source.   This feature is emphasized by Priestley as a deduction from entirely independent assumptions.   Priestley and Ball also consider the effect of departure from equality and Gaussian shape in the profiles.

The actual representations of the loss of momentum and buoyancy by mixing differ in the treatments by Priestley and Ball, and Morton *et al.* In the former the plume is assumed to experience a vertical drag proportional to the square of the ascending velocity on the axis of the plume.   In the latter a physical entrainment into the plume at a rate proportional to the ascending velocity, and to the surface area of the plume element, is assumed. Otherwise, according to Priestley, the formulations are identical, and lead to virtually identical estimates of the height at which a plume attains neutral buoyancy in a calm atmosphere with a standard lapse rate of $6.5°C\ km^{-1}$. It is noteworthy that the solutions give this height as dependent on the 1/4 power of the rate of heat supply to the plume.

For the case of a hot plume in a horizontal wind Priestley (1956) has set out a 'working theory' which combines an extension of the Priestley and Ball analysis (as determining the early stages of ascent) with his treatment of the ascending parcel in a turbulent environment (as determining the later stages of ascent).   A system in which the mixing of the plume is at first controlled by its own relative motion and then by atmospheric turbulence is thus explicitly recognized.   Application of the calm environment treatment is based on the premise, following Sutton's earlier treatment of the bent-over plume, that the relative horizontal motion between the plume and the surrounding air may be neglected.   Priestley argues that the same functional forms of solution should then apply in terms of height z above the source.   The only modification introduced is that the spreading coefficient relating plume-radius linearly with height above the source is now logically regarded as dependent on wind speed, as far as the *along-wind* dimension of the horizontal section through the plume is concerned. With the simplifying assumption that this spreading coefficient is actually proportional to wind speed, and hence that the (geometric) mean radius of the oval section is proportional to $\bar{u}^{1/2}$, a solution for the first phase of the plume is obtained. This is adopted up to the height at which dw/dz coincides with that specified by the second-phase solution appropriate to mixing by environmental turbulence, and thereafter the more rapid decrease of vertical velocity given by the latter solution is followed.

As the working formulae deduced by Priestley (1956) have not as yet been included in any general discussion they are reproduced here for reference purposes. For the first phase, in neutral conditions,

$$w^3 = \frac{3Ag}{2\theta_e c^2}\left[\frac{1}{z}-\frac{z_0{}^2}{z^3}\right] + \frac{w_0{}^3 z_0{}^3}{z^3} \qquad (3.106)$$

where w = upward velocity on the axis of the plume,
   A $= Q_H/\pi\rho\, C_p$,
   Q_H = the rate of supply of heat to the plume,
   θ_e = environmental potential temperature,
   c = the plume-spreading coefficient (defined by R/z where R is the effective radius of cross section of the plume in a horizontal plane) to be determined from observation,
   z = height measured from a virtual release point where $R=0$,

and subscript zero denotes values measured at efflux height. For arbitrary thermal stratification it is necessary to use graphical solutions, given by Priestley and Ball (1955). With these solutions applying to the transition level z_1, the final equilibrium level $z_{\max}$ reached in the second phase, for arbitrary thermal stratification, is

$$z_{\max} - z_1 = \left(kw_1+\frac{g\theta'_1}{\theta_e}\right)\Big/\left(\frac{g}{\theta_e}\frac{\partial\theta_e}{\partial z}+k^2\right) \qquad (3.107)$$

where k = a mixing rate, given by $8K/R_1{}^2$, with K the eddy diffusivity for momentum.

   θ' = excess potential temperature of the plume over its environment and the subscript 1 refers throughout to values at the transition level. A value of $z_{\max}$ exists not only with a lapse rate which is equal to or less than the dry adiabatic, but also with a superadiabatic lapse rate provided.

$$\left|\frac{g}{\theta_e}\frac{\partial\theta_e}{\partial z}\right| < k^2$$

In the original discussion of the method the transition level is determined by a trial and error graphical method, but it has since been pointed out (Spurr and Priestley, 1957) that z_1 can be expressed in a cubic equation which can be solved by well-known techniques.

As regards the statistical effect of natural convection on transport processes in the atmosphere attention has been mostly devoted to the vertical flux of heat from the ground.   In this connection Priestley has argued that even in the bottom 100 m of the atmosphere the effects of the day-time surface heating are such as to encourage the idea that naturally induced thermal plumes play a vital part.   If a close array of small-scale plumes is envisaged, then for continuity of mass to be preserved the spreading of individual plumes must ultimately lead to an assimilation into fewer larger plumes.   However the transformation into the distinct *thermal* of penetrative convection, in the form exploited by glider pilots and evident in cumulus clouds, has yet to be elucidated, and it is clear that this constitutes a major question of structure which must be resolved before any real progress can be made with the problem of representing the effects of convection on the detailed vertical distribution of windborne material over appreciable depths of the atmosphere.   The only analysis so far reported in connection with this latter problem is that provided by F. B. Smith (1957b and c), and summarized in 3.2, for a simplified combination of diffusive and convective action.

4

Experimental Studies of the Basic Features of Atmospheric Diffusion

The diffusion of material released into the atmosphere is basically described by the dimensions and shapes of the distributions which are developed down-wind of the source. In this chapter are collected details of these features, as revealed by experiments which were designed specially for the purpose, and carried out with sources of an idealized nature, usually in selected conditions of terrain and weather. Many important surveys which were concerned with the determination of the maximum or average levels of pollution arising from practical sources are excluded from consideration here, but are discussed later in the more practical context of Chapters 5 and 6.

4.1 Principles of technique and analysis

Most of the experimental studies of atmospheric diffusion fall into one or other of three main groups in which different techniques are adopted for describing and measuring the effects of diffusion. These are:

(a) *Optical outline* methods, using a suitable form of smoke.
(b) The measurement of trajectories of individual *marked particles*.
(c) Measurement of the concentration of a *tracer element* introduced into the air.

Optical outline methods

The examination of the development of the visible size and shape of a smoke cloud is at first sight the most attractive and economical method of studying diffusion. By taking distant photographs of smoke clouds it is usually possible subsequently to draw some outline around the image of the cloud, and so to specify a shape and size. When the source of smoke is continuously operated at a fixed point, an average or *time-mean* description may be achieved by using prolonged exposures (as with a pin-hole camera), or by superimposing a number of instantaneous photographs.

Simple as these techniques may be in action, there are however several difficulties in the analysis and interpretation.

The inherent lack of smoothness in atmospheric diffusion processes results in a frequently ragged appearance of smoke clouds, and it is not always easy to define a usable instantaneous outline without introducing some smoothing of the apparent irregular form. Furthermore, the real meaning of the boundary of the smoke, however unequivocally this may be recognized, is open to some doubt. It obviously depends in a complex way on the optical qualities of the background against which the smoke is observed, the nature of the incident and background illumination, and the absorbing and scattering properties of the smoke material, as well as on the density or concentration of smoke in the plume or puff. In practice no attempt has been made so far to take into account the detailed physical features, and progress has depended entirely on simple interpretations of visible outline. The most widely used treatment is that due to Roberts (see 4.5). However, even when a usable simple relation between cloud outline and smoke concentration is adopted, it is still necessary to make some *a priori* assumptions about the distribution of concentration in the smoke cloud. In earlier applications of the method theoretical expressions for this distribution were used to derive expressions for the visible outline, which were then compared with observation. It has, however, been made clear in discussions by Gifford, which are considered in more detail in 4.5, that it is not necessary to anticipate the relation between the *size* of a cloud and the distance or time of travel, but merely to make some assumption about the *shape* of the distribution of concentration in the cloud. This development eliminates a good deal of what has previously seemed to be a rather intractable difficulty in the effective interpretation of observations of puffs and plumes of smoke.

It will be seen in 4.5 that important deductions have recently been made from observations of smoke puffs, and it seems likely that further development and use of the techniques might profitably be made (see Gifford 1959c). There is, however, an important limitation in the range over which the process of diffusion can be studied in this way; unless the smoke cloud is diffusing very slowly satisfactory observations are unlikely to be practicable beyond a few hundreds of metres of travel. Although in theory extension of range should merely require an appropriate increase in the amount of smoke released, the improvement in practice may be disappointing. Not only may the observational procedure be complicated by the use of much larger volumes of smoke, but there is also the further difficulty that concentrated smoke clouds might absorb solar radiation in sufficient amount to introduce buoyancy effects and lifting of the cloud.

Trajectories of marked particles

The observation of the trajectories of *markers* floating in the air is theo-retically the ideal way of directly observing the basic processes of diffusion, but there are difficulties in making true *Lagrangian* observations, which have already been discussed in principle in 2.5. In practice the problem is to arrange markers which are sufficiently neutral, i.e. which have neg-ligible motion relative to the air surrounding them, and which can then be assumed to display the dispersive action of turbulence components of larger scale than the size of the marker itself. Soap bubbles, thistledown and dandelion seeds have been used for short-range observations, but by far the most widely used marker is the balloon. An advantage of using balloons is that the latest techniques of observing their trajectories, ranging from the traditional visual-reading theodolite systems to elaborate radar-tracking networks, are always immediately available from the operational systems of wind observation on a synoptic scale. The latest exploitation of the method in the form of the long-range constant-level balloon flights orga-nized in the United States of America (see Angell 1959) constitutes a major contribution to the study of long-range large-scale horizontal diffusion in the atmosphere. It is also appropriate to mention here the use of computed air trajectories, as initiated by Durst (see 2.5). Although in this case there is no real physical marking of the air, the velocities of a hypothetical air parcel being computed at intervals from successive meteorological charts, the trajectories obtained represent approximations to those of constant-level balloons. Both the observed and computed horizontal trajectories exclude the vertical motion which a real element of air will experience, and thus do not reproduce those contributions to spread which arise from the systematic variation of wind speed and direction with height. Moreover, all trajectory methods suffer from the drawback of requiring a large number of repetitions to provide a statistically satisfactory result, so that apart from the operational effort a large computing effort is also involved.

Measurement of tracer-element concentrations

Undoubtedly the most rewarding experimental studies of diffusion in the atmosphere have been those in which some easily detected *tracer* element is introduced into the atmosphere, and the concentrations occur-ring at various times and positions down-wind are measured by precise chemical or physical techniques. The method possesses the obvious advantage of enabling the distribution within a diffusing cloud to be directly explored, a feature which is not provided at all by the visible-outline tech-nique and is a laborious matter by the trajectory method. It also has the attraction of being most directly relevant to the assessment of the hazards arising from the release of toxic materials.   The first known measurements of this type were carried out on Salisbury Plain, England, at the War Office Chemical Defence Experimental Establishment, Porton, in 1923.   By present standards the method may seem rather crude, but by careful attention to the details of the procedure results which still serve as basic data were obtained.   The method comprised the release of a harmless smoke formed by burning 'candles' of a pitch composition, and the estimation of the concentration of smoke in the air by a 'stain-meter' technique, devised by F. J. Scrase on the principle of the Owens Automatic Filter for early measurements of air pollution.   In Scrase's method a hand-pump was used to draw the smoke-laden air through a small orifice backed by a filter paper.   By comparing the resulting stain on the filter paper with a series of standard stains, obtained by taking samples in an enclosed chamber in which a known quantity of smoke had been released, an estimate of the smoke concentration could be obtained.   From samples taken by a team of observers at specified stations down-wind of the source, the cross-wind distribution of smoke was examined, and in later work the vertical distribution was also explored by stationing the observers at various heights on a tower.

Air-sampling methods using gases, smokes and larger airborne particles as tracer elements have since been developed and improved in various ways. One of the most important steps in this process was the application of precise laboratory techniques of chemical estimation to samples obtained by drawing the gas-laden air through a suitable liquid absorbent.   However, in practice the use of sensitive gaseous tracers did not easily extend the range over which diffusion could be observed beyond the few hundred metres which were possible with the earlier smoke techniques.   None of the gases which were suitable from the point of view of chemical estimation were sufficiently free from irritant or toxic effects at the level of concentration required, and the experiments had to be designed to exclude any possibility of unpleasant or harmful concentrations being set up outside the experimental area.   The big step in the extension of the range of diffusion experiments, to the order of 100 km, came with the introduction of the fluorescent-particle tracer, first described in this connection by Perkins, Leighton, Grinnell and Webster (1952).   The material which has been used most is a pigment, zinc cadmium sulphide, which can be finely dispersed, one gram providing approximately 10^{10} particles with diameters mainly in the range 1–5 microns.   With ultra-violet illumination these particles can be individually recognized and counted under a good laboratory microscope.

Air-sampling for particulate tracers is carried out by filtering, impaction, or impingement techniques, for a general authoritative discussion of which see Green and Lane (1957).   In the conventional *impactor*, the air is drawn through a nozzle to emerge at very high speed from a narrow slit positioned close to a surface coated with glycerine jelly.   Particles impact on the surface, are held there by the jelly, and may subsequently be examined and counted under a microscope.   For convenience in obtaining a series of collections at different times or positions, the receiving surface usually takes the form of a cylinder or drum which can be rotated either continuously or in steps.   In the *impinger* the jet of air is directed into a liquid in which the particles are retained and from which they are subsequently separated by filtering.   Only one sample is obtainable with an impinger, and in the present application the method is preferable to the drum impactor arrangement only when water droplets are likely to be collected with the particles, since in this case the particles and jelly coating may be washed off the receiving surface of the impactor.   The design and construction of impactors requires considerable care, and as fairly powerful air-pumps are necessary in order to draw air through them at the appropriate rate, sampling in the open at a number of positions simultaneously is a fairly elaborate procedure.   For this reason natural impaction techniques, in which the particles are impacted on an object by the action of the wind alone, may sometime be profitable, especially when fairly large particles are involved.   This method was effectively demonstrated in Gregory's (1951) wind-tunnel studies of the collection of *lycopodium* spores on adhesive cylinders, of various diameters, with their axes normal to the air-stream.   In this case the number of particles caught on a cylinder is proportional to the number of particles which would otherwise have passed through the cross section occupied by the cylinder, the proportionality factor, or collection efficiency, being a function of the diameters of the cylinder and the particles, and of the velocity of the air-stream.   In field applications the important requirement is that cylinder and particle size should be chosen so that not only is the collection efficiency of a reasonable order (say 50 per cent), but that it does not vary rapidly with wind speed.

Terminology of diffusion data

Although much of the nomenclature for expressing the effects of diffusion has already been used in the theoretical discussions of Chapter 3, it will be helpful to summarize the various parameters at this stage, in relation to the particular forms of diffusion measurements which are made.

The chemical analysis or physical examination of a *sample*, collected in one or other of the ways briefly outlined above, leads to an estimate of the mass of material, M, or of the number of particles, N, in a given volume of air $S\tau$, where S is the known rate at which air is drawn through the apparatus and τ is the duration of the sampling process.   In the case of sampling by natural impaction the effective value of S is given by uAE where u is the air speed relative to the object, A is the area presented normal to the flow, and E is the collection efficiency.   Theoretically a correction for the efficiency of collection, retention or absorption, should be made in all the forms of sampling, but in practice the methods in which air is forcibly drawn through a piece of apparatus are deliberately designed to give near 100 per cent efficiency.

If χ (mass per unit volume or number of particles per unit volume) is the instantaneous concentration at the sampling position then the average concentration over the duration of sampling is

$$\bar{\chi} = \frac{1}{\tau} \int_0^\tau \chi \, dt = \frac{M}{S\tau} \quad \text{or} \quad \frac{N}{S\tau}$$

The quantity $\int_0^\tau \chi \, dt$, which is termed the *dosage*, D, during the time τ, is simply M/S or N/S.   When, as in the present chapter, the interest is in the fundamental properties of the size of and distribution within a diffusing cloud of material, it is of course unnecessary to evaluate concentrations and dosages as such, as long as the sampling rate and duration are standard, or corrections for departures therefrom are subsequently made.   The quantities M and N, observed as a function of cross-wind (Y) or vertical (Z) displacement from an axis along the mean wind direction, may then be used directly in describing the properties of a plume of material extending from a point source.   When dealing with a detached cloud or puff these quantities may additionally be observed as a function of distance along-wind (X) from the centre of the cloud.

The cross-wind dimension of a cloud is conventionally represented either by the width between positions at which concentration or dosage falls to a given fraction [usually one-tenth] of the central or peak value, or alternatively by the standard deviation of the cross-wind displacement of the material, in practice defined by

$$\overline{Y^2} = \frac{\Sigma M Y^2}{\Sigma M} - \left[\frac{\Sigma M Y}{\Sigma M}\right]^2$$

or by a similar expression involving N.   When the distribution is of Gaussian form, and the fraction adopted in specifying cloud-width ($2Y_0$) is one-tenth,

$$2Y_0 = 4\cdot30 \, (\overline{Y^2})^{1/2}$$

Corresponding definitions apply to the along-wind dimension, and also to the vertical dimension of a cloud which is well clear of horizontal boundaries, but when the cloud is generated at an impermeable boundary ($z = 0$), then the cloud-height Z_0 is defined as the height at which concentration or dosage falls to one-tenth (say) of the ground value. The root mean square displacement of material above the boundary, equivalent to the standard deviation in the foregoing cases, is defined by

$$Z^2 = \frac{\Sigma M Z^2}{\Sigma M}$$

If the fall of concentration with height is according to the Gaussian form

$$Z_0 = 2 \cdot 15 \, (\overline{Z^2})^{1/2}$$

4.2 The form of the cross-wind distribution at short range from a maintained point source

The earliest measurement with smoke candles showed that the cross-wind variation of smoke concentration at 100 m down-wind of the source was basically of 'cocked-hat' shape (see Sutton, 1953, p. 275), with irregularities of some degree or other according to the steadiness of the wind direction. At first sight this basic shape seemed to conform fairly obviously to the *normal error* or *Gaussian* form, and this form has since been widely used in analytical expressions of the distribution down-wind of sources. It will be recalled (see Chapter 3) that the theoretical treatments of *Fickian-type* diffusion lead directly to this form of distribution. Although diffusion processes in the atmosphere cannot be expected to be *Fickian* in practice, except perhaps at long range in the special case when the spectrum of turbulence falls off fairly sharply at low frequencies (large eddies), this theoretical result may be regarded at least as supporting the adoption of a Gaussian distribution when the distance down-wind, and hence the spread of the material, is large compared with the scale of the turbulence. Another indication comes from the statistical result (see 3.4) that close to a fixed source the variation of spread with distance tends to a linear form, i.e. the particles or elements of fluid have effectively moved with the eddy velocities at the point of release, and these eddy velocities have been seen (2.6) to have probability distributions approximating closely to the Gaussian form. However, these considerations are in no sense a proof of the existence of this form in the distribution of material undergoing diffusion in the atmosphere, and the final demonstration must rely on observation.

The first recorded determination of the analytical form of the cross-wind distribution which has been found is that described in 1925 by R. F. Budden in official records of Porton work.   This was based on an average cross-wind distribution at 100 m down-wind, composed from five experiments, at very similar wind velocities (near 7 m/sec), extracted from the 1923 series of smoke trials referred to in 6.1.   Fitting the distribution to a form

$$\bar{\chi}/\bar{\chi}_0 = \exp - ay^r \qquad (4.1)$$

where $\bar{\chi}_0$ is the axial or peak concentration and $\bar{\chi}$ the concentration at cross-wind distance y from the position of the peak value, the exponent r was found to have the value 1·55, rather than 2·0 as required in the Gaussian form.   More detailed determinations from similar experiments carried out at Cardington, Bedfordshire, in 1931 were reported by E. Ll. Davies, and the results are reproduced in Table 4.I.   These experiments were carried out with different times of sampling, 'instantaneous' values referring to those obtained from a single filling of the sampling pumps, while the remainder were obtained from sequences of pump strokes at intervals of 10 sec.   The whole series of experiments was carried out in two periods of about an hour on separate days, in near-neutral conditions of stability, and with wind speeds near 2·5 m/sec and 6·5 m/sec respectively.   A wide variation in the exponent r is shown in Table 4.I, though without any simple trend in relation to sampling time, and it was noted at the time that the unweighted mean of the series of values of r was 1.6, in good agreement with the original determination.

Table 4.I

Shape of cross-wind distribution at 100 m down-wind of a maintained point source.
(From experiments at Cardington, Bedfordshire, 1931)

Time of sampling (min)	No. of cases	r in Eq. (4·1)
'Instantaneous'	60	1·6
$\frac{1}{2}$	51	1·2
1	30	1·1
$1\frac{1}{2}$	24	1·6
2	18	1·9
$2\frac{1}{2}$	11	1·8
3	9	2·4
$3\frac{1}{2}$	2	1·3

An examination of the distribution curves corresponding to a range of values of r (see later, Chapter 5) reveals that a variation of r from 1·5 to 2·5 is associated with a fairly small change of shape.   This fact, and the rather erratic variations in r, obviously raise some doubt regarding the significance of many of the departures from the Gaussian value of 2·0.   Apart from a reference to an isolated case by Hay and Pasquill (1959) no formal statistical tests of this feature have been reported.   Some further indication of the statistical form of the cross-wind distribution is provided however by analysis of more recent data on diffusion.

Fig. 4.1 shows four average cross-wind distribution curves derived from various diffusion experiments carried out on the open downland site at Porton in near-neutral conditions.   The curves are plotted on 'arithmetical probability' graph paper, on which a Gaussian distribution appears linear.   The process leading to an average distribution was as follows. Each individual cross-wind distribution consists originally of a series of values equal to or proportional to the dosage of the tracer material at consecutive positions on a cross-wind line, or on an arc centred on the point of release.   To an approximation each value may be adopted as the average for the cross-wind interval centred on the appropriate position. Cumulative addition at successive sampling positions gives values which are proportional to *cumulative-dosage*, equivalent to the *cumulative-frequencies* of statistical terminology, and conversion to percentages of the overall total gives *cumulative-percentage dosages* which are plotted against cross-wind or arc position.   A suitable composition of a group of such distributions may then be obtained, firstly by adjusting the cross-wind scales to zero at a cumulative-percentage value of 50 per cent, and then by averaging the resulting cross-wind displacements at selected values of the cumulative-percentage.

Of the distributions shown in Fig. 4.1 only those at (a) have been published hitherto in this form, those at (c) are an analysis of published raw data on cross-wind distribution, while those under (b) are based on unpublished figures obtained from Porton records.   It is interesting to note that of the four average distributions two (fluorescent smoke and lycopodium spores at 100 m or yd) contain no obvious deviation from linearity.   In the other two (fluorescent smoke at 300 m and sulphur dioxide at 80 m) there are clear deviations from linearity especially at one side of the distribution in each case, but the deviations are in opposite senses in the two cases and correspond to values of r (Eq. 4.1) of approximately 1·5 for the fluorescent smoke distribution and 2·5 for the sulphur dioxide distribution.

A different criterion for the agreement with Gaussian form has been employed by Cramer (1957) in his analysis of the *Prairie Grass* series of diffusion experiments in the U.S.A.   These were carried out with sulphur dioxide, and refer to a wide range of stability conditions.   For each

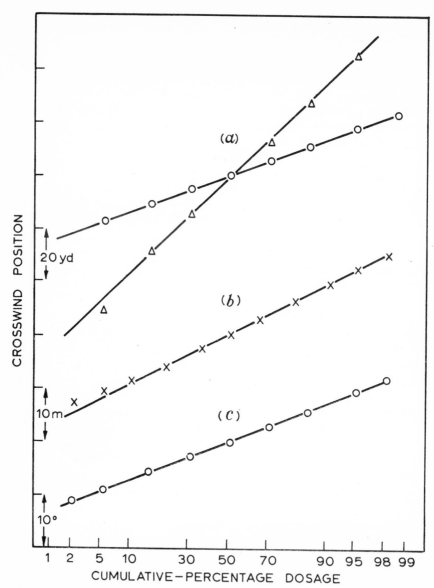

Fig. 4.1 Average cross-wind distributions at short range from a point source at ground level, in near-neutral conditions over downland, Porton, England.

Material	Duration of release (min)	Number of releases	Distance of travel (m)	
(a) Fluorescent smoke	30	7	⊙ 100 △ 300	Hay and Pasquill 1959
(b) Sulphur dioxide	4–7	13	80	unpublished
(c) Lycopodium spores	3	6	100	Hay and Pasquill 1959 (runs 1, 2, 3, 5, 6, 7)

cross-wind distribution, which corresponded to an average over a period of 10 min, Cramer evaluated both the standard deviation of the distribution, and the plume-width as defined by the distance between the points at which the concentration fell to one-tenth of the peak or axial value.   For a

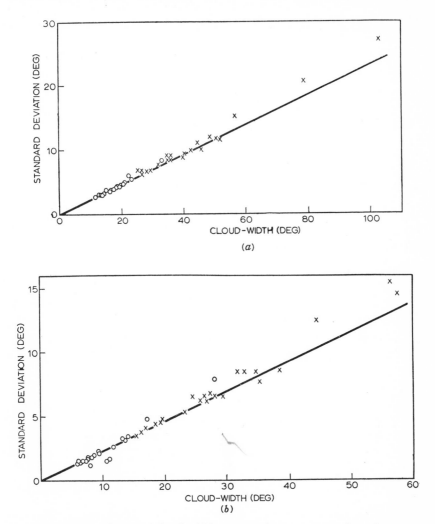

FIG. 4.2   Relation between cloud-width, appropriate to one-tenth peak concentration, and standard deviation, of cross-wind distributions from a continuous point source.   From measurements at O'Neill, Nebraska, at distances (a) 100 m; (b) 800 m; × day-time, ⊙ night.   The straight lines correspond to a Gaussian distribution.   (Cramer 1957)

Gaussian distribution the ratio plume-width/standard deviation is 4·30, and Fig. 4.2 reproduced from Cramer's paper shows that the individual values of plume-width and standard deviation are generally quite close to this relation. However, it is necessary to consider the significance of the deviations from the *Gaussian* lines in Fig. 4.2, and to this end the theoretical values of the plume-width/standard deviation ratio for various values of r in Eq. (4.1) are given in Table 4.II. The value of r is evidently very sensitively dependent on the ratio, and it is clear that the departures of the points from the straight lines in Fig. 4.2 represent departures of r of 0·5 and more from the value of 2·0.

Table 4.II

Ratio of width $2Y_0$, as defined by one-tenth peak concentration, to standard deviation $(\overline{Y^2})^{1/2}$, for a distribution of material as in Eq. (4.1)

r in Eq. (4.1)	$\dfrac{2Y_0}{(\overline{Y^2})^{1/2}}$
2·5	4·34
2·0	4·30
1·5	4·06
1·0	3·26

To sum up, the available observational data on the cross-wind distribution at short range from a ground-level continuous source in level open country show that individual distributions over periods of the order of 10 min may require values of r in Eq. (4.1) widely different from the Gaussian value of 2·0. Even composite distributions may require values as different as 1·5 and 2·5. However, there is so far no indication of a systematic departure from the Gaussian value, and it is tempting to conclude that the variations in both directions are a reflection partly of the quality of the sampling data and analysis, and partly of the inherent lack of homogeneity in the structure and effects of atmospheric turbulence over the sampling times involved. It is clear at least that on present evidence there is no good reason to adopt an analytical form different from Gaussian, especially as the practical features of the distribution do not vary greatly with quite substantial departures from the Gaussian value of r in Eq. (4.1).

4.3   The magnitude of the cross-wind spread at short range from a maintained point source

Early Porton experiments

The 1923 smoke experiments at Porton provided the much quoted figure of 35 m for the width of cloud, as defined by one-tenth peak concentration, at 100 m down-wind of a maintained source at ground level. These experiments were carried out in thoroughly overcast conditions, i.e. in near-neutral conditions of stability, over open gently-rolling downland. The duration of release of smoke in each case was 4 min. It is important to realize, however, that even in the carefully selected near-neutral conditions the individual widths of cloud varied widely, the value of 35 m being the mean of fifty values ranging from 23 to 47 m. Table 4.III shows the distribution of the individual values (this distribution is approximately Gaussian with a standard deviation of 5 m). The individual values are also shown in Fig. 4.3 plotted against the wind speed at a height of 1·8 m, from which it is seen that there is no marked systematic variation with wind speed.

Table 4.III

Frequency distribution of cloud-width at 100 m down-wind of a ground-level point source, in neutral conditions of atmospheric stability over downland at Porton, England

Range of cloud-width	20 to 22	23 to 25	26 to 28	29 to 31	32 to 34	35 to 37	38 to 40	41 to 43	44 to 46	47 to 49	50 to 52
No. of cases	0	1	5	9	10	11	8	5	0	1	0
Percentage of cases	0	2	10	18	20	22	16	10	0	2	0

(Each value of cloud-width was derived from an average cross-wind distribution measured during a 4-min release of smoke, the boundary of the cloud being identified with a concentration equal to one-tenth of that on the axis of the plume.)

Similar smoke experiments carried out by Porton staff at Cardington in 1931 were notable in giving cloud-widths which were generally larger than those obtained at Porton. In the approximately 2½ hours of experiments which were carried out at Cardington, 10 samples of duration 3–6 mins were obtained, and the average cloud-width was 44 m. At the time this result was considered all the more surprising in view of the fact that the site at Cardington was locally even flatter and smoother than that at Porton. A second series of experiments was carried out at Cardington in 1934, over a moderate range of atmospheric stability, with the object of clarifying this feature.   The relatively large values of cloud-width in neutral conditions were substantially confirmed.   In this later series of experiments measurements of gustiness were made, using bi-directional vanes of the type described in 2.1, with the object of ascertaining whether or not the difference between the Cardington and Porton results was associated with a difference in gustiness.   Unfortunately, corresponding measurements of gustiness had not been made at the time of the 1923 experiments, so that direct

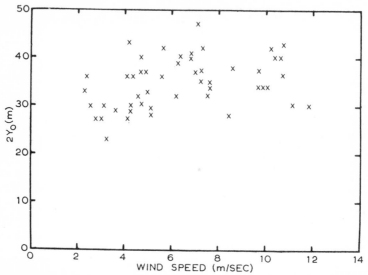

Fig. 4.3   Observed cloud-width ($2Y_0$) at 100 m down-wind of a source of smoke, in relation to wind speed at a height of 1·8 m.   Over downland, Porton, England (1923).   Duration of release 4 min.   Near-neutral conditions of stability.

comparison was not possible.   However, it is stated in the report on the 1934 experiments that for small temperature gradients in the vertical, the gustiness subsequently observed on the Porton site was less than that observed at Cardington.   That this could have been the explanation is borne out by the fact that the Cardington results show an obvious correlation between the individual estimates of cloud-width and the corresponding lateral dimensions of the bi-directional-vane traces, over a threefold range of the latter quantity.   This is demonstrated in Fig. 4.4 which contains the twenty-one cases for which reliable estimates of the cloud-width could be made.

The implications of the above first demonstration of a relation between the lateral spread of a cloud at short range and a direct though crude measurement of turbulence were not immediately followed up, either in relation to the difference in the Porton-Cardington results, or in connection with the fundamental problem of relating diffusion to atmospheric conditions.   In the latter respect it is noteworthy that the departures of the

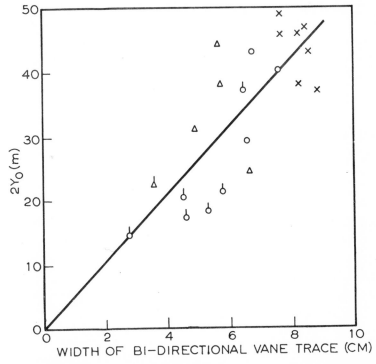

FIG. 4.4   Relation between cloud-width $(2Y_0)$ from a maintained point source, and turbulence as indicated by the lateral width of a bi-directional-vane trace. The different symbols refer to different dates, the primed symbols to the more stable conditions.   (Unpublished data from smoke experiments at Cardington, England, 1934)

individual values of cloud-width from the simple linear relation drawn in by eye are mostly less than 30 per cent—a consistency which now seems quite remarkable in view of the well-known variability in atmospheric turbulence.   Furthermore this result can now be seen (see 3.4) to follow directly from the basic statistical treatment of diffusion from a continuous source, according to which the spread of particles at a given distance of travel should be proportional to the intensity of turbulence and hence, to a good approximation, to the corresponding dimension of the bi-directional-vane trace. It is also noteworthy that the 1934 Cardington results were at the time shown to display a close relation between cloud-width and atmospheric stability as indicated by the Richardson number.

Although the early Porton smoke experiments were extended (in 1925) to distances of travel of 300 and 1000 m, the main preoccupation was with the variation of the peak or axial concentration, and no figures were given immediately for the cross-wind dimensions of the smoke clouds at these distances. The results of eighteen experiments at 300 m were analysed from this point of view some years later, and the mean cloud-width obtained has been quoted by Hay and Pasquill (1959) as 79·1 m, this again referring to near-neutral conditions of stability. If cloud-width is taken to follow a power-law variation with distance, i.e. $Y_0 \propto x^p$, the results for 100 m and 300 m are satisfied by $p = 0·74$. An independent though indirect evaluation of this index may also be made from the analysis of the 1923 and 1925 data. In these analyses power-law indices were derived for the variation with distance of

(a) the axial concentration at ground level

(b) the integral of the cross-wind distribution curve.

Now if the shapes of the cross-wind and vertical distributions are invariant with distance, and if the dimensions of these distributions vary with x^p and x^q respectively, it follows that the power-law index for axial concentration will be $-(p+q)$, while that for the integral of the cross-wind distribution curve will simply be $-q$. The values derived were respectively $-1·76$ and $-0·98$, from which $p = 0·78$, in good agreement with the value obtained directly from the cloud-widths at distances of 100 and 300 m.

The main conclusions to be drawn from the earliest systematic observations of the distribution of smoke concentration down-wind of a continuous point source at ground level are thus as follows. They refer to open grassland with either very flat or only gently rolling contours, and to sampling or release times of 4 min.

(a) The width of cloud in neutral conditions at 100 m down-wind, as defined by one-tenth axial or peak concentration, has an average value in the region of 40 m, but with individual variations of up to perhaps ±15 m from this figure.

(b) In the range 100–1000 m, again in neutral conditions, cloud-width increases with distance raised to a power of approximately 0·8.

(c) As the atmospheric stability changes from near-neutral to moderately stable there is a systematic decrease of cloud-width, and a close correlation between cloud-width and the lateral component of the intensity of turbulence.

Statistical data obtained in the U.S.A. on the cross-wind distribution from a ground-level point source

Experiments carried out at the Round Hill Field Station of the Massachusetts Institute of Technology (in 1954, 1955, and 1957) and during *Project Prairie Grass*, an extensive co-operative programme carried out in 1956, have substantially extended the data on cross-wind spread from a ground-level point source. The tracer employed was sulphur dioxide, and an important feature of these investigations was the inclusion in the meteorological measurements of accurate observations of the lateral and vertical wind fluctuations using fast-response instruments. A description of the techniques and instruments is given in the full reports of the investigation by Cramer, Record and Vaughan (1958), Barad (1958) and Haugen (1959). Another important feature is that the two field sites involved are radically different in aerodynamic roughness. The Round Hill site is described by Cramer (1957) as having a roughness parameter [z_0 in Eq. (3.5)] greater than 10 cm, with trees, houses, small buildings and differences in elevation of the order of 30 m within a distance of 0·5 to 1 km immediately up-wind of the release area. On the other hand the *Prairie Grass* experiments were carried out on the smooth, level Nebraska plains at O'Neill, on a site for which $z_0 < 1$ cm.

Cramer's analysis of the Round Hill and O'Neill data has been largely focused on the empirical relations between the statistics of diffusion and the fluctuations of wind direction near the source. The data on cloud-width at distances of 100 m are displayed in Fig. 4.5, which is taken from Cramer's 1957 paper. Both the diffusion data and the wind data refer to a sampling time near 10 min, the wind being measured at a height of 2 m near the source. A good correlation exists, the deviation of the points from the regression line being very similar to that found in the analysis of the 1934 Cardington data in terms of cruder measurements of the wind-direction fluctuations. The most striking feature is that the American data from two sites of very different roughness, obtained over a substantial range of atmospheric stability, fit closely to a single relation between plume-width and the wind-direction fluctuation, over a tenfold range of the latter parameter. As Cramer points out, no similar consistency is apparent if the diffusion results are plotted against a stability parameter equivalent to the Richardson number, because in neutral conditions the standard deviation of the wind azimuth at Round Hill is approximately double that at O'Neill. The implication is of course that the simple statistics of wind fluctuation directly reflect the diffusing power of the atmosphere, a feature which, as already noted, is to be expected on any logical statistical treatment of turbulent diffusion.

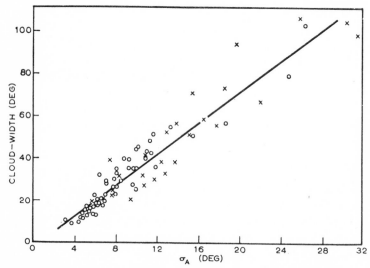

FIG. 4.5 Relation between angular cloud-width and standard deviation (σ_A) of wind direction. From point source experiments at Round Hill Field Station, Massachusetts ($\times$), and O'Neill, Nebraska ($\bigcirc$). Cloud-widths refer to 100 m down-wind of source. (Cramer, 1957)

The O'Neill experiments also included simultaneous measurements of cross-wind distribution at 50, 200, 400 and 800 m, and hence provide a major contribution to the knowledge of variation of cloud-width with distance of travel. Cramer (1957) presents values of the index p in the relation

$$(\overline{Y^2})^{1/2} \propto x^p$$

between the standard deviation of the cross-wind distribution of concentration and the distance x down-wind. Values of p were computed for the four intervals of distance, 50–100, 100–200, 200–400 and 400–800, and for various magnitudes of the standard deviation, σ_A, of the wind azimuth. Some variation of p with distance is evident in the tabulated values, the main trend being a decrease with distance at high values of σ_A (unstable conditions) and an increase with distance at very low values of σ_A (stable conditions), but it is not clear how significant this variation is, and Cramer emphasizes the questionable character of the indication in very stable conditions, in view of the small number of experiments falling in this category. Furthermore, in the final report, Cramer, Record and Vaughan (1958) conclude that the exponent p tends to be invariant with distance, with values as follows,

unstable conditions	0·8–0·9
near-neutral conditions	0·8
stable conditions	0·6

The above analysis of the *Prairie Grass* experiments substantially confirms the early Porton results in neutral conditions, firstly in the sense that the widths of cloud at 100 m are consistent.   Cramer's (1957) analysis gives the magnitude of $(\overline{Y^2})^{1/2}$ in neutral conditions as approximately 10 m, and assuming a Gaussian distribution this implies a cloud-width of 43 m, which is to be compared with values of 35 and 44 m, obtained at Porton and Cardington respectively, with a shorter sampling time (4 min as compared with 10 min in the *Prairie Grass* measurements).   Secondly, the power-law variation of cross-wind spread with distance up to 800 m is very similar to that indicated by the Porton experiments at 100, 300 and 1000 m, the index in both cases being near 0·8.

The explicit relation between cross-wind spread and the statistics of the wind fluctuations

The demonstration of the existence of a good correlation between cloud spread and the intensity of turbulence, as indicated in the fore-going discussion, is an important step in the general specification of the characteristics of diffusing clouds.   The ultimate interest, however, is in the question of the explicit relation between these quantities, particularly in the light of the statistical treatment of diffusion discussed in Chapter 3.   From this it will be recalled, that the spread of particles serially released from a fixed point must initially increase linearly with respect to time T or distance x of travel.   The absolute magnitude of the spread in this case is given simply by

$$\overline{Y^2} = \overline{v'^2}T^2$$

$$\simeq \frac{\overline{v'^2}x^2}{\bar{u}^2} \tag{4.2}$$

This deduction holds strictly only for homogeneous turbulence which is statistically invariant with time, but it may not be unreasonable to consider it in relation to atmospheric conditions away from the immediate effect of the earth's surface, or even close to the surface in the case of horizontal spread.

A demonstration of the approximate validity of an equation corresponding to Eq. (4.2) was first obtained in a study of the vertical spread from an elevated source (Hay and Pasquill 1957), which will be discussed later, and from the data already discussed on cross-wind spread near the ground it can now be demonstrated that the relation holds to a reasonable approximation in this case also. The recent analysis of the statistics of wind direction fluctuation on the Porton site (see 2.8) gives the average standard deviation for a 4-min sampling time and a wind speed of 5 m/sec as 5·25°, in neutral conditions. This means that the intensity of the lateral component of turbulence $\sqrt{(\overline{v'^2})}/\bar{u}$ is approximately 0·09, and that $(\overline{Y^2})^{1/2}$ in Eq. (4.2) is 9 m for $x = 100$ m. Assuming a Gaussian distribution the corresponding cloud-width is 39 m, as compared with the average value of 35 m observed. Again, from the data given by Cramer (reproduced in Fig. 4.5) it is clear that the ratio of angular cloud-width to standard deviation of wind azimuth is about 3·5. Assuming a Gaussian distribution in the cloud, the corresponding ratio of the angular standard deviation of the cloud distribution to that of the wind azimuth is 0·8, whereas from Eq. (4.2) the value would be 1·0. The failure to recognize the approximate validity of Eq. (4.2) at a much earlier stage was of course directly attributable to the lack of accurate absolute measurements of the appropriate component of the intensity of turbulence.

The theoretical expression for the spread of serially-released particles involves the Lagrangian correlation coefficient, and as discussed in Chapter 3, progress depends on the introduction of some explicit form for this quantity in terms of the measurable Eulerian structure of turbulence. It is now appropriate to consider the experimental evidence, provided by diffusion experiments, for the simple hypothetical form suggested by Hay and Pasquill (1959). Full details of the argument are given in Chapter 3 and for the present discussion it suffices to recall Eq. (3.68), i.e.

$$\overline{Y^2} = \overline{v'^2_{\tau,s}} T^2 \quad \text{for } \tau > T$$

where $\overline{v'^2_{\tau,s}}$ is the variance of the lateral component of eddy velocity, *averaged* over a time s equal to T/β, and *sampled* over a time τ equal to the duration of release of particles (or to the duration of the sampling of the distribution of particles). The quantity β is the ratio of the *Lagrangian* time-scale of turbulence to the time-scale deduced from (Eulerian) measurements of the turbulent fluctuations at a fixed point. For practical purposes it is convenient to convert the above into angular form, and for small angles

$$\sigma_p{}^2 = \overline{\theta'^2_{\tau,s}} \qquad (4.3)$$

where $\overline{\theta'^2_{\tau,s}}$ is the variance of wind direction for sampling time τ and averaging time s as specified above, and $\sigma_p{}^2$ is the variance of the bearings of the particles from the point of release.

Experiments have been carried out by Hay (see Hay and Pasquill 1959) with the special object of deducing the values of β required to satisfy Eq. 4.3. *Lycopodium* spores were released at a steady rate from a simple type of mechanical dispenser, and samples of the resulting plume were collected on small adhesive cylinders arrayed on an arc 100 m down-wind, on a site near that used in the earlier Porton experiments. The duration of release of particles was usually 3 min and the sampling cylinders were exposed during the entire time of passage of the plume of particles. A continuous record was taken of the variation of wind direction near the point of release, with a responsive vane. Values of β were easily obtained by first evaluating the standard deviation of the wind direction record, over the 3-min duration of release and for various averaging times, and reading off the magnitude of the averaging time s at which this standard deviation was equal to the observed σ_p. Then $s = T/\beta = x/\bar{u}\beta$, with $x = 100$ m and $\bar{u}$ the mean wind speed during the time of release. The magnitude of τ/T, i.e. the ratio of the time of release to the time of travel always exceeded five. Table 4.IV shows the essential data and values of β obtained, with corresponding wind speeds and temperature gradients. Although there is a considerable variation in β (from 1·1 to 8·5) there is no strong indication of a systematic variation with either wind speed or stability. The large variations could be of a random character arising from small errors in the measurement of σ_p and $\overline{\theta'^2_{\tau,s}}$, since the estimates of β by this method are very sensitive to variation in the foregoing quantities. The practical acceptability of a constant value of β equal to the arithmetic mean of the values in Table 4.IV, i.e. approximately 4, is demonstrated by the comparison of observed and computed values of σ_p in Fig. 4.6, the two worst discrepancies being 10 per cent and 30 per cent. Comparisons are also given for values of β equal either to 1 (i.e. Lagrangian and Eulerian properties identical) or to the time of travel T (i.e. taking $s = 1$ sec, the basic averaging time employed in reading the wind traces in this analysis). Both values lead to significantly poorer agreement than that obtained with $\beta = 4$.

In addition to showing that a small number of special experiments suggest an approximate value of 4 for β, Hay and Pasquill have examined the

Table 4.IV

Data on cross-wind spread and wind direction fluctuation, leading to values of β, the ratio of the Lagrangian and Eulerian auto-correlogram time-scales. (Hay and Pasquill, 1959)

Experiment No.	1	2	3	4	5	6	7	8
$\bar{u}$ in m/sec	4·4	5·3	8·3	3·8	3·3	4·3	3·8	2·8
Temp. diff. °F (23 ft–4 ft)	−1·3	−1·1	−0·6	−1·3	0	0	0·7	1·5
$(\overline{\theta'_{\tau,1}})^{1/2}$ at source (deg.)	7·9	6·3	8·2	15·3	6·8	7·2	5·4	4·8
σ_b at 100 m downwind (deg.)	6·8	5·4	5·6	12·8	5·5	6·7	4·6	3·1
β satisfying Eq. (4.3) with $s = T/\beta$	3·5	5·4	1·1	1·6	5·2	8·5	4·3	3·2

(All wind measurements and the release of the particles were at a height of 2 m. The subscripts of θ' refer to a sampling duration τ equal to the period of release of particles, and an averaging time of 1 sec.)

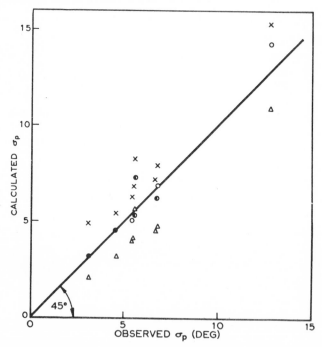

FIG. 4.6   Comparison of observed angular cross-wind spread (σ_p), at 100 m from a continuous point source, with that calculated from Eq. (4.3)

$\beta = 1$ △;

$\beta = 4$ ● stable, ◐ neutral, ○ unstable;

$\beta = T$ (in sec) ×.   (Hay and Pasquill 1959)

more general support provided for this by other experimental data on cross-wind diffusion. They point out that values of σ_p (Eq. 4.3) calculated from overlapping 4-min samples of wind direction fluctuation, obtained recently over a period of 30 min on the Porton site in thoroughly overcast conditions and with wind speed in the region of 5 m/sec, range from 4·1° to 7·5°. Assuming a Gaussian distribution, the cloud-widths measured in the 1923 experiments correspond to a range of σ_p of 3·1 to 6·2°, so both the mean value and the range now calculated are in fair agreement.

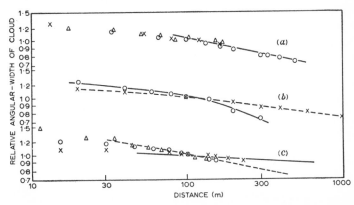

FIG. 4.7 Various aspects of the relation between cloud-width and distance, computed from wind-direction fluctuations and Eq. (4.3). (a) Experiment No. 3(⊙), 5(×), 6(△) in near-neutral conditions; (b) Time of sampling 5 min (⊙), 30 min (×); (c) Experiment No. 4 (×) in unstable conditions, 7 (⊙) and 8 (△) in stable conditions. (Hay and Pasquill, 1959)

A number of other interesting results, concerning the computed variation of cloud-spread with distance, based on Eq. (4.3) with $\beta = 4$, are displayed in Fig. 4.7. Section (a) was derived from the wind fluctuation data for the three cases in Table 4.IV corresponding to near-neutral conditions, and the line fitted by eye to the values beyond 100 m corresponds to a power-law variation

$$\sigma_p \propto x^q$$

with $q = -0·21$. The Porton diffusion data already discussed yield an exponent of approximately 0·8 in the power-law variation of cloud-width in *linear* measure, and hence a value of q (which refers to angular measure) of approximately $-0·2$. Section (b) shows the variation of angular cloud-width with distance for sampling times of 30 min and 5 min, based on the 30-min record of wind direction fluctuation referred to in the preceding paragraph. This indicates that by increasing the sampling time from 5 to 30 min there is a closer approach to a simple linear spread, such that the ratio of the angular cloud-widths at 300 and 100 yd increases from 0·74 to 0·89. The early Porton experiments with release times of 4 min gave a ratio of 0·77, while later experiments with 30-min releases of fluorescent smoke and simultaneous sampling at various distances gave a ratio of 0·89 [the data leading to this figure are those shown at (a) in Fig. 4.1]. Section (c), which uses the wind fluctuation data of cases in Table 4.IV, implies that the variation of angular cloud-width with distance is slower in unstable conditions (Expt. No. 4) than in stable conditions (Expt. Nos. 7 and 8). This variation with stability is in the same sense as that demonstrated in the analysis of diffusion data reported by Cramer, Record and Vaughan (1958), though the computed variation is obviously not sufficiently representative to provide a decisive comparison.

Preliminary analyses of the *Prairie Grass* data, in which the variation of cloud-width with distance between 50 and 100 m is used to calculate values of the Lagrangian correlation coefficient from the differential form of Taylor's equation [i.e. $d^2\overline{Y^2}/dt^2 = 2\overline{v'^2}R(\xi)$, see Eq. (3.36)] have been reported by Barad (1959) and Panofsky and Rao (1958). On the basis of thirteen experiments (twelve of them in stable conditions) Barad's findings, described as tentative, are that for a given time-lag the values of the derived Lagrangian correlation coefficient, R_L, are sometimes higher than the observed values of the Eulerian autocorrelation coefficient, R_E, but not always, there being some indication that $R_L - R_E$ decreases as wind speed decreases and stability increases. This implies that the ratio of the Lagrangian and Eulerian scales (i.e. β in the preceding discussion) decreases with increase in stability, and may be less than 1, in contrast to the values deduced by Hay and Pasquill. On the other hand Panofsky and Rao conclude that the general shapes of the Lagrangian and Eulerian correlation tend to be similar, with the ratios of the scales (β) equal to 4 in the night-time cases, but near 1 in the day-time cases.

A series of measurements of the diffusion of a plume of smoke from an elevated source in stable conditions, at Hanford in the U.S.A., have been reported by Hilst (1957a, 1957b), and the results of these have been examined by Hay and Pasquill (1959) on the basis of Eq. (4.3). The source was operated at a height of 200 ft above the ground, and aerial photographs of the plume were taken at 1-min intervals for 25 min or more during a period of steady meteorological conditions. From the photographs the cross-wind positions of the plume centre and the visible widths of the plume were measured for a number of distances down-wind of the source, and the former values used to determine $\overline{D^2}$, the variance of the

cross-wind positions of the plume.   Making the reasonable assumption
that the distribution within the plume was independent of plume position,
the variance $\overline{Y^2}$ of the time-mean cross-wind distribution was obtained
from Eq. (3.91)

$$\text{i.e.}\quad \overline{Y^2} = \sigma^2 + \overline{D^2}$$

where σ^2 is the variance of the distribution within the plume.   The quantity σ^2 was not observed directly, but approximate values were estimated

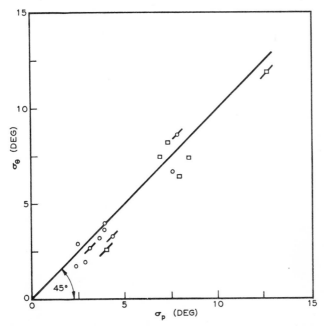

Fig. 4.8   Comparison of observed angular cross-wind spread (standard deviation
σ_p), after 1-min travel from a continuous elevated point source, with the
standard deviation (σ_θ) of the wind direction averaged over 15-sec periods.
Data from Hilst's experiments in stable conditions at Hanford, U.S.A.
/ appreciable effect of cross-wind shear; $\odot$ $\sigma^2 \geqslant \overline{D^2}/3$; $\boxdot$ $\sigma^2 < \overline{D^2}/3$; where σ^2
is the variance of the distribution *within* the instantaneous plume, and $\overline{D^2}$
the variance of the cross-wind position of the plume.   (See Hay and Pasquill,
1959)

theoretically from the measurements of visible width; for details of the
method used reference should be made to the original papers.   The
parameters in a power-law representation of $\overline{Y^2}$ against distance x down-
wind are tabulated in both papers, and the mean wind speed and variance
of wind direction at the source are tabulated in the 1957a paper.   Since

the wind direction statistics are based on 15-sec averages, then according to Eq. (4.3), with $\beta = 4$, the tabulated standard deviation of wind direction should be equal to the time-mean angular spread of the plume for a time of travel of 1 min, the latter being immediately obtainable from Hilst's power-law representation of the diffusion data. The comparison of the two quantities is shown in Fig. 4.8, the data being separated according as σ^2 is less than or greater than $\overline{D^2}/3$, and according as the variation of wind direction with height ('cross-wind shear') was estimated to provide an appreciable contribution to the lateral spread. The agreement is reasonable throughout, though Hay and Pasquill point out there is little to choose between this agreement and that which would be obtained with $\beta = 10$.

The foregoing discussions bring out the important point that data on diffusion at short range can provide only a coarse indication of the form and scale of the Lagrangian correlation coefficient. It has been seen that there are some conflicting features in the early results of this type of analysis, and it is clear that satisfactory clarification will require the critical examination of many measurements of diffusion. Conversely, however, it follows that even a coarse specification of β will provide useful estimates of diffusion from measurements of wind fluctuation. For as pointed out in 3.5 these estimates of diffusion will be proportional to β^p, where p varies from zero for very short distances of travel, to 0·5 at most for very long distances. Thus in practice the approach seems likely to be particularly profitable for estimating diffusion at short and moderate distances.

4.4 Vertical diffusion at short range

The problems of the vertical spread of material at short range from a source may be considered in two categories, according as the source is at ground level, or at some appreciable height above the surface. In the former case the vertical diffusion is influenced from the beginning by a turbulent structure which changes systematically with height above ground, whereas in the latter case the early stages at least of vertical spread involve a height range over which the variation of the turbulent structure may be quite small. The latter case may therefore be considered in essentially the same category as the cross-wind spread discussed in the previous sections, that is, as a case of diffusion in approximately homogeneous turbulence, and will be dealt with first.

Vertical spread from an elevated source

A useful introduction to the characteristic features of vertical diffusion at short range from a continuous source well clear of the ground is provided by some hitherto unpublished data obtained by J. Crabtree and

F. Pasquill at Harwell in 1951.   The experiments involved the release of small puffs of smoke at fixed time-intervals, from a generator carried on the cable of a large captive balloon.   From measurements with a theodolite stationed 1000 m across wind from the generator, and with a camera obscura set up immediately below the generator, the vertical displacements of the estimated centre of each smoke puff were derived at selected intervals up to a distance of horizontal travel of approximately 120 m.   For each experiment, in which 50 puffs were released at 15-sec intervals, the standard deviations of the corresponding vertical displacements were obtained. Table 4.V summarizes the data from twenty-seven experiments carried out in day-time unstable conditions, with the source at a height of 100 m.

Table 4.V

Vertical displacements of smoke puffs released at a height of 100 m in day-time unstable conditions

Distance of travel, x, (m)	31	62	93	124
$\phi = \overline{(D_z^2)}^{1/2}/x$	0·123			
$\dfrac{\phi_{31}}{\phi_x}$		1·00 ($\pm$0·01)	0·98 ($\pm$0·02)	0·97 ($\pm$0·02)

$\overline{(D_z^2)}^{1/2}$ is the standard deviation of the vertical displacements of 50 puffs released at 15-sec intervals.   Data are means of 27 experiments, figures in brackets are standard deviations.

In ancillary experiments carried out in similar conditions it was found that the average diameter of the puffs was only about one-half of the standard deviation $\overline{(D_z^2)}^{1/2}$ of the vertical displacements of the centres of the puffs.   With the reasonable assumption that the puff diameter was, say, five times the standard deviation σ of the distribution of smoke particles within the puff, it follows that $\sigma/\overline{(D_z^2)}^{1/2}$ may be taken to be 0·1.   For the time-mean vertical distribution of smoke concentration during the whole of an experiment the standard deviation, $\overline{(Z^2)}^{1/2}$, may then be written [see Eq. (3.91)]

$$\overline{(Z^2)}^{1/2} = \overline{(D_z^2 + \sigma^2)}^{1/2} = 1·005\overline{(D_z^2)}^{1/2}$$

i.e. the data given in Table 4.V may be taken as representative of the standard deviation of the time-mean vertical distribution of smoke concentration from a continuous release maintained for approximately 12 min. These data show remarkably little deviation from a simple linear variation with distance of travel up to a maximum distance of 120 m, and suggest that an equation corresponding to Eq. (4.2) ,with $\overline{Y^2}$ replaced by $\overline{Z^2}$ and

v' by w', probably holds quite closely for the first 100 m of travel from a source in unstable conditions at a height of a few hundred feet above ground.

An extension of this type of investigation, in which the vertical distribution was observed by an air-sampling procedure, and in which the corresponding variation of the inclination of the wind near the point of release was also measured, has been reported by Hay and Pasquill (1957). In these experiments spores of *lycopodium* released at a uniform rate from a mechanical dispenser carried on the cable of a captive balloon were collected at some distance down-wind, on adhesive cylinders spaced along the cable of another captive balloon. Subsequently the cylinders were scanned under a microscope, and the number of particles deposited on a given length of cylinder counted. These numbers effectively represented the dosage of particles at a given level relative to the height of release, and were used to derive the standard deviations of the apparent vertical distribution of the particles. The standard deviations so obtained were then corrected for the vertical movements of the sampling devices, which were observed by means of a theodolite. Corrections were also applied to the record of wind inclination, from theodolite observations of the bodily vertical movement of the wind vane.

Table 4.VI

Data on vertical spread from a continuous point source at a height of 150 m.
(Hay and Pasquill, 1957)

Expt. No.	Distance of travel (m)	σ_p (deg.)	σ_w (deg.)	σ_p/σ_w	$\bar{u}$ m/sec	ΔT °F (23 ft–4 ft)
4	100	1·7	3·1	0·55	6·7	−0·6
7	100	3·7	3·0	1·23	8·0	+0·2
8	100	3·5	2·8	1·25	7·4	0
12	300	4·9	4·6	1·07	7·7	−0·4
13	300	3·9	3·8	1·03	7·3	+0·6
14	300	4·1	4·0	1·03	6·3	−0·4
15	300	4·9	4·9	1·00	6·1	−0·6
16	500	3·0	3·2	0·94	7·3	−0·7
17	500	2·9	2·7	1·07	6·8	−0·3
19	300	6·0	4·0	1·50	9·5	+0·2

(σ_p is the standard deviation of the vertical spread of the particles, expressed as angular elevation from the source; σ_w is the standard deviation of wind inclination near the source, based on readings at $2\frac{1}{2}$-sec intervals.)

Table 4.VI summarizes the results of ten successful experiments, in each of which the particles were released for a period of about 30 min, at a height near 150 m, and in which the distance of travel was 100, 300 and 500 m. The standard deviation, σ_w, of the wind inclination was computed from readings extracted from the wind inclination record, at $2\frac{1}{2}$-sec intervals over the whole period of release. With two exceptions (Nos. 4 and 19) the values of σ_p and σ_w are remarkably similar, apparently irrespective of the distance of travel and the conditions of wind speed and vertical gradient of temperature. It is possible that these two anomalies, and also the occurrence of the moderately high values of σ_p/σ_w for Nos. 7 and 8, are simply a consequence of the difficulty of obtaining mutually representative measurements of the turbulence and the diffusion. The main source of difficulty was that the positioning of the balloon cable carrying the sampling apparatus was dependent on visual estimation of the continuously varying wind direction at the position of the dispenser. According to the success with which this positioning was achieved, it is clear that the sample collected could be mainly associated with a relatively small proportion of the duration of release of the particles. In the original discussion of this work Hay and Pasquill conclude that there is no evidence for a significant departure from linearity in the relation between vertical spread and time of travel, and point out that this suggests a value of not less than about 10:1 for the ratio of the *Lagrangian* time-scale to the time-scale of the (Eulerian) autocorrelation of the wind inclination. This ratio is at least of the same order as the more reliable values obtained later from the measurements of cross-wind diffusion discussed in the previous section.

Hilst and Simpson (1958) have given a brief preliminary report of measurements of vertical distribution from a continuous source in stable conditions. The fluorescent pigment used as a tracer was emitted from a tower at a height of 185 feet, and its vertical distribution was sampled simultaneously at 500, 1000, 2500 and 5000 ft down-wind by arrays of adhesive cylinders suspended from captive balloons. Positioning of the sampling arrays was guided by a visible smoke plume emitted with the pigment. No data on the vertical component of turbulence are given, so it is not possible to analyse the results in the manner just discussed. However it is particularly noteworthy that the standard deviations of the vertical distributions increase with distance much more slowly than linearly, even more slowly in fact than the square root of the distance. Using empirical equations for this variation with distance, and applying the differential form of Taylor's equation, Hilst and Simpson demonstrate that the results require a form of the Lagrangian correlation coefficient which becomes negative for large values of time-lag. The physical

11—A.D.

significance of this interpretation is by no means clear, and it should be borne in mind that in the stable conditions of these experiments the properties of the vertical component were unlikely to be uniform with height, as required in Taylor's analysis.

Vertical spread from a source on the ground

The figure of 10 m usually quoted for the height of the cloud from a continuous cross-wind line source in neutral conditions, at a distance of 100 m (see Sutton 1947a), is based on experiments carried out on the Porton site in 1923 and 1924.   In these cases the source was provided by smoke candles distributed uniformly across wind at 3 m or 5 m spacing, the sampling being carried out by hand-pump, as in the observations of cross-wind spread, the only difference being that the operators were stationed at various heights on a tower.   A re-analysis of these results, together with the analysis of an extended series of trials at Cardington, was presented in 1932, and the findings of this later analysis are summarized here.

The official records of the analysis contain graphs of the mean vertical distributions obtained from twenty-nine experiments carried out at Cardington in 1931, with a distance of travel of 229 m, and from seven experiments carried out at Porton with a distance of travel of 100 m.   All experiments were carried out with small temperature gradient in the vertical and are considered to be representative of the effect of purely mechanical turbulence over a level, fairly smooth site.   The values given for the height of cloud, Z_0, as defined by the height at which the smoke concentration χ fell to one-tenth of the concentration χ_0 at the surface, and for the exponent s in the form

$$\chi/\chi_0 = \exp(-bz^s) \tag{4.4}$$

are as follows:

	$Z_0(m)$	s
Cardington measurements at 229 m down-wind	24	1·5
Porton measurements at 100 m down-wind	10·1	1·3

The above figures were based on a graphical analysis which involved an unspecified extrapolation of the concentration profile to the surface, the lowest sampling position being at a height of 1 m in both series of experiments.   From the magnitude of the concentration at three heights z_1, z_2, z_3, such that

$$z_3 = 2z_2 = 4z_1,$$

the value of s may be computed conveniently and objectively, i.e. without subjective extrapolation of the concentration profile, since from Eq. (4.4)

$$2^s = \frac{\log \chi_2 - \log \chi_3}{\log \chi_1 - \log \chi_2} \tag{4.5}$$

The values of s so deduced from concentrations read off the graphs of vertical distribution are $1 \cdot 4$ and $1 \cdot 15$ for the Cardington and Porton experiments respectively, but the corresponding values of Z_0, being somewhat insensitive to s, are not substantially changed.   As in the case of the cross-wind distribution, the inference is that the parameter describing the shape of the distribution has not been determined with precision, though in the present case there is a more compelling indication of a departure from the Gaussian form.

No analysis of the shape of the vertical distribution has yet been provided from the *prairie grass* experiments, but Cramer (1957) has presented the data on the vertical spread $(\overline{Z^2})^{1/2}$ at a distance of 100 m, and demonstrated that these are well correlated with the standard deviation of the wind *azimuth* (σ_A) over a sevenfold range of the latter quantity.   No comparison with the standard deviation of the *inclination* of the wind is given.   The magnitude of $(\overline{Z^2})^{1/2}$ ranges from 2 m in very stable conditions, through approximately $3 \cdot 5$ m in neutral conditions, to 11 m in very unstable conditions.   Comparison of these *standard deviations* with the Porton data on *height of cloud* at a distance of 100 m can be made by adopting an appropriate magnitude for s in Eq. (4.4).   So far this is only roughly determined to be in the range $1 \cdot 1$–$1 \cdot 5$, and unfortunately, as the figures in Table 4.II show on replacing Y by Z, $Z_0/(\overline{Z^2})^{1/2}$ is fairly sensitive to variations in s below $1 \cdot 5$.   Taking an intermediate value of $s = 1 \cdot 3$, the corresponding value of this ratio is interpolated as $1 \cdot 95$ so that from the Porton figure of 10 m for height of cloud the corresponding standard deviation is approximately 5 m, appreciably larger than Cramer's figure for neutral conditions.

The most familiar theoretical interpretation which is at present available for the above data is that provided by the solutions of the two-dimensional parabolic equation of diffusion (Chapter 3), which assumes that the vertical flux of material is given by the product of the gradient of the concentration and an eddy diffusivity.   For the shape of the vertical distribution reference to Eq. (3.20) shows that the exponent s in Eq. (4.4) is equal to $2\alpha + 1$, where α is determined by the conjugate variations of wind velocity and eddy diffusivity with height, i.e.

$$\bar{u} \propto z^\alpha$$
$$K \propto z^{1-\alpha}$$

The difficulty which arises here from the fact that the vertical distribution of wind speed in the lower atmosphere conforms more closely to the logarithmic form [see Eq. (3.5)] has been overcome by Calder (1949) by using power-law approximations to the latter form. As Calder points out, the index α is necessarily a function of the height range over which the wind profile is specified, and therefore some *a priori* knowledge of the amount of vertical diffusion is essential in order that a realistic estimate of the equivalent value of α may be made. Furthermore, since the wind velocity observations made at the time of these early diffusion experiments are inadequate for specific determination of the wind profile index it is necessary to make broad estimates. Calder has given equivalent values of α for various height intervals and for roughness parameters, z_0, of 3 and 0·5 cm. For diffusion over distances of 100 to 1000 m on the Porton site he adopts an average value of 0·187, and in the absence of alternative data this is presumably a reasonable figure to take for the Cardington site. This value of α leads to an index s equal to 1·37, which is within the range of the experimental values, and supports the indication of a departure from Gaussian form.

Turning to the magnitude of the vertical spread, Calder's treatment gives a value of 10·5 m for the height of cloud Z_0 at 100 m down-wind in neutral conditions, which is in striking agreement with the observed magnitude in the Porton experiments. According to this treatment

$$Z_0 \propto x^{1/(2\alpha+1)}$$

and extrapolation to the distance of the Cardington trials (229 m), using the same value of α (0·187) gives $Z_0 = 19$ m. This is appreciably smaller than the observed value of 24 m, and it may be significant that this latter figure was derived from the mean of three sets of data, for which the separate values of height of cloud and wind speed were as follows:

	$\bar{u}$ (at height of 2 m) (m/sec)	Z_0 (m)	No. of experiments
25.11.31	3·6	26	2
26.11.31	7·9	20	7
2.12.31	3·5	23	20

The relatively large values of Z_0 are thus associated with the relatively low wind speeds, which suggest the possibility either that there was a variation (with wind speed) of the vertical component of turbulence which is not taken into account in this application of the theoretical treatment, or that there was some elevation of the cloud due to the heat of the smoke sources, to an extent which would be expected to increase with decreasing wind speed.   Unfortunately, on the data available it does not seem possible to resolve this discrepancy, but it is noteworthy that the result at high wind speed agrees well with Calder's value.

With regard to the previously noted discrepancy between the Porton and *Prairie Grass* data, it should be remembered that the roughness parameter z_0 of the O'Neill site is given by Cramer (1957) as < 1 cm, while Calder associates the Porton diffusion data with a z_0 of 3 cm.   According to Calder's treatment a reduction in z_0 from 3 cm to 0·5 cm produces a reduction of 20 per cent in the calculated height of cloud at 100 m downwind of the source, so that the difference in results may be due to a difference in site roughness.

Kazanskii and Monin (1957) have reported measurements of the vertical spread of smoke plumes from cross-wind line sources on the ground (see also Monin 1959).   The visible vertical boundaries of the plumes were recorded photographically, and the vertical distributions were explored by means of air-sampling apparatus mounted on masts at heights up to 12 m. In the analysis of the photographic records the form of the plume near the source was disregarded as being dominated by the thermal rise of the initially hot smoke, the upper boundary of the smoke further down-wind being approximated to a straight line, the inclination of which to the horizontal was then read off, and taken as a measure of the (linear) rate of growth of the cloud due to diffusion.   The magnitudes of the inclination were found to be systematically related to stability as specified by the length parameter L introduced by Monin and Obukhov (1954) (see 3.1).   In neutral conditions the inclination was about $\tan^{-1} 0·07$, i.e. the visible height of cloud at 100 m was about 7 m.   As the mean roughness parameter z_0 of the site is quoted as 0·4 cm this result may be compared directly with the *Prairie Grass* measurements.   There is the obvious difficulty of comparing a visible dimension with a dimension based on a concentration distribution, but as previously noted Cramer's analysis gives $(\overline{Z^2})^{1/2} = 3·5$ m in neutral conditions, which with the value of $Z_0/(\overline{Z^2})^{1/2}$ also previously suggested (i.e. 1·95) corresponds to $Z_0 = 7$ m.   Furthermore, the value of Z_0 given by Calder's treatment for $z_0 = 0·5$ cm is 8·1 m.

The results of the vertical distributions reported by Kazanskii and Monin are given in a graphical form from which it is not possible readily to deduce either the heights of cloud or the shape of the vertical distribution for direct comparison with the data already discussed.   It is interesting to note, however, that the results are claimed to demonstrate a quality of similarity, in that the shape of the distribution is a unique function of z/H where H is implicitly the visible height of the plume, and that this unique function is in good agreement with functions derived theoretically by Monin from solutions of the hyperbolic equation of diffusion, which he suggests is preferable to the classical parabolic equation (see 3.3).

Indirect estimates of vertical spread

In view of the practical difficulties of obtaining direct observations of the vertical spread, except at very short distances, estimates of this quantity are sometimes made from measurements of the surface distribution of concentration.   It is obvious that the surface concentration down-wind of an infinite cross-wind line source (or the equivalent cross-wind integral of the surface concentration from a point source) is determined by the shape and dimension of the vertical distribution.   If the shape is *similar* irrespective of distance, i.e. is described universally by a function of z/H, where H is a characteristic vertical dimension such as the height as previously defined, then it follows that the variation of the concentration at ground level with distance is the inverse of the variation of H with distance.   An investigation of the distribution of ground-level concentration down-wind of a long cross-wind line source was undertaken at Porton in 1925, using the smoke-candle and stain-meter technique.   In all, twenty-six experiments were carried out, in approximately half of which the concentrations were measured at 100, 200 and 300 m down-wind, while in the remaining half the distances were increased to 300, 600 and 1000 m.   Approximately neutral conditions of stability obtained on all occasions.   Two separate analyses were made of the results to give the index in the power-law variation of concentration χ with distance x, i.e.

$$\chi \text{ (infinite line source)} \propto x^{-q},$$

the values of q obtained being 1·0 and 0·9 respectively.   The value of q derived from the cross-wind integral of the concentrations at 100, 300 and 1000 m from the point source experiments referred to in 4.3 was 0·98, again for neutral conditions of stability.   From the *Prairie Grass* data on the variation of peak concentration and cloud-width Cramer (1957) has inferred for q a value of 'approximately 1·0' in neutral conditions, while Kanzanskii and Monin's (*loc. cit.*) line source results also support $q \simeq 1·0$, in a range of conditions of stability which is not specified.

Cramer's analysis also includes estimates of the index q in conditions of stability other than neutral.   It appears that in such conditions the simple power-law variation does not hold over the whole range of distance from 50 to 800 m, and that the inferred *local* value of q tends to increase with distance to values greater than 1·0 in unstable conditions, and to decrease with distance in stable conditions.   The implication is that in unstable conditions the vertical spread of the plume increased more rapidly than in proportion to distance. In view of the indirect derivation this striking result should be accepted with some caution until confirmed by direct measurements of vertical spread at a number of distances simultaneously. However it is noteworthy that this effect of stability on the variation of vertical spread with distance is given by Monin's theoretical treatment, described in his 1959 paper and in the paper by Kazanskii and Monin. From a physical standpoint the *direction* of the observed change of q with change of atmospheric stability is not unreasonable, since it merely demands that the vertical component of turbulence should increase more rapidly with height in unstable conditions than in neutral conditions, but whether the value of q in neutral conditions is exactly 1·0 is a point which has yet to be established.

4.5 Relative diffusion

Reference has already been made to the existence of two distinct forms of dispersion, manifested in the meandering of a plume of smoke and in the widening of the plume itself, and the distinction between these two forms has been emphasized in the theoretical discussions of Chapter 3. The preceding sections of the present chapter have been concerned with the combined effect of the two processes, and it is now appropriate to consider the observational data relating to the latter form of diffusion alone, i.e. the relative separation of the particles or elements of a diffusing cloud. In its elementary form this relative diffusion is represented in the growth of an individual cluster of particles, but it also determines the *instantaneous* distribution in the cross section of a continuous plume of material. To the extent that there may be no important *vertical* meandering process in the case of the continuous plume emitted from a source on the ground, this case might logically have been included in the present rather than in the previous section. However, this case is special in the sense that as the cloud develops vertically it is affected at different horizontal levels by different scales of turbulence. The discussions of the present section will be confined to the effects of nominally homogeneous turbulence, in which case all parts of the diffusing cloud are subject to the action of the same spectrum of turbulence.

The earliest indications of the instantaneous width of a plume come from the early Porton smoke experiments, in which it was clear that the resultant cross-wind distribution over some finite period (i.e. the *time-mean* distribution) was determined to a considerable extent by the cross-wind movement of the smoke plume as a whole. The *instantaneous* cross-wind distribution in the plume was substantially narrower than the time-mean distribution, and indeed it is noteworthy that in the 1923 experiments the visible width of the smoke plume at 100 m down-wind was observed to be approximately 16 m, as compared with the time-mean width of 35 m. However, the first measurements of the near-instantaneous distribution in a smoke plume were obtained in the Cardington experiments in 1931. The so-called instantaneous samples were provided by a single filling of the sampling pump, and it is stated in the records that in this operation a large percentage of the sample was obtained in 2–3 sec. The widths of cross-wind distribution so obtained, as defined by the fall of concentration to one-tenth of the peak value, averaged 25 m in neutral conditions, whereas the corresponding value for a sampling-time of 3 min was 44 m.

The growth of smoke-puffs

Because of the difficulty of measuring the instantaneous values of con-centration simultaneously at a sufficient number of positions the observa-tion of relative diffusion has tended to rely mainly on the visual methods, and especially on the observation of the growth and dissipation of puffs of smoke. Earliest examples are contained in discussions by Roberts (1923) and Sutton (1932), in which photographic observations of the growth of anti-aircraft shell bursts were used to test theoretical treatments. Later and more extensive series of observations of this type have been reported by Kellogg (1956) and Frenkiel and Katz (1956). In Kellogg's experi-ments in New Mexico, vials of titanium tetrachloride and water, attached to trains of balloons, were exploded at predetermined altitudes by small charges of cordite set off by baroswitches. The altitudes of release ranged from 23,600 to 63,000 ft and the resulting puffs of smoke were observed by photo-theodolites, from the records of which both the positions and visible sizes of the puffs were obtained at intervals. Eighteen usable sets of observations were reported in the form of graphs of visible diameter against time, up to a maximum time between 3 and 11 min. The smoke puffs used by Frenkiel and Katz were released within the first 100 m above the surface, over water off Maryland, U.S.A., in unstable conditions. The puffs were generated by exploding small pill-boxes of gunpowder carried by a tethered balloon. Positions and sizes of the smoke puffs at 1-sec intervals were obtained from cine-photographs, and the data on smoke-puff radius were tabulated by Frenkiel and Katz for nineteen cases, with total durations of observation ranging from 7 to 20 sec. In experiments of this type the puffs obtained are usually not of perfectly spherical shape, and some system has to be adopted for obtaining a consistent measurement of puff size. The system adopted by Frenkiel and Katz was to measure the visible *area*, and from this to obtain the radius of the equivalent circular area. In

Kellogg's experiments the puffs were elongated horizontally by wind shear, and it was argued that the minimum diameter was the relevant dimension for the diffusive spread.   However, it was found to be more satisfactory to determine this dimension in an indirect way, by measuring the visible area and the *maximum* diameter, and calculating the minimum diameter for an assumed elliptical shape.

In general the smoke puff results show a rate of visible growth which is fairly constant to start with, and is then progressively reduced.   This is well illustrated in the average curve taken from Kellogg's paper and reproduced here as Fig. 4.9.   Some cases actually show the visible size reaching

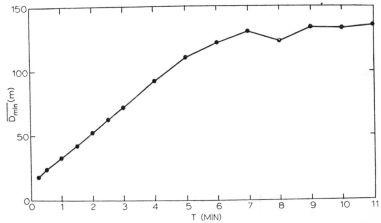

FIG. 4.9   Growth of the visible diameter of a smoke-puff as a function of time of travel T.   Average curve from eighteen releases at heights ranging from 23,600 to 63,000 ft over New Mexico.   (Kellogg, 1956)

a maximum value and then diminishing with the further lapse of time. However, as pointed out by Gifford (1957a) in a reappraisal of Kellogg's data, many of the observations in the stratosphere show a distinct tendency for the graph of diameter against time to be slightly convex to the time axis in the early stages (see Fig. 3 of Kellogg's paper).   The same effect is indeed slightly evident even in the average curve, for times between 0·5 and 3 min.   This property immediately points to an accelerated growth of the cloud, as predicted in 3.6.

For the proper interpretation of observations on the growth of smoke puffs, it is essential to make some assumptions about the way in which the visible outline is related to the smoke concentration in the cloud.   The method which is most commonly employed is that introduced by Roberts

(1923).   In this treatment of *opacity* it is assumed that the smoke particles produce a loss of intensity of the light from some further object or background by direct screening only, and that the background or object is obscured (i.e. the smoke puff is outlined) when this intensity is reduced to a certain fraction of its magnitude in the absence of intervening smoke. Thus, for obscuration to occur the integrated smoke concentration along the line of sight must have a certain limiting value.   This limiting value must depend on such factors as particle size distribution and the nature of the background, but for given circumstances it is assumed to be constant. The procedure followed from this point by Roberts, Sutton, Kellogg, and Frenkiel and Katz, was to use a theoretical relation for the distribution of concentration in the puff as a function of time, in order to derive a relation for the variation of visible size with time.   Comparison with the observations then enabled the correctness of the original diffusion treatment to be assessed, and parameters such as diffusion coefficients and intensities of turbulence to be evaluated.   Roberts' treatment of diffusion used the concept of a constant eddy diffusivity which is not generally acceptable, while the remaining treatments were all based ultimately on Taylor's statistical treatment which, as discussed in Chapter 3, is applicable to the diffusion from a fixed continuous source, but not to the relative diffusion now under discussion.   However, it has since been recognized and emphasized by Gifford (1957a), that in order usefully to interpret smoke puff data it is not necessary to adopt any particular solution for the variation of concentration with time, though it is necessary to make some assumption about the *shape* of the distribution of smoke concentration within the puff.

Following custom Gifford assumes that the statistical distribution of concentration in the puff follows the Gaussian form, with variance σ^2 at time t after release.   For a given quantity of smoke Q the concentration at x, y, z relative to the puff centre is then given by

$$\chi(x, y, z, t) = \frac{Q}{(2\pi\sigma^2)^{3/2}} \exp \left[-\left\{ \frac{x^2+y^2+z^2}{2\sigma^2} \right\} \right] \qquad (4.6)$$

If the puff is viewed from some distance along the y axis, the visible outline will be determined by the condition

$$N_0 = \int_{-\infty}^{\infty} \chi \, dy = \frac{Q}{2\pi\sigma^2} \exp - \left[\frac{r^2}{2\sigma^2} \right] \qquad (4.7)$$

where $r = (x^2 + z^2)^{1/2}$ is the visible radius of the puff, and N_0 is a constant independent of t.   Differentiation of (4.7) with respect to time leads to

$$\frac{dr^2}{dt} = \frac{d\sigma^2}{dt} \left[\frac{r^2 - 2\sigma^2}{\sigma^2} \right] \qquad (4.8)$$

so at the time of maximum visible radius r_m it follows that

$$r_m{}^2 = 2\sigma^2.$$

Substitution in (4.7) gives

$$N_0 = \frac{Q}{e\pi r_m{}^2} \tag{4.9}$$

and equating 4.7 and 4.9, and rearranging

$$\sigma^2 = \frac{r^2}{2}\left[\ln\left(\frac{r_m{}^2 e}{2}\right) - \ln \sigma^2\right]^{-1} \tag{4.10}$$

Thus the absolute values of σ may be derived as a function of time from observations of the growth of a smoke puff, provided these observations are maintained for a sufficient period to enable the maximum radius to be specified.

In the re-examination of the smoke puff data reported by Kellogg, and by Frenkiel and Katz, Gifford found that in both cases a number of observations were characterized by the existence of a definable maximum radius, so that Eq. (4.10) could be applied. The values of σ^2 obtained by Gifford $(\overline{Y^2}$ in his notation) are shown in Fig. 4.10. The curves correspond to the theoretical relations for the separation of a pair of particles, which follow from Batchelor's (1952) application of the Kolmogoroff similarity theory, i.e.

$$\overline{y^2}(T) - \overline{y^2}(0) \propto T^2 \quad \text{small } T \tag{4.11}$$

$$\overline{y^2}(T) \propto T^3 \quad \text{intermediate } T \tag{4.12}$$

and which have been discussed in 3.6. It was assumed that $\overline{y^2}(0) \ll \overline{y^2}$ for all applicable T values in the case of (4.12), and even in the case of (4.11) for Kellogg's data. In the fitting of (4.11) to the results of Frenkiel and Katz a reasonable value of $\sigma_0{}^2$ ($=400$ cm^2) was adopted, but it was pointed out that any other value between zero and the obvious upper limit of 550 cm^2 would give an equally acceptable fit. It can be seen that Gifford's representation of the data strongly supports the existence of the predicted t^2 and t^3 régimes. Apart from the agreement with these specific laws Gifford's analysis is particularly notable in demonstrating an increase of dispersion (σ) more rapid than linear with time, whereas all previous analyses of diffusion data have been considered to show a growth slower than linear.

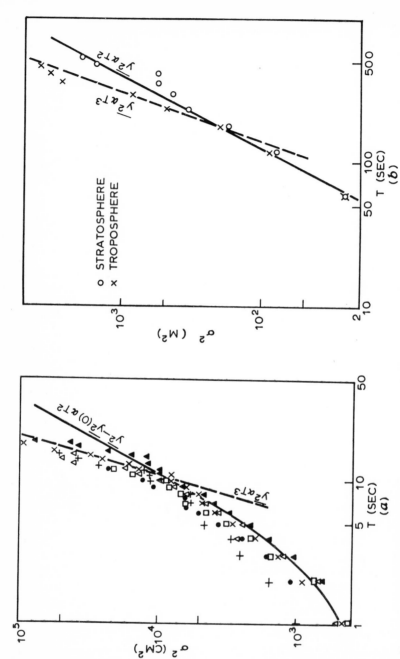

FIG. 4.10 Gifford's (1957a) re-analysis of data on the growth of smoke-puffs, for comparisons with predictions from the Kolmogoroff similarity theory. σ^2 is the variance of the distribution in a smoke-puff. (a) Frenkiel and Katz, 1956, individual puffs; (b) Kellogg, 1956, averaged data.

Trajectory studies

The more direct but analytically more laborious technique of evaluating the variation with time of the relative separation of pairs of *particles* has been followed by Charnock (1951) and Wilkins (1958a). Charnock used data obtained by Durst (1948) from camera obscura observations of the trajectories of pairs of smoke puffs fired from an aircraft flying at heights in the range 2000–5000 ft. The results tabulated by Charnock include values of

$$l_0 = \overline{l(0)}$$

and
$$F(t, l_0) = \overline{[l(t) - \overline{l(0)}]^2}/t$$

for $t = 10, 20, 30, 40$ and 50 sec, where $l(0)$ is the initial separation between two puffs at an arbitrary time zero (not necessarily the time of release), and $l(t)$ the projection on a horizontal plane of the separation t seconds later. The bar implies averaging over a number of observations with similar initial separation. The quantity $F[t, l(0)]$ was examined as a function of time for comparison with the similarity-theory prediction corresponding to Eq. (4.11), i.e. $F(t, l_0) \propto t$. Charnock found that there was some support for the relation in winds less than 5 m/sec, but that the results obtained with stronger winds were too scattered to provide any definite conclusion. Wilkins has reported and analysed analogous experiments in which pairs of neutral balloons were released at ground level, with initial separation either 10 or 100 m, and tracked for several minutes by pairs of theodolites on a 1600-m base line. Average results for the variation of $\overline{[l(t) - l(0)]^2}$ with time for each initial separation, based on ten experiments in each category, were presented graphically. These confirm Gifford's previous analysis in indicating dispersion régimes corresponding to (4.11) and (4.12) for $l(0) = 100$ m. For $l(0) = 10$ m an increase in the exponent of T was evident, but owing to scatter there was no clear indication of a T^2 régime followed by a T^3 régime.

It is noteworthy that the full forms of Eq. (4.11) and (4.12), as given by dimensional analysis and similarity theory, contain the rate of dissipation, ϵ, of turbulent kinetic energy, and a dimensionless constant. Assuming the latter to be unity estimates of ϵ can therefore be made from observations of relative diffusion. The estimate obtained by Charnock (0·2–0·9 cm² sec⁻³) from observations at heights of 1–2 km is intermediate between those obtained by Gifford from the surface observations by Frenkiel and Katz (2–5 cm² sec⁻³) and the stratospheric observations by Kellogg (0·02 cm² sec⁻³). Wilkins' estimate from his surface observations (70–200 cm² sec⁻³) does not fit in with the foregoing trend in variation of ϵ

with height, and is a reminder of the extremely crude nature of these estimates of ϵ.

Observations of relative diffusion by tracer-sampling

The visual methods also suffer from the disadvantages that it has not so far proved possible, except by inference, to derive from them information on the form of the distribution of concentration within a cloud of material. On the other hand direct observation of the distribution by virtually instantaneous sampling measurements is very difficult if not impossible, and probably the best measurement that can be readily achieved is a compromise in which some element of *finite-time* sampling is involved. Such material as is at present available for discussion was obtained by arranging for a puff of gaseous or particulate material to pass over a horizontal line or grid of sampling positions, or for a line of material released from an aircraft flying across-wind at high speed to cross a vertical array of sampling positions. In either case the results are expressed in the form of dosages, or numbers of particles collected, during some interval, and error will arise unless the motion of the cloud is exactly normal to the sampling line. If the standard deviation of the particles from the line of motion is σ_{true}, the apparent value observed on the sampling line will be approximately $\sigma_{\text{true}} \sec \theta$, where θ is the angle between the direction of motion and the normal to the sampling line. This discrepancy in angle may arise from a misjudgment of the mean wind direction when setting out the cross-wind sampling line, but even a magnitude of 20° will introduce an error of only about six per cent in σ. Additionally, the turbulent fluctuations in the cross-wind component will result in fluctuations of θ for successive clouds. Then for clouds which on average cross the sampling line normally the observed standard deviation will average approximately $\bar{\sigma}_{\text{true}} \overline{\sec \theta'}$, i.e. $\bar{\sigma}_{\text{true}} (1 + (\overline{\theta'^2}/2))$ for small values of θ'. The quantity $(\overline{\theta'^2})^{1/2}$, i.e. the intensity of the lateral component of turbulence, will normally be in the region of 0·1 radians (see 2.8), and the error in $\bar{\sigma}$ will then be negligible. This means that provided the experiment is arranged so that the cloud travels in a general direction fairly close to the normal to the sampling line, and that cases of excessive intensity of turbulence are avoided, the error involved in determining the spread within the cloud from an integrated sample is likely to be unimportant.

Sampling data of the above type, from field tests conducted at the Dugway Proving Ground, U.S.A., have been presented by Tank (1957). Clouds of gas released explosively were arranged to pass over arrays of gas samplers on a flat site. Diagrams of the isopleths of total dosage during

the passage of the cloud are given for each of seven tests, for positions
within about 200 m down-wind of the point of release.   Tank's analysis
of these data was carried out in terms of Robert's (Fickian) solution of the
instantaneous point source (see Sutton, 1953, p. 134), modified so as to
allow for the initial finite size of the cloud.   The general assumption of
Fickian-type diffusion for this case is of course entirely unacceptable, and
the results as presented by Tank are for this reason of somewhat limited
empirical value.   An analysis in the light of Batchelor's applications of the
Kolmogoroff similarity theory has been given by Gifford (1957b), using the
total dosage on the along-wind axis of the ground-level dosage pattern.
This total dosage is taken to be inversely proportional to the mean-square
particle dispersion [$\overline{y^2}$ in the notation of Eq. (4.12)].   From a plot of
axial dosage against time T after burst Gifford concludes that with the
exception of two tests in stable conditions all cases showed a T^{-3} régime,
which corresponds to a T^3 régime in $\overline{y^2}$.   It is noteworthy that in two stable
cases the fall of dosage with time after burst was slower than as T^{-1},
implying that the increase of $\overline{y^2}$ was slower than as T, i.e. slower than would
be expected from Fickian-type diffusion, but this was probably owing to
the fact that the finite initial size of the clouds was not negligible in these
cases.

   Smith and Hay (1961) have given the results of an experimental study
in which clusters of *lycopodium* spores were formed near the ground by
catapulting the material from a small container.   Within a few metres of
travel the spores were dispersed into a cloud approximately 1–2 m in
height and 2–4 m in down-wind length, and these were taken to be the
initial dimensions of the cluster, subsequent growth being ascribed to
turbulent diffusion.   Samples of the cloud were collected on adhesive
cylinders set out on cross-wind lines at distances of 100, 200 and 300 m
down-wind of the point of release.   The experiments are of particular
interest in that in conjunction with these observations of lateral diffusion
fairly detailed records were taken of the fine-structure variation of wind
direction θ at a height of 2 m, at four positions with cross-wind separation
ranging from 5 to 35 m.   From the numbers of spores collected on a
specified length of cylinder, which were taken to be measures of the total
dosage during the passage of the cloud, the standard deviation of the cross-
wind distribution was computed in each case.   The results are summarized
in Table 4.VII with other relevant data.   To a close approximation the
values of $\sigma_\theta[=(\overline{\theta'^2})^{1/2}]$ represent the intensity of turbulence $i=(\overline{v'^2})^{1/2}/\bar{u}$.
The values of scale of turbulence, which showed no systematic connection
with the other meteorological factors observed at the time, were obtained

from the correlograms of wind direction against cross-wind separation, using equations corresponding to (1.2) and (1.3). Both the intensities and scales of turbulence are appropriate to averaging and sampling times (see 1.4) of 1 sec and 3 min respectively.

Table 4.VII

Experimental data on the expansion of clusters of particles in near-neutral conditions. (Smith and Hay, 1961)

Expt. No.	σ_p in m at			σ_θ (rad)	$\bar{u}$ (m/sec)
	100 m	200 m	300 m		
1	4·76	10·80	17·70	0·136	6·1
2	3·16	7·64	—	0·153	5·6
3	3·68	6·80	13·98	0·151	6·1
4	5·04	10·28	14·40	0·126	5·0
5	5·38	11·92	—	0·147	4·3
6	—	5·80	9·24	0·140	5·9
7	3·48	—	—	0·113	9·5
8	4·70	—	—	0·085	9·1
9	2·20	—	—	0·091	9·7
10	5·37	—	—	0·095	9·0

(σ_p is the standard deviation of the cross-wind distribution. σ_θ is the standard deviation of wind direction for an averaging time of 1 sec and a sampling time of 3 min. Horizontal scale of turbulence 5–25 m. All wind measurements at a height of 2 m).

It is noteworthy that at each distance the sizes of the cloud as represented by the standard deviations show roughly a twofold variation, without any obvious relation with the intensity of turbulence. This is perhaps not surprising in view of the relatively small range of intensity, and the fact that these estimates of intensity, by virtue of the sampling time of 3 min, include the effect of *eddy sizes* much larger than those which could possibly have contributed directly to the spread of the clouds. The final dimensions (i.e. about six times the standard deviation) of the clouds were about 100 m, which would be equivalent to a sampling time of 10–20 sec. In any case it is known from the observations of turbulence discussed in 2.7 that the intensity of turbulence for a sampling time even as long as three minutes fluctuates widely over short intervals of time or space, so that the diffusion and turbulence data of the type given in Table 4.VII can be compared only on a statistical basis.

On the assumption of a Gaussian distribution within the cloud the average value of the standard deviations of the particle distribution at

100 m. i.e. 4·2 m, would correspond to a cloud-width (as defined by one-tenth peak concentration) of 18 m. This may be compared with the average 'instantaneous' cloud width of 25 m measured in the experiments with continuous sources at Cardington in 1931. A further point is that the data of Table 4.VII contain evidence of an accelerated increase in cloud dimension with distance of travel, in the sense that the exponent in the power-law variation of standard deviation with distance tends to be greater than unity. There is however no clear indication of an exponent as large as 1·5, corresponding to a T^3 régime as in Eq. (4.12). This feature is not surprising when it is remembered that the T^3 régime is predicted for diffusion which is dominated by eddies in the inertial sub-range. In the conditions of Table 4.VII it is clear that *eddy sizes* of 10 m or more would be effective, and at the heights of a few metres involved it seems unlikely that these eddies would have the properties of the inertial sub-range. Further consideration of these results in relation to statistical theory is given in the following section, in conjunction with data obtained on a larger scale.

4.6 Diffusion on a large scale

For the most part the material which has been discussed so far in this chapter has been concerned with the diffusion occurring over distances of travel of a few hundred metres. The relative diffusion data obtained by Kellogg using smoke puffs, and by Wilkins using neutral balloons, involved times of travel up to about 10 min, and hence distances up to a few thousand metres. Recognition of some rational system in the effects of diffusion over a larger range of distances has of course been one of the main aims of diffusion studies, and, as is well known, significant moves in this direction were provided at a very early stage by L. F. Richardson's remarkably penetrating theoretical investigations. The observational information available at this time, however, was of a rather crude and heterogeneous nature, and of the data collected in Richardson's 1926 paper (p. 724) only those obtained from observations of the scattering of balloons can be expected to have some basic value as regards diffusion at long range from a point source.

Richardson's balloon data were obtained largely from balloon competitions organized at Brighton and in Regent's Park, London, and the results obtained from these were published in detail by Richardson and Proctor (1925). Values were given of the standard deviation σ of balloons from their mean track, for groups of balloons at various mean distances from the starting point. Applying Eq. (3.17), which is applicable to Fickian-type

12—A.D.

diffusion, Richardson and Proctor obtained values of the eddy diffusivity K and examined the support provided for Richardson's (1926) deduction that

$$K \propto \sigma^{4/3}$$

In fact the proportionality constant was found to be systematically dependent on wind speed, and when observations at about the same speed were selected Richardson and Proctor found that for σ in the region of 30 km

$$K \propto \sigma^{5/3}$$

However, in considering the implication of these results in relation to the theoretical ideas on diffusion the significance of the nature of the release of the balloons does not seem to have been taken into account. According to the original paper the balloons in any one group had been released over a period usually in the region of 10 hr, and not instantaneously as a cluster. The effective maximum separation of the balloons, *owing to the release process*, was therefore in the region of 300 km, i.e. somewhat greater than the separation observed in the arrival positions. This means that it is probably more logical to treat the data as appertaining to a *continuous* point source than to a cluster or instantaneous source of initially small dimensions, as is usually implied in discussion of these data. If this is so, then it would be appropriate to regard the apparent increase of K as at least partly a consequence of the persistence of Lagrangian correlation, as discussed in 3.4, rather than an indication of the accelerative nature of relative diffusion as discussed in 3.6.

In a re-analysis of Richardson and Proctor's data, Sutton (1932) gives a graph of log σ against log x for groups formed from results corresponding to similar distance x from the source. The points with one exception lie close to the relation

$$\sigma \propto x^{0.875}$$

for distances ranging from 50–500 km, but they could also be represented fairly well by a simple linear relation between σ and x, with σ/x approximately 0·07.

Data from the fluorescent-particle tracer technique

Other data on diffusion in the first 100 km of travel are of much more recent origin and have been derived from the fluorescent-pigment tracer technique, in which greater sensitivity is achieved by the process of actually counting the very small individual particles. The first results to be reported in the literature are due to Braham, Seely and Crozier (1952), who carried out their studies in 1951 from the New Mexico Institute of Mining and Technology.   An effectively continuous release of the material at a rate of about 3×10^{10} particles per second was achieved, either by mixing it into the oil fed into a military smoke generator, or by means of a mechanical type of dispenser.   Air-sampling down-wind of the point of release was carried out with a drum impactor mounted on an aircraft, which flew successive traverses through the plume of airborne material at various distances and heights.   By turning the drum of the sampler at pre-scribed intervals of time samples corresponding to successive sections of a traverse were separately collected, so enabling the cross-wind distribution to be determined.   A continuation of the experiments in New Mexico in 1952, and similar experiments in Australia in 1953, have been described by Crozier and Seely (1955).   Since 1955 (see Pasquill, 1955, 1956) the techniques have been used at Porton in connection with Meteorological Office studies of the diffusion of cloud-seeding agents for the artificial stimulation of rain.   In the latter work, in order more effectively to study the vertical as distinct from the cross-wind distribution, the tracer experi-ments have also been carried out in a converse manner, that is, with release of the particles from a dispenser carried rapidly across-wind on a motor vehicle or aircraft, the sampling being carried out with apparatus at various heights on the cable of a captive balloon flying at a fixed position down-wind of the release-line.   An additional advantage of this arrangement is that suitable meteorological instruments can also be carried on the tether-ing cable.

All the experiments reported so far have been conducted in the daytime and, for the most part, with at least a slight amount of convection.   In general terms the results show cross-wind distributions which are similar in shape and regularity to those obtained at much shorter range.   Crozier and Seely (1955) have examined the data obtained in New Mexico and Australia in terms of an equation corresponding to Eq. (4.1), i.e.

$$N/N_{\max} = \exp -ay^r$$

where N is the number of particles collected in a section at a cross-wind distance y from the position of the peak value $N_{\max}$.   Using composite cross-wind distributions, derived from the combined samples above given ground positions in successive traverses at various heights, they obtained values of r ranging from 1·5 to 2·7 in four of the 1952 experiments, at distances of five to ten miles.   These distributions included the cross-wind movements of the plume in the successive traverses at various heights. In an alternative analysis Crozier and Seely combined the individual distri-butions after displacing them laterally so that the individual centres of gravity were coincident, and found that the distributions of these 'average individual traverses' gave values of r with a smaller spread and with an average of about 1·7. They also found that this value of r gave a reasonable fit to the distributions composed in the same way from the 1951 experiments, but the Australian data required a fairly wide range of r, namely 1·7 to 2·8.

In the analysis of the Porton data on cross-wind distribution, successive traverses at the same distance were combined, irrespective of height and without any relative displacement. The total number of particles collected in each cross-wind section were added cumulatively along the composite traverse, and reduced to percentage values which were then plotted against cross-wind position on arithmetical probability paper. Each such distribution was normalized by expressing the cross-wind distance in terms of the standard deviation (σ) of the distribution. The distributions were combined by superimposing on 50 per cent, and averaging the cumulative percentage values at selected normalized cross-wind positions. The resulting average distribution, based on 105 traverses in eighteen experiments at distances of 5–46 miles, is reproduced in Fig. 4.11. A slight

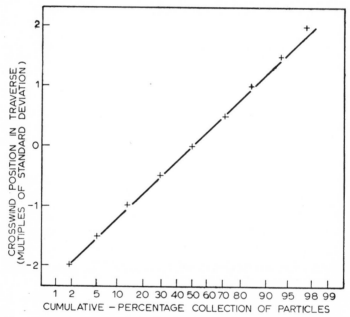

FIG. 4.11 Composite cross-wind distribution at medium range from a point source at ground level (obtained from aircraft traverses at 5–46 miles downwind). (Unpublished Porton data)

skewness is evident in this distribution, but in view of the spread of the individual points no significant deviation from the Gaussian form is indicated.   As in the analysis of the short-range data in 4.2, individual plots showed considerable departure from linearity, but these departures are again evidently eliminated where large numbers of results are combined. While assigning an average value of $r = 1 \cdot 7$ to their distributions Crozier and Seely do not attach any great precision to this value, and the net impression from the data so far obtained is that on the average the Gaussian form is the most satisfactory representation of the cross-wind distribution.

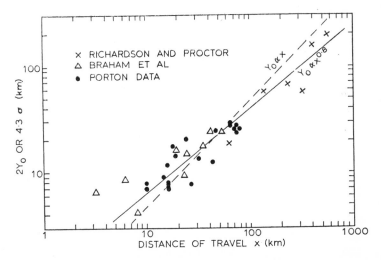

FIG. 4.12   Data on cross-wind spread at medium and long range from a point source. $2\overline{Y}_0$ is the cloud-width defined by one-tenth axial concentration, σ^2 is the standard deviation of the cross-wind distribution.

Cloud widths from the New Mexico (1951) and Porton measurements are shown as a function of distance in Fig. 4.12, and Richardson and Proctor's balloon data as re-analysed by Sutton (1932, Fig. 1) have been entered on the same diagram in the form of values of $4 \cdot 3\sigma$, which is equal to the cloud-width on the assumption of a Gaussian distribution.   The consistency of the data is at first sight remarkable, though obviously it is not good enough to specify with accuracy a single universal exponent in the power-law representation of the variation of cloud-width with distance, i.e. $Y_0 \propto x^p$.   Nevertheless, it can be seen from the lines inserted on the diagram that the data are consistent with an index (p) near $0 \cdot 8$, as in the short-range results, and show no sign of a trend toward the index of 0·5 which is expected in the limit for homogeneous turbulence. However, the possibility must be considered that the trend indicated by the combined fluorescent particle and balloon results may be misleading, owing to the different sampling times involved. These varied considerably, and indeed in view of the nature of the experiments it is difficult to assign precise values, but they were evidently equivalent to about an hour or less in the fluorescent particle measurements, and about ten hours in the balloon observations.

At the present stage the understanding and generalization of data such as those shown in Fig. 4.12 are hindered by the lack of a satisfactory theoretical framework, much more so than for diffusion at short range. On scale considerations alone there is no objection to the statistical treatments which appear to be making some headway in the short-range problems, but in the present context the problem is further complicated by the systematic variation of the airflow with height in the first few thousand feet of the atmosphere, in respect of both the mean wind velocity, and the intensity and scale of turbulence. Crozier and Seely (1955) conclude that 'crosswise' shear (i.e. the systematic variation of wind direction with height) has an important effect on the cross-wind distribution, though, presumably due to the vigorous vertical mixing, this did not noticeably appear as a shear in the cross-section of the plume. In the unpublished analysis of the Porton data an attempt has been made to represent both the large-scale turbulence and the angular shear by the standard deviation of the mean wind directions in 500-ft layers, as given by successive pilot balloons released near the source, up to a height comparable with the measured or anticipated top of the particle cloud. The relation with cloud spread is not established to a high degree of significance, but an approximately 2:1 ratio is suggested between this standard deviation of the wind direction and the standard deviation of the (angular) cross-wind spread of the particles. Much more data would be required to establish a relation, but this first indication is at least a pointer to the effect that correlation with actual wind fluctuation data may well be the most profitable line to follow in the practical analysis of horizontal diffusion at medium range.

Vertical diffusion at medium range

Little progress has yet been reported in the systematic assembling of data on vertical diffusion at medium range. The adequate description of the vertical distribution in a plume from a fixed source requires sampling traverses at a number of heights, preferably with repetition, so that with a single aircraft, effective sampling is likely to be confined to relatively short distances, where the plume is narrow and can be traversed frequently. From their observations Crozier and Seely note that there appeared to be a tendency towards a uniform vertical distribution over a considerable portion of the depth of a plume and attribute this to vigorous mixing. In preliminary experiments reported briefly by Pasquill (1955) the conditions were moderately unstable in the lower layers of the atmosphere, with overhead inversions at heights ranging from 2000 to 7500 ft. Here also the rather inadequate sampling of the vertical distribution indicated a tendency towards uniform vertical distribution.

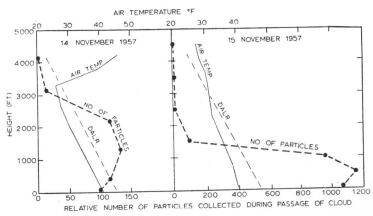

Fig. 4.13 Examples of vertical distribution at medium range from a cross-wind line source of fluorescent particles. DALR = dry-adiabatic lapse-rate. (Porton experiments)

It was to be anticipated that the existence of a strong inversion in the temperature profile at some level would decisively halt the upward spread of the fluorescent particles by convection, and also that in the absence of convection, even without marked stability, the vertical spread well clear of the ground would be very slow. Demonstrations of these effects are contained in two distributions, obtained by releasing the fluorescent material from an aircraft flying across-wind, and collecting samples at various heights on a balloon cable down-wind of the release line. In these cases the samples were collected in impingers, in order that simultaneous collection of water from the natural clouds should not spoil the samples of particles. Fig. 4.13 shows the number of particles collected at various levels during the passage of the particle-cloud, and the data on temperature gradient. The occasion of 14 November 1957 was a typical example of a subsidence inversion, with a continuous layer of strato-cumulus cloud. Although the inevitably fairly wide spacing of the samplers precludes an exact description of the vertical distribution near the inversion, it is clear that while the particles were almost uniformly mixed in the first 2000 ft, virtually none had penetrated the base of the inversion. By the following day the inversion had been replaced by a generally sub-adiabatic layer up to about 5000 ft, the overcast of strato-cumulus being maintained. On this occasion, although at 44 miles down-wind the particles had effectively diffused to the ground (they were released at a height of 1000 ft), the upward vertical spread had not reached 2500 ft and indeed few particles were collected at 1500 ft. This remarkably slow vertical spread was consistent with the fact that instrumental records taken at 1000 and 3000 ft showed very small vertical gustiness.

The data described in the preceding paragraph are isolated examples from which only tentative and rather qualitative deductions may be made. During 1958 and 1959 a few further observations were made using the same techniques, but at a rather shorter range, chosen deliberately so as to measure the vertical distribution before it was complicated by the 'reflect-ing' effect of the ground. The heights of release were in the range 1500–2500 ft. More detailed measurements than hitherto were made of the statistics of the fluctuations of wind inclination at three heights (usually 1000, 2000 and 3000 ft), by using measuring and recording systems des-cribed by Jones and Butler (1958) and Jones and Pasquill (1959). By the arguments already presented in 4.5, observations of the total numbers of particles collected during the passage of the cloud may be taken as a good approximation to the instantaneous vertical distribution in a cylindrical cloud with its axis lying across wind.

Smith and Hay (1961) have presented the data of the experiments des-cribed in the last two paragraphs, with those obtained using small isolated puffs near the ground (see 4.5), in an approximate test of a result derived theoretically for the relation between the maximum rate of spread of a cluster and the statistics of turbulence. This result is given in Eq. (3.89); expressed in finite difference form for application as an approximation over finite sections of travel it may be written

$$\frac{\Delta\sigma}{\Delta x} = \frac{2}{3}\beta i^2 \qquad (4.13)$$

Fig. 4.14, a simplified version of that given by Smith and Hay, shows how the available data support the approximate relation over a tenfold range of the intensity of turbulence i, a thousandfold range of distance, and a thousandfold range of cluster size. Considerable approximation was involved in applying (4.13) to the medium-range data, for with only one sampling distance it was necessary to use σ/x. Furthermore the estimates of σ were frequently rather crude in view of the lack of detail in the observed vertical distribution, and this is reflected in the wide limits set on these data in Fig. 4.14. Similarly wide limits are also given for the intensity of turbulence in these cases, because of the observed variation of i over the height range covered by the diffusing cloud. In a general way the results

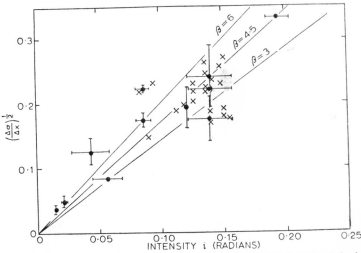

FIG. 4.14   Observations of the spread of a cluster of particles (standard deviation σ) in relation to the intensity of turbulence i (the standard deviation of the wind direction or wind inclination). × cross-wind spread of small puffs of *lycopodium* spores travelling distances (x) 100–300 m; ● vertical spread of a cross-wind line release of fluorescent particles, at distances 3–100 km. The vertical and horizontal lines indicate limits of uncertainty. The lines through the origin correspond to the theoretical maximum values of $(\Delta\sigma/\Delta x)^{1/2}$ according to Eq (4.13), for indicated ratios β of the Lagrangian and Eulerian time-scales. (Smith and Hay, 1961)

support an approximately linear relation between $\sqrt{(\Delta\sigma/\Delta x)}$ and i, and imply a value of β (the ratio of the Lagrangian and Eulerian time-scales) near 4·5. It is to be noted that the definition of this ratio is here based on the so-called trace correlogram, and is not identical with that used by Hay and Pasquill (1959). For further details of this feature the original papers should be consulted, but it suffices to note that, for isotropic turbulence, the β used by Smith and Hay should be $\frac{2}{3}$ of the β as defined by Hay and Pasquill. Since the latter β was considered to average 4, from a rather limited amount of data on short-range diffusion from a continuous source, the agreement is reasonable.

Long-range diffusion as indicated by trajectory studies

Air trajectories observed physically by tracking balloons, or computed from successive charts of the wind velocity field, provide a direct description of diffusion which is particularly valuable when the horizontal distribution on a global scale is of interest. The principles and techniques have already been discussed in 2.5, in that case in relation to the determination of the Lagrangian properties of the airflow. As is implicit in Taylor's well-known analysis (see 3.4), the statistics of the dispersion of serially-released particles and the statistics of averaged Lagrangian velocities are one and the same thing.

A very early study of the dispersion of the end-points of computed air trajectories was made by Defant and published in 1921. Defant plotted the trajectories of air masses over Europe from a starting point at the southern extremity of Ireland. According to Sutton (1932) the results for over a hundred trajectories showed that for a mean trajectory length of 1400 km the standard deviation of the end-points of the individual trajectories was 1200 km. The possibilities inherent in this sort of analysis were not followed up, however, until about 1950, when C. S. Durst began the work later published by him and his colleagues (as an official report, 1957, and in the open literature, 1959). Durst *et al.* and Edinger and Rapp (1957) also examined the data of the early transosonde balloon flights from this point of view, and the data of subsequent more numerous transosonde flights have been reported and analysed in detail by Angell (1959).

As already discussed in 2.5 Durst *et al.* were able to show from their trajectories that the Lagrangian correlation coefficient describing the large-scale variation of the wind would be closely fitted by a simple exponential law. In addition, their results contain two features of special interest, both of which emerge from a consideration of dispersion as a simple power-law function of distance in the form

$$S = \frac{C}{\sqrt{2}} x^a \qquad (4.14)$$

where S is the standard vector deviation of the end points of the trajectories, x the mean vector distance from the point of initiation, and C and a are arbitrary constants. Equation (4.14) will be recognized as formally identical with Eq. (3.63), due to Sutton, but as Durst *et al.* point out the derivation of this equation cannot be used in the context of the data involved here.

The first feature of interest is that for sampling times τ ranging from half a minute for some balloon data, to three months for the longest period of initiation of geostrophic trajectories, the variation of C is given closely by

$$C = 0 \cdot 18\tau^{1/2} \qquad (4.15)$$

where C is expressed in $\text{km}^{1/8}$ and τ in hours (the exponent in the length unit arises from the fact that a in (4.14) is near $\frac{7}{8}$). It should be remembered that the data which have gone into this relation are of a rather heterogeneous nature. Furthermore, the use of a common unit for C means that the empirical laws of the form of Eq. (4.14) have in effect been extrapolated, sometimes well outside the range for which they were established, for C is simply the value of $\sqrt{2S}$ at unit distance. For these reasons the precise magnitudes of the parameters in Eq. (4.15) may be of somewhat doubtful significance. Disregarding the above difficulty concerning the extrapolation of Eq. (4.14) and regarding C as $\sqrt{2S}$ at a short distance, then from Eq. (4.2) for the initial rate of spread of particles, it follows that

$$\frac{C}{\sqrt{2}} \simeq \frac{\sqrt{\overline{v'^2}}}{\bar{u}}$$

Thus the parameter C can be regarded as approximately proportional to the intensity of turbulence, and the relation expressed in Eq. (4.15) as simply a reflection of the well-known variation of intensity with sampling time.

The second feature of special interest in Durst *et al.*'s results is also concerned with an effect of sampling time, though not in the immediately obvious form just discussed. They found that the mean values of the exponent a (Eq. 4.14) all lay in the range 0·8 to 0·9. As these refer to diffusion over distances of several hundred kilometres it is very striking that they are so similar to the exponent in the corresponding power-law expression for the variation of cloud-width with distance over a few hundred metres. However, this does not necessarily mean that Eq. (4.14), with $a = 0 \cdot 8$–0·9, would apply to diffusion from a *given source* over the whole range from 0·1 to 100 km. The significant point is that the long-range data refer to a release time or sampling time which is measured in days and weeks, compared with minutes in the case of the short-range data. With this in mind a simple interpretation follows on lines given by Hay and Pasquill (1959). If, to simplify the argument, the Lagrangian correlation coefficient is assumed to be exponential in form and of time-scale t_L [see Eq. (3.51)], the dispersion at time T is a function of the time-ratio T/t_L, as in Eq. (3.54). Thus, for diffusion experiments in which the time-ratio, or equivalent distance-ratio $x/\bar{u}t$, covers a similar range, the variations of dispersion with distance-ratio will be identical, and if these variations are represented as power-laws the exponents will be the same. Hay and Pasquill were able to demonstrate that in the two sets of results the difference in distance was accompanied by a difference in the scale $\bar{u}t_L$ such that the ranges of $x/\bar{u}t_L$ were indeed very similar (0–2 approximately). This difference in scale was clearly a consequence of the enormous difference in sampling time. It is noteworthy that data on diffusion from a fixed source in a wind tunnel, over distances corresponding to a similar range of $x/\bar{u}t_L$, were also found to be represented by a similar value of a (0·75).

Also with regard to the variation of dispersion with distance an interesting feature emerges from the results of the transosonde flights analysed by

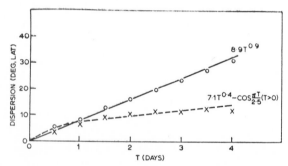

FIG. 4.15 Dispersion (standard deviation) of serially-released constant-level balloons after time T. Routine transosonde flights, from Japan, at the 300 or 250 mb level. The lines represent the indicated analytical expressions. ○ zonal dispersion; × meridional dispersion. (Angell, 1959)

Angell (1959). Figure 4.15, taken from Angell's paper shows the zonal (E–W) and meridional (N–S) dispersion of the balloons for all 1957–59 flights of four or more days' duration. These flights were at the 300 mb or 250 mb level. It will be seen that the zonal results show a sustained growth which is only slightly less than linear with time, the exponent a in Eq. (4.14) being 0·9. More striking, however, is the fact that rapid increase of the meridional values is confined to the first two days.

Lagrangian autocorrelograms obtained by Angell (1960) from an analysis of the 1957–8 flights only are represented by Eq. (2.18) and (2.19). Although these are not exactly comparable with the dispersion data of Fig. 4.15, since the latter include the 1959 flights, they may be expected to be adequate for broad comparisons. It is interesting to note that the scale $\left[\int_0^\infty R(\xi)d\xi\right]$ of the correlogram for the zonal component is approximately

20 hr, very similar to that found by Durst *et al.* (22 hr) in their analysis of geostrophic trajectories at 700 and 500 mb. In view of the relation between dispersion and time of travel expressed in terms of this time scale (see the detailed discussion of this point in 3.5 and Fig. 3.4) the fact that Durst *et al.*'s data on diffusion up to 36 hr and Angell's data up to 5 days both give high values of the exponent *a* is therefore not surprising. Durst *et al.*'s dispersion data refer to vector deviations, and although the correlation coefficients are derived for the zonal and meridional wind components, as well as for the vector magnitude, no reference is made to their relative magnitudes. There is in fact some trend (see Table 3 of their 1959 paper) for the correlograms to fall off more rapidly in the meridional case than the zonal case. A much more pronounced difference is evident in the correlograms of Eq. (2.18) and (2.19), where indeed the meridional case shows large negative values at lags near 20 hr and, furthermore, a well-marked periodicity. As noted previously this correlogram may be regarded as a superposition of an exponential function and a sinusoidal term of 2-day period. It is easily seen that $\int_0^t R(\xi)d\xi$ becomes quite small at $t = 48$ hr and, as would be expected from Taylor's analysis (see 3.4), this is reflected in the approximate constancy of the dispersion after two days. It is important to note that this well-marked departure from linear increase of dispersion with distance is not simply a tendency towards the Fickian law as represented in Eq. (3.17) and (3.39), but appears to be a consequence of a well-defined sinusoidal component in the average pattern of the zonal flow in which Angell's data were obtained.

4.7 Recapitulation

The discussions in the present chapter complete the present survey of the various basic aspects of atmospheric diffusion to the current stages of development. It will be useful at this point to summarize the position by emphasizing the features which have been more or less established, and the more important questions which remain to be clarified.

1. In circumstances in which a reasonable approximation to quasi-steady, quasi-homogeneous turbulence exists, the turbulent spread of material has been shown to be related to the observable intensity and scale of turbulence in a rational way. An approximation to a simple connection between the frequencies of the velocity fluctuations experienced by a particle and those observed by an instrument at a fixed point is implied, but has yet to be given theoretical basis.

(a) The relation has been most clearly demonstrated for lateral spread near the ground, or vertical spread well away from the ground, at distances up to about a kilometre from a maintained source. It also applies in a more approximate way to the expansion of an isolated cloud of material, over distances up to about 100 km and depths of atmosphere of several hundreds of metres.

(b) The relation is most questionable in the case of horizontal spread in very stable conditions near the ground, and generally in the case of horizontal spread at longer range, when further complication arises in the form of the systematic variation of wind direction with height.

2. There are two major aspects of vertical diffusion not included in the above generalizations.

(a) Vertical spread in the characteristically sheared layer near the ground has been related to the vertical profile of mean wind in near-neutral conditions, in fashions which though empirical are physically reasonable. There are signs of extension on similar lines to unstable and stable conditions. The analysis of the problem in terms of the actual structure of turbulence has so far made little progress, and this is a field in which careful and detailed measurements of both diffusion and structure would be rewarding.

(b) For diffusion over appreciable depths of the atmosphere, apart from the indication that vertical spread is slowed or halted by thermally stable layers, there is as yet no coherent description of the effects of the convective and large-scale vertical motions of the atmosphere.

3. For horizontal spread (and also vertical spread in regions clear of the ground or stable layers) the shape of the distribution of material from a maintained source is on average a close approximation to Gaussian form. However, individual cases display considerable irregularities and distortion from this simple form. There are indications that the vertical distribution from a ground-level source may be systematically different from Gaussian, but further observational evidence is needed. Furthermore, no useful details have yet been provided for the distribution developed within an expanding puff or plume.

4. All the preceding considerations imply a statistical type of homogeneity in the horizontal structure of the airflow. When the flow is systematically patterned by the dynamical and thermal influence of topography and surface characteristics, major modification of the distribution of material may be imposed. Little general information is at present available, but some particular features are discussed in Chapter 6.

5

The Estimation of Diffusion from Meteorological Data

This chapter deals with the application of the foregoing ideas and results to the practical problem of estimating the magnitude of air pollution produced by a given discharge of material into the atmosphere. The methods proposed are valid only in the somewhat idealized conditions of airflow which were deliberately specified or selected in the theoretical and experimental studies. In particular it should be stressed that the methods as they stand cannot be expected to give reliable estimates in the following circumstances:

(a) when the airflow is indefinite (calm conditions),

(b) when there are local disturbances of the airflow, e.g. in the immediate vicinity of buildings and obstacles, unless the diffusing cloud has already attained dimensions considerably bigger than the disturbances,

(c) when the airflow is channelled, or when it contains circulations or drainage set up by the heating and cooling of undulating or hilly terrain.

5.1 Qualitative features of diffusion and its variation with meteorological conditions

There are certain aspects of diffusion which are obvious from the visible behaviour of puffs and plumes of smoke in the atmosphere, and an appreciation of these features forms a useful introduction to the more quantitative applications which follow. It is well known that the smoke trail from a source on the ground takes a variety of forms according to the weather conditions and the time of day, and that certain characteristic properties may be recognized. In open country, with at least a moderate wind speed and a thoroughly cloudy sky (or even with a clear or partly clear sky as long as the wind is strong), the smoke forms into a fairly straight well-defined trail which increases perceptibly and steadily in width and height

179

as distance from the source increases.   If, however, the wind is light, and there is sufficient sunshine to warm the ground surface, a much greater degree of irregularity appears in the form of the plume.   Apart from the obvious effect that the smoke itself may be heated by absorption of solar radiation, it is clear that the movement of the air itself leads to a more rapid spread of the smoke in the vertical, and to an erratic variation in the direction of travel of successive sections of the smoke plume.   The result is that the plume has a sinuous and sometimes even disconnected form, and rapidly reaches a stage when it is no longer visible.   On the other hand, at night, if the sky is sufficiently clear to result in appreciable cooling of the ground, and the wind is light, bodily rise and vertical spread are considerably reduced and the smoke trails off down-wind in a compact visible form for appreciable distances.

The three categories just described constitute the simplest classification of diffusive conditions.   They are associated with characteristic vertical gradients of temperature and associated stabilities in the lower atmosphere, i.e.

near-zero gradient   — neutral stability,

lapse (decrease of   — unstable,
   temperature with
   height)

inversion (increase   — stable.
   of temperature
   with height)

In accordance with the dimensions attained by a smoke plume the concentrations within the plume tend to be relatively low in unstable conditions and relatively high in stable conditions.   In addition the irregularities which occur (to various extents), in the instantaneous appearance of a plume of smoke, have important consequences on the average cross-wind distribution of smoke concentration.   These irregularities arise from the fact that successive sections of the plume travel from the release point along different (approximately straight) trajectories (see Fig. 5.1).   The result is that in the area down-wind of the source the cross-wind distribution of smoke concentration at any instant is characterized by relatively high values on a narrow front, while the distribution averaged over some period of time possesses lower values extending over a wider front.

When the source of smoke is elevated above the ground, as in the case of effluent from an industrial chimney, the preceding modes again appear in the horizontal structure, and the smoke plume also assumes characteristic shapes in the vertical.   These are easily identifiable when viewed from the side some distance away.   The vertical displacements are undoubtedly amplified if the smoke is hot, as was clearly recognized in an early discussion of smoke plumes (Etkes and Brooks, 1918), but there are basic patterns which are essentially determined by the properties of turbulence and convection in the atmosphere.   In the recent American literature on the

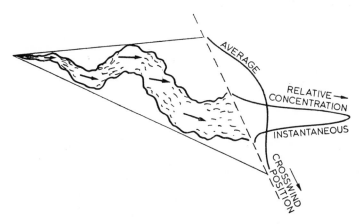

FIG. 5.1   Instantaneous and average aspects of the cross-wind spread of a smoke-plume

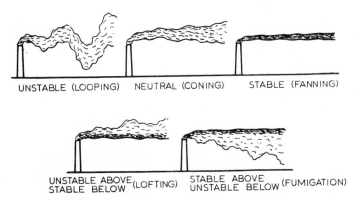

FIG. 5.2   Characteristic forms of smoke-plumes from chimneys.   (Church, 1949, and United States Weather Bureau, 1955)

behaviour of effluent from chimney stacks certain graphic terms are commonly applied to the modes of behaviour in the vertical (see Church, 1949 and U.S. Weather Bureau, 1955, Chapter 5).   The three basic modes are:

looping — in unstable conditions
coning — in near-neutral conditions
fanning — in stable conditions

The looping form is produced by successive sections of plume travelling with different inclinations, not by the up and down motion of a given section.   In coning, the successive sections follow trajectories which are not widely different, and the plume as a whole tends to assume a steady conical form.   In fanning the cross-wind spread is maintained, and there may be a certain amount of meandering of the plume as a whole, but the spread in the vertical is greatly reduced and sometimes entirely absent.   The schematic diagrams in Fig. 5.2 illustrate these three main forms, and also two transitional conditions.   *Lofting*, in which vertical spreading occurs much more effectively on the upper side of the plume than on the lower side, occurs with the diurnal transition from unstable to stable conditions, near sunset in clear weather.   *Fumigation* is the reverse of lofting, and occurs with the reverse transition in stability in the early morning.   For a more detailed discussion of these properties, and of their implication as regards the ground-level distribution of effluent from a high stack, reference should be made to the U.S. Weather Bureau publication.   One of the most important implications, in obvious contrast to the situation arising with a ground-level source, is that relatively unstable conditions, and not stable conditions, are the most conducive to the intermittent appearance of heavy smoke concentrations on the ground close in to a stack.   On the other hand a temporary occurrence of very heavy concentrations, even at a great distance from the stack, may result from the fumigation action associated with the onset of unstable conditions.

Because of the clear association between diffusive action and the thermal stability of the atmosphere, temperature gradient was adopted from the beginning as the main indicator, and much effort has been expended in many countries towards obtaining statistics and maintaining current measurements of this quantity.   Although it may be particularly effective in indicating the likelihood of extreme conditions such as fanning and fumigation, there has been a growing recognition of its inadequacy on its own as a general indicator.   This arises partly from the observation that the influence of stability involves the vertical gradient of wind speed, as well as that of temperature, and partly from the observation that diffusion is manifestly affected by the roughness and topography of the terrain (see, for example, the discussion of Cramer's analyses in 4.3).   Accordingly, there is a growing tendency, supported both by practical experience and by

Table 5.1

Wind direction trace classifications and related conditions at Brookhaven National Laboratory, New York. (Singer and Smith, 1953, see also United States Weather Bureau, 1955)

Type	Angular width of trace	Type of turbulence	Stability condition	Average stack-height wind, m/sec	Time of day	Season	Remarks
A	>90°	Largely thermal (convective)	Great instability	1·8	0900–1500 only	Uncommon in winter	The stronger the lapse the greater the wind speed possible before trace becomes type B
B₂	45°–90°	Largely thermal	Great instability	3·8	0900–1500 only	Mostly summer	Same as above
B₁	15°–45°	Thermal and mechanical	Moderate instability	7·0	0600–1800 (occasionally night with steep lapse)	Any	Generally associated with brisk winds and moderate lapse
C	15°	Mechanical	Moderate stability	10·4	Night (or day with heavy cloud cover)	Any	Typical trace under overcast skies and neutral lapse rate
D	0°–15°	None	Great stability	6·4	Mostly night	Any	Typical inversion trace

the development of the fundamental understanding of diffusion processes, to utilize simple wind observations which contain some measurement, albeit crude, of the intensity and scale of the turbulence.

The widths of the ink traces obtained in routine instrumental records of wind speed and wind direction were used as a measure of turbulence at a very early stage (see 2.1).   An application of this method in a qualitative way is implied in the classification of types of wind fluctuation by Giblett *et al.* (1932), based on records of wind speed and direction at Cardington. In this classification eddies were divided into four types, ranging from a Type I, which was characterized by gusts of large amplitude and long period, typical of well-developed convection and thunderstorms, to a Type IV represented by the fluctuations of very small amplitude which tend to occur on a clear night.   This classification may be regarded as the fore-runner of a more detailed system established at the Brookhaven National Laboratory, U.S.A.   In this case the range and appearance of the fluctuations of horizontal wind direction were used to define the type of airflow. An original division into four categories by M. E. Smith [1951(a)], was later extended to five categories (Singer and Smith, 1953), which are listed with explanatory data in Table 5.I.   There is an obvious association to be expected between wind-trace types, A, C and D, and the *looping, coning* and *fanning* types of plume respectively.

The foregoing classifications of smoke plumes and gustiness provide a useful approach to the broad specification of diffusion in terms of general weather conditions.   They may be used in assessing or forecasting the quality of diffusion effects on particular occasions, or in drawing up statistics of the frequency of occurrence of the various categories.   Examples of the latter application are given by Singer and Smith (*loc. cit.*).   However, apart from the qualitative nature of the results, there are definite limitations in the approach, which are recognized in the papers by Singer and Smith and others (U.S. Weather Bureau, 1955).   In particular, any such data are partly characterized by the properties of the instrument, and the topography and climatology of the site, and the application of criteria established on one site to the assessment of behaviour on another site needs to be made with care.   For the achievement of more quantitative and more reliable estimates of diffusion it is necessary to apply the formal treatments and physical observations which have been discussed in the preceding chapter.

5.2   Functional forms for the distribution of material from a source

Any complete expression for the spatial distribution of airborne material released at a point must contain three features:

(1) The *shape* of the distribution of concentration at any given time or down-wind position, i.e. the manner in which the concentration varies across wind, vertically and along-wind (the latter being relevant only to the case of a puff or isolated cloud of material).

(2) The dimensions of the diffusing cloud in the cross-wind, vertical (and along-wind) directions.

(3) An expression of the so-called *continuity* (or conservation) condition which will here be restricted to the case when no material is lost by deposition or decomposition.

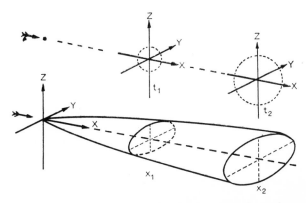

FIG. 5.3   Idealized representation of instantaneous and continuous sources.

All three features are contained in the various solutions (see 3.2) of the differential equations of diffusion, and as already discussed these solutions possess varying degrees of acceptability according to the tests of physical principle and direct observation.   On the other hand only feature (2) is at present specified by the statistical treatments considered in Chapter 3, and it is necessary to introduce (1) and (3) separately.

As an introduction to the working formulae which will be discussed in the next section, it is useful to consider certain convenient expressions which may be looked upon either as formal solutions of the type discussed in Chapter 3.2, or as empirical equations in which to substitute features (2) and (3) above, the former of these being provided either in a purely empirical way or on the basis of the statistical treatments of Chapter 3. Consider idealized cases of instantaneous and continuous sources (see Fig. 5.3) in a homogeneous airstream, with the x-axis in the direction of the mean wind, supposed horizontal, the y-axis across wind and the z-axis vertical.   The mean wind is assumed to be constant in space, while the mean components of velocity in the cross-wind and vertical directions are zero. Ideally it is assumed that the instantaneously-generated cloud moves in a straight line parallel to the x-axis, expanding in all directions, while the fixed continuous source generates a symmetrical plume around the fixed x-axis, with an expanding cross section in the y, z plane.

Forms in which concentration falls off with distance from the centre of the cloud (or axis of the plume) according to an exponential function may be written as follows:

Instantaneous point source

$$\chi(x, y, z, t) = A_1[\exp -(a|x|^p + b|y|^r + c|z|^s)] \qquad (5.1)$$

where χ is the concentration of airborne material (units of matter per unit volume) and x, y, z, are measured from a moving origin situated at the centre of mass of the cloud. The exponents p, r, s are positive.

Continuous point source

$$\chi(x, y, z) = A_2 \exp[-(b|y|^r + c|z|^s)] \qquad (5.2)$$

where x, y, z are now measured from a fixed origin at the site of release. The parameters a, b, c are dependent on the *dimensions* of the diffusing cloud in the appropriate directions, while $A_1 [=\chi(0, 0, 0, t)]$ and $A_2 [=\chi(x, 0, 0)]$ will be seen to be functions of these dimensions when the continuity condition is applied.

As the mathematical form adopted in Eq. (5.1) and (5.2) allows concentration to fall completely to zero only at infinite values of x, y or z, the dimensions of the puff and of the plume cross section are matters of arbitrary definition. They may be conveniently defined by the root mean square deviations $\sigma_x, \sigma_y, \sigma_z$, of the displacements of the material particles along or parallel to the appropriate axes. For example, considering any vertical line through the puffs or plumes

$$\sigma_z^2 = \frac{\int_0^\infty z^2 \chi \, dz}{\int_0^\infty \chi \, dz} \qquad (5.3)$$

and similar expressions may be written for σ_x and σ_y.

For sources of inert permanently airborne material the continuity conditions are

Instantaneous point source (quantity Q of matter released)

$$\int\!\!\int\!\!\int_{-\infty}^{\infty} \chi \, dx \, dy \, dz = Q \qquad (5.4)$$

Continuous point source (quantity Q of matter released per unit time)

$$\int\int_{-\infty}^{\infty} \bar{u} \chi \, dy \, dz = Q \tag{5.5}$$

Applying (5.4) and (5.5) and substituting the forms of σ specified in Eq. (5.3), (5.1) and (5.2) become

Instantaneous point source

$$\chi(x, y, z, t) = \frac{Q}{B_1 \sigma_x \sigma_y \sigma_z} \exp\left\{-\left[\left(\frac{\Gamma(3/p)}{\Gamma(1/p)}\right)^{p/2}\left(\frac{x}{\sigma_x}\right)^p + \left(\frac{\Gamma(3/r)}{\Gamma(1/r)}\right)^{r/2}\left(\frac{y}{\sigma_y}\right)^r + \left(\frac{\Gamma(3/s)}{\Gamma(1/s)}\right)^{s/2}\left(\frac{z}{\sigma_z}\right)^s\right]\right\} \tag{5.6}$$

Continuous point source

$$\chi(x, y, z) = \frac{Q}{B_2 \sigma_y \sigma_z} \exp\left\{-\left[\left(\frac{\Gamma(3/r)}{\Gamma(1/r)}\right)^{r/2}\left(\frac{y}{\sigma_y}\right)^r + \left(\frac{\Gamma(3/s)}{\Gamma(1/s)}\right)^{s/2}\left(\frac{z}{\sigma_z}\right)^s\right]\right\} \tag{5.7}$$

where

$$1/B_1 = \frac{prs}{8} \frac{[\Gamma(3/p)\,\Gamma(3/r)\,\Gamma(3/s)]^{1/2}}{[\Gamma(1/p)\,\Gamma(1/r)\,\Gamma(1/s)]^{3/2}}$$

and

$$1/B_2 = \frac{rs}{4\bar{u}} \frac{[\Gamma(3/r)\,\Gamma(3/s)]^{1/2}}{[\Gamma(1/r)\,\Gamma(1/s)]^{3/2}}$$

The spatial distributions of concentration are thus expressed completely in terms of the *dimensions* and *shapes* of the cloud along the component axes, and in terms of the wind speed, and the source strength. In reality the dimensions of the cloud are usually different for instantaneous and continuous sources.

Practical interest will frequently be concerned with sources which operate for some finite interval, τ, and in general it is necessary to consider the effect of this on the dimensions of the cloud. Furthermore, owing to the effect of diffusion in the direction of the wind, on the leading and trailing edges of a detached plume, Eq. (5.7) will apply only for some period shorter than τ. This period will decrease with increase of distance down-wind and will ultimately reach zero, after which the distribution will tend to that given in (5.6). More complex mathematical expressions for the intermediate stages can be derived, but are not of sufficient concern to warrant discussion here.   Eq. (5.7) can, however, be taken to apply when χ is replaced by $\int_0^\infty \chi \, dt$ (i.e. the total dosage), and Q is the total quantity of material released.   As dosage rather than concentration is often the important practical quantity the equation is frequently applied in this form.

A further simplification may be introduced when a number of sources of equal strength are closely spaced on a long cross-wind line, so providing an approximation to an infinite line source of uniform strength.   In this case the concentration or dosage is a function of x and z only, and is given simply by the cross-wind integral of the point source distribution, $\int_{-\infty}^{+\infty} \chi(x, y, z) \, dy$.

Continuous line source of effectively infinite cross-wind extent (quantity Q of matter released per unit length per unit time)

$$\chi(x, z) = \frac{Q}{B_3 \sigma_z} \exp \left[-\left(\frac{\Gamma(3/s)}{\Gamma(1/s)}\right)^{s/2} \left(\frac{z}{\sigma_z}\right)^s \right] \tag{5.8}$$

where

$$1/B_3 = \frac{s[\Gamma(3/s)]^{1/2}}{2\bar{u} \, [\Gamma(1/s)]^{3/2}}$$

As in the case of the point source the right-hand side of Eq. (5.8) also represents the dosage corresponding to the release of a quantity Q per unit length of the line.   In practice the distribution down-wind of a cross-wind line source will be appropriate to Eq. (5.8) only over a central zone, the cross-wind width of which will shrink as the edge-effect of lateral diffusion extends inward.   The width of this zone will be effectively the length of the source-line minus the cross-wind width of the cloud from a point source at the same distance down-wind.

In Chapter 4 it was seen that the experimental data on the form of the distribution of concentration produced by plumes indicates a wide range of values of r (the exponent in the cross-wind distribution), though with a tendency towards $r=2$ (i.e. a Gaussian or normal distribution) as a statistical average.   For the vertical distribution the evidence is much less plentiful.   The general impression is in favour of a Gaussian shape ($s=2$) when, as implied so far in the present discussion, the source is at a distance from the earth's surface.   When the source is at ground level (for other implications of which see later) the vertical distribution evidently requires a different value of s, which has yet to be generally determined, but which on preliminary evidence is nearer unity.   For longitudinal distribution (in a puff) no data have yet been reported, but it seems reasonable to expect similarity with the cross-wind distribution.   With these possible variations of p, r and s in mind it is of practical interest to examine their effect on the levels of concentration in a cloud.   This is easily seen from Fig. 5.4 in which values of $[2u\chi(x, z)\sigma_z]/Q$ from Eq. (5.8) are plotted against z/σ_z. The purpose of this form of presentation is merely to indicate the effect of diffusion on concentration-profile shape in one direction.   For identical

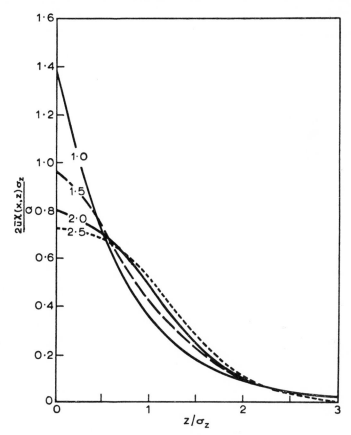

FIG. 5.4   Concentration profile according to Eq (5.8), with values of s 1·0, 1·5, 2·0, 2·5

changes in profile shape in two directions the relative effect on concentration would be the square of that indicated in Fig. 5.4, while for three dimensions it would be the cube.   It follows that departures in peak concentration (at $z/\sigma_z = 0$) from that corresponding to Gaussian distributions will not be of practical significance unless the appropriate exponents (all three for the instantaneous point source, r and s only for the continuous point source) simultaneously fall to 1·5 or rise to say 3·0 (using a fairly obvious extrapolation), or unless one exponent falls to much nearer unity. On the available evidence important variations in p and r away from 2·0 seem relatively unlikely, but it may be desirable to take account of the tendency for s to approach unity in certain conditions.

The assumption of Gaussian distribution in all directions ($p=r=s=2$) greatly simplifies the above equations, for

$$s(\Gamma(3/s))^{1/2}/(\Gamma(1/s))^{3/2} = \sqrt{(2/\pi)} \quad \text{etc.}$$

and

$$(\Gamma(3/s)/\Gamma(1/s))^{s/2} = \tfrac{1}{2} \quad \text{etc.}$$

Eq. (5.6), (5.7) and (5.8) then become

Instantaneous point source (Q units of matter released)

$$\chi(x, y, z, t) = \frac{Q}{(2\pi)^{3/2}\sigma_x\sigma_y\sigma_z} \exp\left[-\tfrac{1}{2}\left(\frac{x^2}{\sigma_x^2}+\frac{y^2}{\sigma_y^2}+\frac{z^2}{\sigma_z^2}\right)\right] \qquad (5.9)$$

Continuous point source (Q units of matter released per unit time)

$$\chi(x, y, z) = \frac{Q}{2\pi\bar{u}\sigma_y\sigma_z} \exp\left[-\tfrac{1}{2}\left(\frac{y^2}{\sigma_y^2}+\frac{z^2}{\sigma_z^2}\right)\right] \qquad (5.10)$$

Continuous line source of effectively infinite extent across-wind (Q units of matter released per unit length per unit time)

$$\chi(x, z) = \frac{Q}{(2\pi)^{1/2}\bar{u}\sigma_z} \exp\left[-\frac{z^2}{2\sigma_z^2}\right] \qquad (5.11)$$

An equation in the particular form of Eq. (5.9) seems first to have been stated by Frenkiel (1952b), though (5.10) and (5.11) are implicit in Sutton's (1947a) formulae for continuous point and infinite-line sources.

Usually the main interest lies in the distribution of concentration at ground level, and in this connection the simplest extension of the previous formulae is obtained when the source is itself at ground level. Assuming that the ground exerts no chemical or physical action on the airborne material, and merely constitutes an impervious boundary, the idealized forms of puff and plume would be represented in Fig. 5.3 by the parts of the diagram lying above the x, y plane, which is now taken to represent the ground. Neglecting the variation of wind speed with height above the ground, the continuity conditions (5.4) and (5.5) now apply with integration limits 0 to ∞ in the z direction, but otherwise unchanged, with the obvious result that the concentrations in Eq. (5.6)–(5.11) are simply doubled. To be exact the characteristic variations of wind structure with height above ground should be taken into account. When this is done by introducing power-law forms for the mean wind speed and the eddy diffusivity, i.e.

$$\bar{u} \propto z^m \quad \text{and} \quad K(z) \propto z^n$$

Roberts' solution of the equation of diffusion [see Eq. (3.20)] gives a vertical distribution of concentration as in Eq. (5.8) with

$$s = m - n + 2$$

In this case a complete expression for the point source may still be written as in (5.7), with s as above, but the value of B_2 determined by the continuity condition will be different.

The case of the ground-level distribution of concentration from an elevated point source at height H above the ground may be dealt with by using a *reciprocal theorem* (see 3.2). This states that the concentration at ground level due to a source at height H is the same as the concentration at height H due to a source at ground level. Such an approach is useful as long as the process of vertical spreading continues, but ultimately this may be more or less suddenly halted by a stable layer at some height in the atmosphere. No convenient formula is immediately available for this case, when in effect the vertical diffusion is occurring between two impervious boundaries, though solutions which can be numerically evaluated have been given independently by Rounds and F. B. Smith (see 3.2).

Application of the reciprocal theorem to the simple forms in Eq. (5.9)–(5.11) is not strictly valid, since these equations do not satisfy the differential equation of diffusion with diffusivity and wind speed appropriately regarded as a function of height above ground. However, it is customary to adapt these equations by assuming that the spreading plume is 'reflected' from the ground without otherwise being altered, or equivalently that the source has an 'image' of equal strength below ground. In these cases the result is exactly the same as that which follows from applying the reciprocal theorem. This means that the variations of diffusivity with height are not being taken into account rigorously, and the procedure must be justified on empirical grounds.

So far the only theoretical analysis which has given a bounded distribution, basically different in this sense from the exponential form of Eq. (5.1) *et seq.*, is that developed by Monin (1959) in the U.S.S.R. Monin's solution for an infinite line source at ground level gives a vertical distribution of concentration which falls to zero at some finite height. However, in neutral conditions of stability, for which this solution takes a simple explicit form, the vertical distribution (see 3.3) is very similar, except at the upper boundary of the cloud, to the expression given by Calder (1952), which is of simple exponential form, i.e. $s = 1$ in Eq. (5.2).

Although interesting fundamental problems are involved in the precise shapes of the cross-wind and vertical distributions from a point source, for many practical purposes it is obvious that these are of secondary importance, and that the essential point is to decide whether the shapes of the distribution are, say, of approximately Gaussian or simple exponential forms. Otherwise the controlling parameters are the cross-wind and vertical dimensions as represented by σ_y and σ_z in the foregoing equations. The practical success of explicit diffusion formulae thus depends on the extent to which correct choices of distribution shape, and of σ_y and σ_z, are contained therein.

5.3   Diffusion formulae for practical use

The formulae which have been most widely used hitherto in making practical estimates of the distribution of concentration down-wind of continuous sources are those developed by Sutton (1932, 1947a, 1947b) and Bosanquet and Pearson (1936). Other approximate formulae are now available from subsequent theoretical and experimental studies of diffusion, notably by Calder (1949, 1952), Cramer (1957, 1959), Monin (1959) and Hay and Pasquill (1959). By derivation Bosanquet and Pearson's and Calder's expressions are tied to the exponential type of distribution as in Eq. (5.7), with $r = 2$, $s = 1$ for the former, and in the case of Calder's simpler form (1952) $r = s = 1$ (i.e. simple exponential distributions in both directions). Monin's vertical distribution is of different form, but as explained previously (see 3.3) the departure from the simple exponential form ($s = 1$) is probably insignificant for practical purposes, and otherwise Monin's result is identical with Calder's (1952) result. For the remainder there is no *a priori* implication of the shape of the cross-wind or vertical distributions. Sutton (1947b) has given exponential-type expressions of non-Gaussian form but in most practical applications of his formulae the simpler Gaussian form of Eq. (5.10) has been used.

Apart from the differences in the shapes of the distributions, the various explicit applications which may now be made differ only in the specifications of σ_y and σ_z. The available formulae by which σ_y and σ_z are expressed semi-theoretically, in terms of parameters related to the turbulence, are summarized in Table 5.II. Cramer's formulae, which are not included in Table 5.II, are empirical relations between plume-spread and gustiness, based on extensive experimental data obtained in the *Prairie Grass* diffusion studies.

Table 5.II

Practical formulae for the cross-wind (σ_y) and vertical (σ_z) spread of the distribution from a continuous point source at distance x

σ is the standard deviation of the material distribution, as defined in Eq. (5.3). The values of r and s are these implied or recommended for use in Eq. (5.7) and (5.12)–(5.14)

	σ_y/x	σ_z/x	Values of r and s	
(i) Sutton (1947a and b)	$\dfrac{1}{\sqrt{2}}\,C_y x^{-n/2}$	$\dfrac{1}{\sqrt{2}}\,C_z x^{-n/2}$	2	2
(ii) Bosanquet and Pearson (1936)	q	$\sqrt{2}(p)$	2	1
(iii) Calder (1952)	$\dfrac{\sqrt{2}(\alpha k u_*)}{\bar{u}}$	$\dfrac{\sqrt{2}(k u_*)}{\bar{u}}$	1	1
(iv) Hay and Pasquill (1959) (see also Pasquill, 1961)	$(\sigma_\theta)_{\tau,\,x/\beta\bar{u}}$	$(\sigma_\phi)_{\tau,\,x/\beta\bar{u}}$	2	2

Notes (also see Chapter 3 for the bases of these formulae):

  (i) C_y and C_z are virtual diffusion coefficients, and n is a turbulence parameter determined by the vertical profile of mean wind speed [see Eq. (3.64)].

  (ii) q is an empirical coefficient, p the numerical coefficient in an assumed form of the vertical diffusion coefficient ($p\bar{u}z$).

  (iii) $u_* =$ friction velocity [see Eq. (3.5)], $k =$ von Kármán's constant, $\alpha = v'/w'$.

  (iv) $(\sigma_\theta)_{\tau,\,x/\beta\bar{u}}$ and $(\sigma_\phi)_{\tau,\,x/\beta\bar{u}}$ are standard deviations of wind direction and wind inclination in radians, measured from a record averaged over elementary intervals equal to $x/\beta\bar{u}$, where β is the ratio of the Lagrangian and Eulerian time-scales, and extending over the period of release or sampling (τ) [see Eq. (3.68)].

Some numerical values of these parameters are given in the notes below Fig. 5.5.

The expressions for σ_z associated with Sutton, Bosanquet and Pearson, and Calder all refer, implicitly if not explicitly, to vertical diffusion in circumstances in which the diffusion coefficient increases with height, and they are all strictly applicable only in neutral conditions of stability. Sutton's and Calder's forms for σ_y rest on an assumed analogy between lateral and vertical spread. Hay and Pasquill's expression for σ_y is not subject to any *a priori* restrictions on the stability conditions, but assumes a homogeneous field of turbulence. The corresponding form for σ_z is therefore formally admissible only at positions remote from the ground, where the variation of turbulence with height is slow, but its use near the ground can be supported by the same analogy, applied in reverse, as that which supports Calder's form for σ_y.

With the above restrictions and qualifications the values of σ_y and σ_z in Table 5.II provide, on substitution in Eq. (5.7) with appropriate values of r and s, explicit formulae for the concentration down-wind of a continuous point source. According to the values of r and s used Eq. (5.7) reduces to the following simple expressions for the peak or axial concentration down-wind of a point source at ground level:

$$r = s = 2 \qquad \frac{\chi \bar{u}}{Q} = \frac{1}{\pi \sigma_y \sigma_z} \qquad (5.12)$$

$$r = s = 1 \qquad \frac{\chi \bar{u}}{Q} = \frac{1}{\sigma_y \sigma_z} \qquad (5.13)$$

$$r = 2, \; s = 1 \qquad \frac{\chi \bar{u}}{Q} = \frac{1}{\pi^{1/2} \sigma_y \sigma_z} \qquad (5.14)$$

A comparison of these formulae with experimental data can be made for ranges of 100–1000 m over grassland in neutral conditions of stability, for which Sutton (1947a and b) and Calder (1952) have prescribed values of their relevant parameters, and for which Smith and Abbot (1961) have reported statistics of wind direction fluctuations (σ_θ in Table 5.II). For the application of his formulae Calder (1952) recommends a value of approximately 2 for α, the ratio of the lateral and vertical components of turbulence, and the same value may be used in estimating the effective σ_ϕ to be used with σ_θ. Bosanquet and Pearson (1936) provide average values of the parameters p and q from a broad consideration of miscellaneous data on wind structure and diffusion. Data obtained from the formulae are shown in Fig. 5.5 in the form of $\chi \bar{u}/Q$ against distance on logarithmic scales. The heavy lines represent the corresponding average experimental data obtained at Porton, and at O'Neill, U.S.A., in the *Prairie Grass* experiments, the latter data being based on values extracted from Cramer's 1957 paper for the applicable magnitude of σ_θ (σ_A in Cramer's notation). Essential numerical details are summarized in the notes below Fig. 5.5. The Porton data refer to sources operating for a period of 4 min and the *Prairie Grass* data (though obtained with a different duration) are effectively adjusted to the same duration by the use of the appropriate value of σ_θ. Sutton's C_y and C_z, and Calder's α, are actually associated with measurements of gustiness over 3-min periods, but it is clear from the data concerning the effect of sampling duration on gustiness (see 2.8) that the difference between 3 and 4 min is of no practical significance in the present consideration.

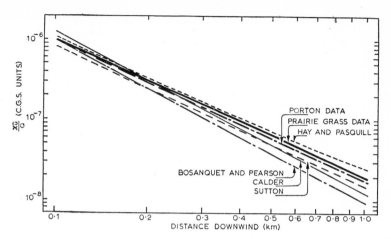

FIG. 5.5   Comparison of working formulae (Table 5.II) and experimental data,
for the peak or axial concentration from a point source maintained for about
4 min, at ground level in open country, in neutral conditions. Q is in g/sec,
$\bar{u}$ in cm/sec, χ in g/cc.   The magnitudes of the parameters used in the formulae of Table 5.II were as follows:

   (i) Sutton (1947a and b), $C_y = 0.21$; $C_z = 0.12$ m$^{1/8}$; $n = \frac{1}{4}$.
  (ii) Bosanquet and Pearson (1936), $p = 0.05$; $q = 0.08$.
 (iii) Calder (1952), $\alpha = 2$; $k = 0.45$; $u_* = 0.5$ m/sec; $\bar{u} = 5$ m/sec.
 (iv) Hay and Pasquill (1959)—the values of $(\sigma_\theta)_{\tau,x/\beta\bar{u}}$ below were obtained
     from the data in Fig. 2.18 by using the relation

$$(\sigma_\theta{}^2)_{\tau,x/\beta u} = (\sigma_\theta{}^2)_{\tau,s} - (\sigma_\theta{}^2)_{x/\beta u,s}$$

where the subscript notation is as in Table 5.II and s is the common
averaging-time imposed by the instrument. $\tau = 4$ min; $u = 5$ m/sec;
and β was taken to be 4.

x	100	300	600	1000 (m)
$(\sigma_\theta)_{\tau,x/4u}$	4·36	3·73	3·23	2·79 (deg)

σ_z/σ_y was assumed to be $\frac{1}{2}$.

Porton data (Sutton, 1947a):
  For a source of strength 1 g/sec and duration 4 min, in a wind of 500 cm/sec,
the axial concentration was 2.0×10^{-9} g/cc at a distance of 100 m, and varied
with (distance)$^{-1.76}$

Prairie Grass data
  For a wind speed of 500 cm/sec and a sampling duration of 4 min, Fig. 2.18
gives $\sigma_\theta = 5.25$ deg.   Using this as σ_A in Fig. 6 of Cramer's (1957) paper,
slight extrapolation gives the following concentrations for a source-strength
of 100 g/sec

Distance	100	200	400	1000	(m)
Concentration	200	65	20	4×10^{-9}	(g/cc)

Bearing in mind the various approximations and assumptions which have been made in applying the above formulae, the results are remarkably consistent, both one with another and with the observed data.   To some extent this is an inevitable consequence of the essentially empirical element in all the treatments.   In particular it should be emphasized that the assumption of complete analogy between lateral and vertical diffusion is strictly incorrect, and that any agreement thereby achieved is somewhat fortuitous.   This feature has been brought out in an analysis by Barad and Haugen (1959) of the *Prairie Grass* diffusion data, in which it is shown that the parameter n in Sutton's formulae must be given different values for lateral and vertical diffusion.   Nevertheless, the results just reviewed show that certain broad features have been established.   The conclusion to be drawn at this point is that the average features of the concentration field at short range from a ground level point source, operating for several minutes in relatively ideal conditions of terrain and airflow, are prescribed with tolerable accuracy by several formulae.

With the more recent demonstrations of the good correlations between diffusive spread and intensity of turbulence, and the encouraging degree of success obtained with simple adaptations of the basic statistical treatments, there is now a reasonable expectation of achieving a similar degree of accuracy with much less restriction as regards sampling or release time and degree of atmospheric stability.   In particular the formula developed by Hay and Pasquill is *a priori* equally acceptable for stability conditions other than neutral, and for any sampling or release time, subject only to this being at least as long as the time of down-wind travel which is involved. As regards stability it has already been demonstrated (see 4.3) that the effect of a moderate range can be satisfactorily prescribed, but a more detailed study in more extreme conditions of stability would be desirable.

Elevated sources

Extension of the formulae to the case of isolated elevated sources, as represented by effluent from chimneys, follows fairly readily in a formal sense, though problems arise as to the magnitude of the parameters used, since the plume behaviour is then dominated initially by conditions at a considerable height, rather than by the conditions very close to the ground. The formulae which have been commonly used, those of Bosanquet and Pearson (1936) and Sutton (1947b), are given in Eq. (5.15) and (5.16) respectively,

$$\chi(x, y) = \frac{Q}{(2\pi)^{1/2} p q \bar{u} x^2} \exp\left\{-\left(\frac{y^2}{2q^2 x^2} + \frac{H}{px}\right)\right\} \qquad (5.15)$$

$$\chi(x, y) = \frac{2Q}{\pi C_y C_z \bar{u} x^{2-n}} \exp\left\{-\frac{1}{x^{2-n}}\left(\frac{y^2}{C_y^2} + \frac{H^2}{C_z^2}\right)\right\} \qquad (5.16)$$

where $\chi(x, y)$ is the ground-level concentration from a source at height H, and the parameters are those listed in Table 5.11.   For arbitrary values of σ_y and σ_z general forms may be written as follows:

$r = s = 2$

$$\frac{\chi(x, y)\bar{u}}{Q} = \frac{1}{\pi \sigma_y \sigma_z} \exp\left\{-\left(\frac{y^2}{2\sigma_y^2} + \frac{H^2}{2\sigma_z^2}\right)\right\} \qquad (5.17)$$

$r = 2,\ s = 1$

$$\frac{\chi(x, y)\bar{u}}{Q} = \frac{1}{\pi^{1/2}\sigma_y \sigma_z} \exp\left\{-\left(\frac{y^2}{2\sigma_y^2} + \frac{\sqrt{2}H}{\sigma_z}\right)\right\} \qquad (5.18)$$

All the above formulae give a ground-level concentration which is zero at $x = 0$, i.e. at the foot of the chimney and rises to a maximum $\chi_{\max}$ on the axis, at a distance $x_{\max}$, when

$$2px_{\max} = H \qquad (5.19)$$

$$\text{or} \quad C_z^2 x_{\max}^{2-n} = H^2 \qquad (5.20)$$

or generally (if σ_y/σ_z is independent of distance) when

$$\sigma_z = H/\sqrt{2} \qquad (5.21)$$

These equations bring out the interesting point that for a given H the distance at which the maximum concentration occurs is dependent only on the rate of vertical spread.   It is in fact the distance at which the standard deviation of the vertical spread is 0·7 times the height of the source.   It is emphasized, however, that the latter result is only true when, as in the above cases, the functional forms of σ_y and σ_z with respect to distance x are the same.

The magnitudes of the maximum concentrations at ground level are as follows:

From Eq. (5.15) (Bosanquet and Pearson)

$$\chi_{\max} = \frac{2^{3/2}Q}{e^2 \pi^{1/2} \bar{u} H^2}\left(\frac{p}{q}\right) \qquad (5.22)$$

From Eq. (5.16) (Sutton)

$$\chi_{\max} = \frac{2Q}{e\pi \bar{u} H^2}\left(\frac{C_z}{C_y}\right) \qquad (5.23)$$

14—A.D.

From Eq. (5.17), with $r=s=2$

$$\chi_{max} = \frac{2Q}{e\pi\bar{u}H^2}\left(\frac{\sigma_z}{\sigma_y}\right) \tag{5.24}$$

From Eq. (5.18), with $r=2$, $s=1$

$$\chi_{max} = \frac{2Q}{e^2\pi^{1/2}\bar{u}H^2}\left(\frac{\sigma_z}{\sigma_y}\right) \tag{5.25}$$

Using these expressions for χ_{max} and the foregoing expressions for x_{max}, Eq. (5.15) and (5.16) may be transformed into convenient non-dimensional forms (see Falk *et al.*, 1954, and Meade, 1960, respectively).

For a given source strength and wind speed Eq. (5.24) and (5.25) show that χ_{max} depends on $1/H^2$, σ_z/σ_y, and on the shape of the vertical distribution, the numerical term and the terms involving e and π being a consequence of the particular shape assumed. For a given value of the ratio σ_z/σ_y it follows that the values of χ_{max} corresponding to Gaussian and simple exponential distributions in the vertical will be in the ratio $1:\pi^{1/2}/e$, i.e. $1:0.65$. According to the experimental evidence obtained by Hay and Pasquill (1957) the vertical distribution from a source at a height of 150 m, at distances up to 500 m, approximates closely to the Gaussian form, so that on these grounds at least Eq. (5.24) would appear to be preferable.

When the material is released at high temperature, or with forced up-draught, the centre-line of the plume is at first inclined to the horizontal. Approximate allowance for this is normally attempted by using an effective value of H, usually the height at which the plume is estimated to become approximately horizontal (see 6.1).

Many of the results which have so far been obtained on the concentrations down-wind of elevated sources (see 6.3) fail to provide any critical appreciation of the validity of Eq. (5.15)–(5.25), either because of inadequate quality in the data on the distribution of concentration, or because of absence of special meteorological observations. These results are discussed in 6.3. There are, however, some particular examples which should be noted here, especially as they provide an indication of the potential value of formulae which directly incorporate values of gustiness or intensity of turbulence. Lowry (1951) has referred to an empirical relation between gustiness and the distance of the maximum ground level concentration from an elevated source, based on the surveys of the distribution of oil-smoke released from a tower. A reference to what is presumably the same data is made by Mazzarella (1952), but the details of the two relations differ, viz.,

as given by Lowry $r_{max} = H \csc \sigma$ (5.26)

as quoted by Mazzarella $x_1 = H \cot s$ (5.27)

where r_{max} is the distance of the point of maximum concentration, x_1 the distance at which the oil-fog first reaches the ground, H the height of release, σ the standard deviation of the *wind direction*, and s the standard deviation of the wind *inclination* both taken over a period of ten to fifteen minutes. The precise reconciliation of these two formulae is not obvious, but it may be noted that they have the same form (for small angles) as the relation which would follow from substituting condition (5.21) in Hay and Pasquill's formula for σ_z at (iv) in Table 5.II. On making this substitution

$$ r_{max} = \frac{H}{\sigma_\phi \sqrt{2}} = \frac{H\sigma_\theta}{\sigma_\theta \sigma_\phi \sqrt{2}} $$

and since for small angles $\sigma_\theta = \sin \sigma_\theta \, (=1/\mathrm{cosec}\ \sigma$ in Lowry's notation) this is identical with Lowry's result if $\sigma_\theta/\sigma_\phi = \sqrt{2}$. There is, however, an element of vagueness in this comparison, for the magnitude of gustiness specified by Lowry is not necessarily associated with the appropriate averaging time and sampling duration as implied in Hay and Pasquill's treatment.

In an experimental study with an elevated source Falk *et al.* (1954) found that the observed characteristics of the dispersion pattern at ground level were related statistically to the fluctuations of wind speed and direction near the point of release. The relations were formed directly in terms of the distances and magnitudes of the maximum ground-level concentrations, and also in terms of the parameters p and q obtained by fitting Bosanquet and Pearson's formula (Eq. 5.15) to the dispersion measurements. Falk *et al.* give a relation of the form

$$ q = a + b\sigma_\theta $$

where σ_θ is the standard deviation of wind direction, and a and b are constants, but it is clear from the data presented graphically in their paper that the approximate relation

$$ q \simeq 1 \cdot 1 \sigma_\theta $$

where σ_θ is measured in radians, is also acceptable. They also give

$$ p = 0 \cdot 57 \sigma_u / \bar{u} $$

where σ_u is the standard deviation of wind speed. Remembering (see Table 5.II) that

$$ q = \sigma_y / x $$
$$ p = \sigma_z / x\sqrt{2} $$

and assuming isotropic conditions (so that $\sigma_u/\bar{u} \simeq \sigma_\phi$, where ϕ is wind inclination) the above empirical values for p and q imply

$$\sigma_y/x \simeq \sigma_\theta$$

$$\sigma_z/x \simeq \sigma_\phi$$

These are effectively the formulae given at (iv) in Table 5.II though again the comparison cannot be made very critically, as the averaging time used in determining σ_θ and $\sigma_u/\bar{u}$ is not specified, and the length of the wind record used was only ten minutes, whereas the dispersion pattern was observed over about an hour.

A preliminary test of a more critical nature has recently been provided by some experiments in the U.S.A., in which sampling of the distribution of concentration at ground-level down-wind of a source at a height H of about 50 m was accompanied by recordings of the inclination of the wind at a similar height (see Pasquill, 1961). For each experiment the integral of concentration with respect to cross-wind position was evaluated at a number of distances from the source, and the distance (x_{max}) estimated at which this integral was a maximum. By integrating Eq. (5.17) with respect to y, and then differentiating with respect to σ_z, it is easily shown that the maximum occurs when $\sigma_z = H$ (cf. $\sigma_z\sqrt{2} = H$ for the maximum of the axial concentration). Substituting this condition in the form for σ_z given at (iv) in Table 5.II,

$$x_{max} = H/\sigma_\phi \qquad (5.28)$$

the appropriate averaging time and sampling duration being implied. Data were provided for thirteen cases, in which x_{max} was observed to be in the range 300–1000 m. For twelve of these the ratio of the x_{max} calculated from Eq. (5.28), to that observed was in the range 0·76–1·38, in one case the ratio was 1·82, and the overall average was 1·14. The first indications, therefore, are that quite useful calculations of diffusion from an ideal type of elevated source can be made in a simple way from measurements of vertical gustiness.

The success of the above application is probably a reflection of a feature which may often be observed in the plume of smoke from an elevated source, especially in unstable conditions. Successive elements of the plume follow trajectories which are different from each other, but have approximately constant inclination for appreciable distances. This behaviour is the counterpart in the vertical plane of that illustrated in Fig. 5.1 for the horizontal plane. The important point here is that such a behaviour appears to occur in downward motion, in unstable conditions, even up to the stage when the element of the plume is nearing the ground.

Further consideration of the applicability of diffusion formulae

In the dispersal problems which arise in the atmosphere there are other complexities and difficulties which have to be taken into account:

(1) In reality the concentration at a fixed point is a fluctuating quantity, so that even if the average level is harmless or tolerable it does not follow that this can be assumed for the fluctuating concentration.

(2) Substantially longer distances of down-wind travel may be of interest when large sources or highly toxic substances are involved.

(3) The modification of the airflow by natural features of vegetation and relief, and by buildings, may significantly influence the travel and spread of airborne material.

(4) Extreme conditions, of low wind speed and of stability, may arise which are not obviously amenable to the forms of treatment so far advanced.

As already emphasized in the introduction to this chapter the problems represented in (3) and (4) above are all concerned with departures from the ideal conditions of airflow which have been assumed in developing the diffusion formulae. These situations have not as yet been subjected to comprehensive investigation, and the tendency has been to deal with them on an *ad hoc* empirical basis, some discussion of which is more appropriately given in the next chapter. The problems in (1) and (2) are in the forefront of current research on atmospheric diffusion, and although it has been seen in Chapter 4 that much remains to be done, there are already a number of advances which might be put to practical use.

The fluctuation of concentration at a point in space is a characteristic feature of mixing in a turbulent atmosphere, and one which reflects the dual nature of dispersion processes affecting a plume. As pointed out at several stages in this book, the elements of the plume are both spread within themselves and scattered with respect to the centre-line of the average cross-wind distribution. (See Fig. 5.1.) The classical procedure of integrating the equation for an instantaneous point source, to give that appropriate to a continuous point source, assumes that individual puffs have the same linear trajectory and implies a straight plume. As far as the magnitude of the concentration *within* the plume is concerned, this idealization is reasonable provided the *instantaneous* dimensions of the plume are used in formulae such as (5.10). On the other hand such formulae will fail to give a correct representation of the *occurrence* of concentrations of a particular magnitude at a fixed point. Formal treatment of this problem has been given by Gifford (1959b), using a simplified model of a fluctuating

plume (see 3.6).   Explicit application of this treatment requires the estimation of the spread of an individual puff, for which a useful approximation
has been provided by F. B. Smith (see Smith and Hay, 1961) in the form

$$\sigma = 3i^2x \qquad (5.29)$$

where σ is the standard deviation of the distribution (assumed Gaussian)
within a cluster of particles, and i is the total intensity of turbulence (in
practice the standard deviation of the wind direction or wind inclination,
according to the component involved).   For present purposes this σ can be
identified with that of the cross section of an instantaneous plume, normal
to the local centre line of the plume, and can be substituted in Eq. (5.10)
et seq.   Thus the practical problem is the specification of i, and the assessment of the frequency of occurrence of plume elements at specified positions
on the ground.   Some progress which has been made with this latter
requirement, for the case of an elevated source, is outlined in 5.4.

In general the peak concentration produced by a continuous plume will
decrease with duration of sampling or exposure, in accordance with the
systematic increase of cross-wind spread.   A similar effect will also be
associated with the vertical spread of an elevated plume, but the effect will
diminish as the vertical spread increases to a magnitude large compared
with the height of the source.   Thus, for a ground-level source, or at long
distance from an elevated source, the variation of the ground-level concentration with sampling duration will be essentially controlled by the cross-
wind spread.   For the simple hypothetical case when the wind direction
over a long period is uniformly distributed around 360 degrees, the long-
term average concentration, χ_∞, at radius x from the source, is related to
the peak value for a sampling duration τ, χ_τ, as follows.   Taking χ_τ
according to Eq. (5.12), say, and assuming σ_y (appropriate to sampling
duration τ) to be small compared with x,

$$2\pi x \chi_\infty = 2\chi_\tau \int_0^\infty \exp\left(-y^2/2\sigma_y^2\right) dy$$

from which

$$\frac{\chi_\infty}{\chi_\tau} = \frac{\sigma_y}{(2\pi)^{1/2}x}$$

For example, with $x=100$ m and $\sigma_y=10$ m (appropriate to $\tau=4$ min in
neutral conditions over open downland),

$$\frac{\chi_\infty}{\chi_\tau} = 0\cdot04$$

In reality the long-term distribution of wind direction will not be uniform, and the long-term average value of χ at a given position will depend on the frequency of the corresponding wind direction (see 6.3).

Extension of the diffusion formulae to longer ranges, say to 100 km, has hitherto frequently been attempted by an extrapolation of formulae such as those of Sutton. However, the use of formulae which were derived and established for short ranges of travel in the lower atmosphere may be quite misleading. To take one simple example, the theories and observations indicate that over distances of hundreds of metres the height of a cloud from a ground-level source in neutral conditions is approximately one-tenth of the distance down-wind. Extrapolation to 100 km would imply a vertical spread through virtually the whole troposphere, whereas it is evident (see 4.6) that with neutral conditions near *the ground* the vertical spread of the cloud at that distance may not exceed 1000 m. However, a tentative but fairly realistic adaptation of the short-range formulae can now be made on simple lines as follows.

Considering first the estimation of the appropriate value of σ_y, this may be approached by an empirical application of the Hay–Pasquill form in Table 5.II, when the interest is in the average distribution from a long-term release of material, or the Smith form in Eq. (5.29) when the interest is in the transient concentrations from a plume or isolated cloud of material. Some evidence in confirmation of the former application has been given by Pasquill (1961) and, taking this as an interim solution, the practical problem reduces to making appropriate estimates of σ_θ, from wind directions averaged over a time interval equal to one-quarter of the time of down-wind travel involved. By the original argument this method should only be applied for release-times at least as long as the time of travel. The suggested application of Eq. (5.29) has yet to be submitted to practical test for lateral diffusion at long range.

Estimation of σ_z may be attempted in a similar way, but there will be the additional complication that vertical spread will be slowed up appreciably or even completely halted at some level in the troposphere, after which there might be expected to be a progression to a uniform vertical distribution throughout the effective mixing layer. An approximation to the development of the distribution within the finite layer may be obtained by considering the expanding plume to be 'reflected' from the top of the mixing layer in exactly the same way as it is supposed to be 'reflected' from the ground in Eq. (5.15)–(5.18). If the values of σ_z are estimated initially without regard for the upper boundary of the mixing layer (at height Z, say, above the source), it is easily seen that Eq. (5.12), for example, may be applied at least until $\sigma_z = Z/2$, at distance x_1 say. When $\sigma_z = Z$ (at distance

x_2), the resulting concentration may be expected to be approximately uniform with height, and of a magnitude appropriate to $\sigma_z = Z$. At greater distances than x_2 the ground level concentration will no longer be reduced by vertical spreading, and the equation may continue to be used with $\sigma_z \simeq Z$ and the appropriate value of σ_y. A practical application of this principle is embodied in the procedures recommended at the end of this chapter.

5.4   Practical systems of estimating diffusion

Diffusion formulae may be applied with a variety of practical objects. The common examples are the estimation of the likely hazards or discomforts, from the effluent of existing or projected industrial plants, and from airborne clouds of toxic or objectionable material released as a result of an accident. According to the circumstances of the requirement and the meteorological data available, the exact mode of application and the achievable accuracy will vary.

The use of predetermined diffusion parameters.   From the engineer's standpoint the simplest and most attractive procedure is the use of a simple formula, with values of the parameters specified according to the broad features of weather and terrain.   It is in this sense that Sutton's formulae in particular have been used.   The values specified by Sutton for n, C_y and C_z for neutral conditions over relatively flat grassland, have already been given with Fig. 5.5   Sutton also gave (1947b) tentative values for other conditions of stability, and for sources at different heights in the atmosphere.   In the latter application the estimates were made by interpolating between results obtained near the ground, and those obtained from an analysis of the growth of smoke clouds from shell bursts.   These latter results could only reflect the properties of small-scale turbulence, and not the larger-scale components which would determine the spread from continuous sources in the first 100 m or so of the atmosphere.

Many other estimates have been given of the parameters n, C_y and C_z, both on the basis of wind profile and gustiness observations, and from the analysis of diffusion measurements.   These will not be reviewed in detail at this point, but it may be noted that a summary has already been given (U.S. Weather Bureau, 1955).   The same publication also presents a number of graphical solutions of formulae of this type.   For the evaluation of Calder's simple equation, which is applicable only in neutral conditions, estimates of the *friction velocity* u_*, and of the ratio of the horizontal and lateral components of turbulence are required.   The former is available to a sufficient accuracy for open country (see Deacon, 1949), but the dependence of the gustiness ratio on roughness has yet to be evaluated.

For the application of Cramer's and of Hay and Pasquill's formulae, statistics of the components of gustiness, as represented by the standard deviation of wind direction and wind inclination, are required. For the latter formula these statistics need to be expressed as a function of averaging time and sampling duration. Until recently this requirement would probably have been regarded as too elaborate to be considered in the present context, but the latest developments in instrumentation and in recording systems (see 2.7 and below) now bring it within the scope of practicable observational programmes. Examples of the quality and quantity of the statistics which are attainable, and of their use in providing statistical estimates of diffusion, have been given in papers by F. B. Smith (1961) and Smith and Abbot (1961).

The use of current measurements of gustiness. The developments in techniques of recording gustiness are of more immediate value when some form of monitoring assessment of dispersal has to be maintained as a routine, say on the site of an industrial plant. An early attempt to satisfy this requirement by a routine measurement of turbulence was contained in Hewson's (1945) employment, at Trail in Canada, of a 'bridle-cup turbulence integrator', an instrument which recorded the number of changes of wind speed over intervals of 2 miles/hr. This was followed, at the Brookhaven National Laboratory, by M. E. Smith's (1951a) use of a broad classification of gustiness based on the records of wind direction (see Table 5.I). The appearance of various vane-type instruments which are both adequately responsive and robust (see Mazzarella, 1952, Jones and Butler, 1958), and of convenient systems of recording (Jones and Pasquill, 1959), means that routine application of the formulae which explicitly involve gustiness may now be contemplated on a substantial scale.

Records obtained with the system described by Jones and Pasquill may be used with a minimum of arithmetic to estimate diffusion for given time of travel T, and duration of release or sampling τ, by the method proposed by Hay and Pasquill (1959). According to this method the standard deviation of the angular cross-wind spread is approximately equal to the standard deviation of the wind-direction fluctuation appropriate to an averaging time $T/4$ and a sampling duration τ, and the vertical spread is similarly given in terms of wind inclination. In practice this standard deviation will be given by the square-root of the difference of the squares of the standard deviations recorded for sampling durations of τ and $T/4$ [see Eq. (2.21)]. The method of recording could also be developed to give the angular spread directly, by using a band-pass filter of which the low-frequency cut-off is equivalent to a sampling duration τ, and the high-frequency cut-off to one-quarter of the time of travel T. Thus, if the band-pass filter corresponded to a sampling duration of 3 min and an averaging time of 30 sec, the recorded standard deviation would represent the standard deviation of the angular spread after a time of travel of 2 min, for a source of duration 3 min, or alternatively for a continuously generated plume sampled for 3 min.

Davidson and Halitsky (1958) have recommended a method of estimating the field of instantaneous concentration from an elevated source, based on measurements of the inclination of the wind near the site of release. The plume of emitted material is supposed to be of cylindrical cross section,

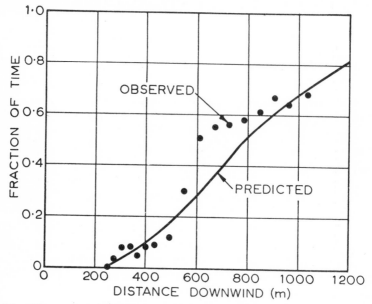

FIG. 5.6   Observed and computed duration of smoke, at ground-level, from an elevated source. (Davidson and Halitsky, 1958)

and to expand linearly with an angle 2β subtended on the release point. Successive elements of plume are assumed to have linear trajectories determined by the wind vector averaged over 10-sec intervals. The fraction of time that plume segments will cross a fixed arc on the ground at distance R is given by twice the probability that the average inclination is downward and numerically greater than $(H/R)-\beta$, where H is the height of the source. The factor of two is based on observations that the speed of plume segments on the ground was about one-half of the mean wind speed at the release point, which in this case was at a height of about 100 m.

Davidson and Halitsky have compared observations of the duration of appearance of smoke at specified distances down-wind, with values calculated in this way from the wind records, taking $\beta = 0.055$ rad, an average figure based on the visible dimensions of the plumes. The useful measure of agreement obtained is illustrated in Fig. 5.6.

Davidson and Halitsky's evaluation of the instantaneous concentration involves other simplifying assumptions, for which reference should be made to the original paper. Some of these will require modification as more advanced treatments of the expansion of a plume are adopted, but the main point which is to be brought out here is the demonstration that the occurrence of intermittent concentration at short range can be estimated in a realistic way from records of wind fluctuation near the site of release of the material.

A suggested general system

It is unlikely that the assessement of the distribution of an air pollutant over a region extending up to say 100 km from the point of release can always be confined to the substitution of a single set of parameters in one simple equation. This is so because the growth of a cloud or plume in the vertical will not necessarily follow a simple (e.g. power-law) variation with distance indefinitely. Even when a simple formula is applicable estimates of the parameters to be used in it will vary according to the quality of the meteorological data available. The latter data will range from the usual routine descriptions of meteorological conditions, as used in synoptic and climatological analyses, to the most advanced and detailed measurements of the structure of turbulence. Moreover, there are aspects of diffusion which have so far been examined only in a very preliminary way, and generalization from the data available is then essentially speculative and should be reappraised frequently.

For the provision of approximate estimates of diffusion, a general system has recently been suggested (Pasquill, 1961) which incorporates the available methods in a simple flexible way, and which can be applied with routine meteorological data or with more sophisticated measurements when these are possible. The basis of the system is the Gaussian type of formula, Eq. (5.10), made appropriate to a ground-level source by multiplying by two, and generalized to allow for the relatively slow variations of wind direction by considering the distribution of concentration on an arc centred on the source, instead of on a cross-wind line. The standard deviations of the lateral and vertical distributions are expressed in terms of an angular *lateral spread* θ and a *vertical spread* h, defined as usual by concentrations one-tenth of the axial or ground-level values respectively.

Then, with practical units as follows:

> wind speed u m/sec (assumed constant with height)
> distance d km
> lateral spread θ deg
> vertical spread h m

the concentration C_0 on the axis of the plume, at ground level, from a point source of strength 1 unit/min, is given by

$$C_0 = \frac{2{\cdot}8 \times 10^{-3}}{ud\theta h} \text{ units/cu.m} \qquad (5.30)$$

It may easily be seen that this expression follows directly from Eq. (5.10) for small values of θ.   It can in practice be applied without restriction on θ, on the assumption that large values of θ will only arise from relatively slow swings of wind direction, and that the resulting arc distribution of concentration is Gaussian.   The point to be emphasized about Eq. (5.30) is that it avoids complex parameters, and brings into prominence dimensions of the plume which are easily visualized and therefore least likely to be miscalculated.   It should also be noted that C_0 can alternatively be taken as the total dosage, in 'units' min/cu.m, corresponding to a total release of one unit.   When detailed measurements or estimates of gustiness are available estimates of σ_y and σ_z (hence of θ and h) may be derived from the Hay–Pasquill and F. B. Smith formulae as discussed in 5.3.   In routine practice, however, the only relevant measurements of gustiness likely to be available are those contained in conventional wind-direction traces.   For releases of long duration (hours) a simple rule for obtaining rough estimates of θ is suggested as follows:

> $d = 0{\cdot}1$ km θ = extreme range of trace over duration of release,
> $d = 100$ km θ = range of trace when averaged over 15-minute periods.

When the release occupies a much shorter duration (minutes) the data provided by the usual slow record of wind direction may not be adequate, and in the absence of special measurements of gustiness tentative estimates of average values of θ (at the same two values of d) are suggested for broad categories of atmospheric stability.   These estimates are tabulated on Fig. 5.7, the stability categories being specified in the accompanying notes. The values for 0·1 km are based on statistics of lateral gustiness over open downland, while those for 100 km are very speculative estimates based on limited data.

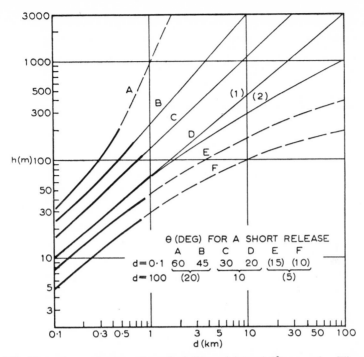

FIG. 5.7   Tentative estimates of vertical (*h*) and lateral (*θ*) spread.   These estimates are for a source in open country

Key to stability categories

| Surface wind speed (m/sec) | Insolation | | | Night | |
	Strong	Moderate	Slight	Thinly overcast or ⩾ 4/8 low cloud	⩽ 3/8 cloud
< 2	A	A–B	B	—	—
2–3	A–B	B	C	E	F
3–5	B	B–C	C	D	E
5–6	C	C–D	D	D	D
> 6	C	D	D	D	D

(for A–B take average of values for A and B etc.)

Strong insolation corresponds to sunny midday in midsummer in England,
slight insolation to similar conditions in midwinter.   Night refers to the period
from one hour before sunset to one hour after dawn.   The neutral category D
should also be used, regardless of wind speed, for overcast conditions during
day or night, and for any sky conditions during the hour preceding or following
night as defined above.   The D(1) curve should be followed to the top of the
dry-adiabatic layer; thereafter, in sub-adiabatic conditions, D(2) or a curve
parallel to D(2) should be followed.   (Pasquill, 1961) (from *The Meteorological
Magazine, February 1961, H.M.S.O.*   Crown Copyright Reserved)

For the vertical spread, tentative values composed from the available data on diffusion and gustiness are given in graphical form, for the same broad categories of stability (see Fig. 5.7). The estimates are most securely based at short range (up to 1 km), where reliable experimental data are available. At longer range they are at best derived from limited experimental data, and the few statistics available on vertical gustiness in the first few thousand feet above the ground, while in the more extreme conditions of stability and instability they are essentially speculative. In general it is emphasized that the data of Fig. 5.7 are extremely tentative, and require progressive confirmation or adjustment as better data become available. Moreover, these data apply to open level country and contain no allowance for the possible disturbing effects of buildings and topographical features.

The procedure for evaluating the distribution of concentration at ground level is set out in detail in the original paper. A summary is given below, and the working out of a hypothetical example is reproduced in Table 5.III and Fig. 5.8 and 5.9. Since the magnitudes of θ at 0·1 and 100 km will not usually be grossly different, those at intermediate standard distances of 1 and 10 km may be interpolated simply by assuming equal changes in θ over the three intervals of distance. This implies a variation with log d, rather than with a power of d, but the difference can hardly be significant in comparison with other uncertainties in the calculations. Magnitudes of h at the four distances are read off Fig. 5.7, and with the corresponding values of θ are substituted in Eq. (5.30) to give C_0 for a wind speed of 5 m/sec (in the original paper a chart is given from which values of C_0 for $d = 0·1$ km may be directly read, and then corrected to the other values of d). The magnitudes of vertical spread are taken from the graphs in Fig. 5.7 until a value (h') equal to the expected vertical extent of convection is attained, at a distance d'. As a rough working rule it is assumed that the development of a uniform vertical distribution, which *per se* introduces a roughly twofold reduction in the ground-level concentration, is accomplished in a further distance d'. Accordingly, for distances equal to or greater than about $2d'$ a constant value of $2h'$ is substituted in Eq. (5.30).

The axial concentrations must then be corrected so as to correspond to the effective wind speed u. This is taken to be the 'surface wind speed' of routine meteorological observation, for distances of 0·1 and 1 km. For distances of 10 and 100 km a speed is adopted midway between this and the 'geostrophic' value as estimated from a chart of the surface pressure distribution. In this way a practical allowance is made for the influence of the wind at greater heights as the vertical spread of the plume increases. The axial concentrations at the four standard distances are then plotted on log–log scales, as in Fig. 5.8, and joined by straight lines to provide for approximate interpolation.   Corrections are next applied, if necessary, for the effective height H of the source, by multiplying by $\exp(-H^2/2\sigma_z^2)$ i.e. $\exp(-2 \cdot 303H^2/h^2)$.   In practice a set of correction factors for standard values of h/H may be used.   This procedure disregards the effect of height of source above ground on the rate of vertical spread, but at present there are insufficient data on which to base any allowance for this effect.

Table 5.III

Example of calculation of the distribution of concentration from a point source of strength 1 'unit'/min.   (Pasquill, 1961)

General data

Site	Southern England
Date	16 June, 1959
Period	1000–1300 GMT
Effective height of release (H)	100 m
Surface wind	4 m/sec 275°
Geostrophic wind	8 m/sec 325°
Vertical extent of convection	1000 m
State of sky	1/8 Cu, 6/8 Sc, 6/8 Ci
Stability category	B–C
Distance at which estimated vertical spread (h) equals vertical extent of convection	5·5 km

Calculation of C_0 [from Eq. (5.30)]

Distance	0·1	1	10	100	km
Effective value of h	20	170	2000	2000	m
Lateral spread θ†	120	93	67	40	deg
Effective value of u	4	4	6	6	m/sec
C	$2 \cdot 9 \times 10^{-6}$	$4 \cdot 4 \times 10^{-8}$	$3 \cdot 5 \times 10^{-10}$	$5 \cdot 8 \times 10^{-11}$	units/cu.m

Allowance for elevation of source (H)

Assumed h/H	½	⅔	⅔	1·0	1½	2·0	4·0
$F_1 = \exp(-2 \cdot 303H^2/h^2)$	10^{-4}	$5 \cdot 6 \times 10^{-3}$	0·027	0·10	0·36	0·56	0·87
Distance at which corresponding values of h occur	0·28	0·37	0·46	0·59	0·86	1·15	2·20
C_0	4600	2700	1800	1200	580	330	82 } 10^{-10} units/cu.m
$F_1 C_0$	0·46	15	49	120	210	185	71 } cu.m

Position of plume axis

Distance	0·1	1	10	100	km
Effective wind direction	275	275	290	290	deg

† Estimated from routine wind-direction trace.

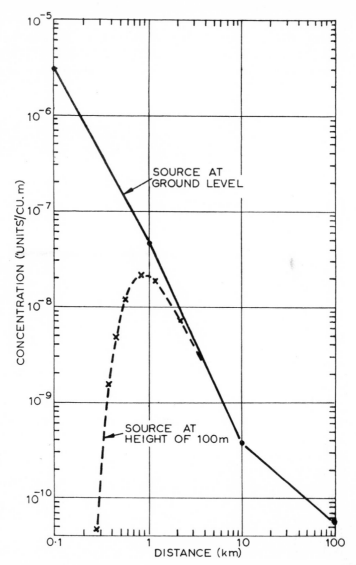

FIG. 5.8   Concentration–distance diagram for the example in Table 5.III.   (Pasquill, 1961) (from *The Meteorological Magazine, February 1961, H.M.S.O.* Crown Copyright Reserved)

The next stage is the drawing of a plan of the plume, as in Fig. 5.9. The positions of the axis of the plume, according to the effective wind direction, and of the edges of the plume according to the values of θ, are plotted to scale and joined by straight lines. Only two of the intervals of distance can be conveniently accommodated on one drawing, and the example in Fig. 5.9 is for the outer range of 1–100 km. The effective wind direction is taken

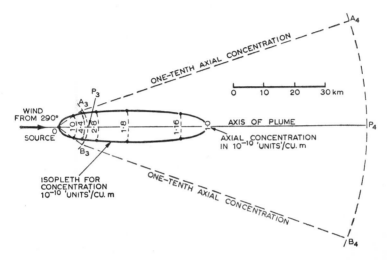

FIG. 5.9   Plan of plume for the example in Table 5.III.   (Pasquill, 1961) (from *The Meteorological Magazine, February 1961, H.M.S.O.*   Crown Copyright Reserved)

to be that of the surface wind for distances of 0·1 and 1 km, and the average of the surface and 'geostrophic' directions backed (i.e. moved anticlockwise) by 10 deg. is suggested for 10 and 100 km. Concentrations interpolated from Fig. 5.8 are now entered on the axis; the edges of the plume (shown as broken lines) represent the arc positions at which the concentrations fall to one-tenth of the axial values. Interpolation of the concentrations α degrees away from the axis is provided by multiplying the axial values by

$$\exp\left[-2\cdot303(2\alpha/\theta)^2\right]$$

For rapid interpolation and construction of isopleths of concentration factors are given for round values of $2\alpha/\theta$, i.e. for convenient deviations from the axis expressed as a fraction of the 'half' lateral spread. The resulting data refer to a source strength of 1 unit/min (or to a dosage for a total release of 1 unit of material). The figures can be adjusted, in direct

15—A.D.

proportion, to any numerical magnitude of source strength (or total release). Alternatively, if the requirement is to delimit the area within which a concentration (or dosage) C' is exceeded, as a result of a release of Q units/min (or a total release of Q units) the results for unit source may be used merely by adopting an equivalent threshold value of C'/Q.

In some circumstances time or interest may not warrant the carrying out of the full procedure and, for example, it may be sufficient merely to specify the direction of the plume and, in the case of an elevated release at height H, the distance $d(\mathrm{max})$ down-wind at which the maximum effect is likely to occur.   The first feature is provided immediately by the appropriate wind directions, and an estimate of the latter may be made directly by using Fig. 5.7 to read off the distance at which $h = 1 \cdot 5H$.   It follows from Eq. (5.21) (with $h = 2 \cdot 15\sigma_z$) that this is the distance $d(\mathrm{max})$ of the position of maximum concentration or dosage.   The corresponding magnitude of the maximum concentration is given by Eq. (5.24), which in the same practical terms as used in Eq. (5.30) reduces to

$$C_0(\mathrm{max}) \simeq \frac{2 \times 10^{-3}}{3uHd(\mathrm{max})\theta} \text{ units/cu.m} \qquad (5.31)$$

where θ refers to the distance $d(\mathrm{max})$.

6

The Distribution of Windborne Material from Real Sources

Release of material into the atmosphere may be accompanied by significant ascent, as in the case of hot gases discharged from industrial chimneys. Moreover, the material may be in the form of solid particles large enough for sedimentation and deposition to occur, or in the form of gases and vapours which are absorbed by vegetation and other surfaces. The complications which are introduced by such features have been disregarded in the preceding chapters. They are now considered with emphasis on practical aspects, and as a preliminary to discussion of various cases of atmospheric dispersion.

6.1 The rise of hot effluent

In the last chapter it was seen that the theoretical maximum concentration at ground-level down-wind of an elevated source is inversely proportional to the square of the height of release, when the material released is of the same density as the atmosphere and possesses no initial vertical motion. It was also pointed out that when the released material does rise in the atmosphere the customary procedure is to estimate the maximum height to which the plume rises above ground, and to use this 'effective height' in place of H in Eq. (5.15) *et seq.* This is clearly only an approximate representation of the real situation, for downward diffusion of the material will be occurring while the plume is rising, and the effect at any down-wind distance will be dependent in a complex way on the average height of the plume up to that distance. However, the obvious practical importance of the effective height of the source, and in particular the possibility that this might be adjusted to some sufficiently high value by the deliberate addition of heat, has led to much theoretical analysis of the ascent of hot gases. This analysis is a very difficult matter requiring knowledge of the rate at which the upward momentum and buoyancy possessed by a plume are reduced by entrainment or by mixing with the surrounding atmosphere. The method which has been adopted by most

215

workers starts with the differential equations governing the momentum and heat content of an element of the plume. Alternatively, as shown by Scorer (1958) certain basic relations may be deduced purely on dimensional grounds. In both approaches ascent in an otherwise calm atmosphere is usually assumed. Also it is necessary to draw upon observational data for specification of the absolute magnitude of the rate of spread of a plume.

In the more recent treatments Priestley's (1956) adaptation of the classical approach, and Scorer's (1959a and b) use of dimensional and simple physical considerations, are both particularly noteworthy in containing attempts to represent some of the real features and conditions of ascending plumes. Priestley's version, which specifically involves the turbulent spreading of the plume, has already been briefly considered in Chapter 3. Its chief interest lies in the introduction of two phases in the ascent of a plume, according as the spreading process is dominated first by induced turbulence, arising from the rapid motion of the plume relative to the air, and later by natural atmospheric turbulence. Scorer's treatment also divides the ascent into two stages, but here the division is in terms of the idealized geometry of the plume. In the early stage the plume is regarded as a vertical jet of fluid, but as this becomes bent over in the wind its development in a vertical plane is regarded as analogous to that of a long cylindrical element with a horizontal axis.

Priestley's analysis leads to a bounded value of the vertical rise, not only in a thermally stable atmosphere, but also in an atmosphere which is neutral or even unstable to some degree. Scorer's analysis, in common with earlier treatments, implies unlimited rise. For practical purposes the rise is regarded as complete when the vertical velocity is reduced to some small fraction (say one-tenth) of the wind speed, and the plume is thereafter regarded as *passive* and dominated by atmospheric diffusion.

An interesting feature which emerges in all treatments is the important effect of wind speed u on the total rise z_{max}. The well-known engineering formula of Bosanquet, Carey and Halton (1950) contains separate terms for the effects of efflux velocity and buoyancy. In the term for efflux velocity u enters as a complex function, but when the efflux velocity is large compared with u the function approximates to a variation with $1/u$. This simple dependence on wind speed is predicted by Scorer's analysis of the bent-over jet. On the other hand Sutton's (1950) and Bosanquet *et al.*'s derivations of the buoyant ascent contain wind speed in the form $1/u^3$, and this very sensitive dependence on wind speed is also given by Scorer's analysis. From a practical point of view there is naturally much concern with the relative magnitudes of the ascent produced by efflux velocity and buoyancy, and with the question whether it is preferable to discharge effluent with high efflux velocity from a narrow chimney, or with low efflux velocity from a wide chimney. On the simple basis that the ratio of the area of the envelope of a plume to its volume increases with a decrease in the width of the plume, Scorer (1955) has argued qualitatively that the buoyancy of a narrow plume will be dissipated more effectively than that of a wide plume of the same output, so leading to a smaller value of z_{max} in the case of the higher efflux velocity. This result has since been derived in Bosanquet's (1957) revision of the earlier treatment by Bosanquet *et al.*, and in Scorer's treatment by dimensional analysis (1959a).

Observations of the ascent of plumes

The first systematic observations to be reported appear to be those quoted by Bosanquet *et al.* (1950) in support of their formula for the combined effect of efflux velocity and buoyancy. These were obtained by plotting the visible shapes of plumes from various plants on a perspex screen. The original paper contains a table giving the ratios of the observed rises to the calculated rises at distances of 100 and 200 ft in all of seven tests, at 300 ft in three tests, and at 400 and 600 ft in only one test. These ratios are stated to have a mean value of 1·13, the range being 0·78 to 1·37. No reference is made to the lapse-rates obtaining during the tests, but in any case Bosanquet *et al.*'s calculations necessarily assume an adiabatic lapse rate. Further details are stated to be contained in an unpublished appendix to their paper (one of a series deposited in the library of the Institution of Mechanical Engineers), and the figures therein for the observed rises have been quoted by Best (1957).

None of Bosanquet *et al.*'s tests showed the attainment of a constant (maximum) value of rise of plume. The values at the maximum distance of observation, extracted from Best's paper, are given in Table 6.I with other relevant data. Bosanquet *et al.*'s observations have been compared with other theoretical formulae, and the results corresponding to the maximum distance of observation are summarized in Table 6.II. It is seen that on average the best agreement is provided by the formulae developed by Priestley and Meade. Taking individual occasions the range of discrepancy is least in Meade's case, but it is to be noted that his calculations involve fitting the formula to the observations at one distance (usually a short distance) in order to obtain the magnitude of the spread of the plume. In the case of Priestley's calculations this feature was specified by appeal to independent observations. A further comparison with Bosanquet *et al.*'s observations has been made by Schmidt (1957), using a

Table 6.I

Bosanquet *et al.*'s observations of plume rise.   (After Best, 1954 and 1957)

Plant No.	W_0 (ft/sec)	Δ (°C)	Q_H (cal/sec)	Wind speed u (ft/sec)	Max. distance from chimney (ft)	Plume rise (ft)
1	31	180	$1·53 \times 10^6$	14	600	186
				33	800	84
				26·5	800	101
				19	800	200
2	28	25	$7·24 \times 10^4$	10	300	67
				13·3	300	47
3	35·5	149	$1·58 \times 10^6$	20·4	600	103

w_0 efflux velocity

Δ excess of effluent temperature over that at which the effluent would have the same density as the air

Q_H heat carried by the effluent

formula in which the determining parameters are the ratio of the efflux velocities associated with the forced efflux and with the buoyancy, and the exponent in the power law describing the growth of the radius of the plume.

Table 6.II

Summary of comparisons of the data in Table 6.I with theoretical formulae

Formula	Range of ratios of calculated to observed rise
Bosanquet *et al.* (see Best, 1957)	0·44–1·13
Sutton (see Best, 1957)	1·21–1·85
Priestley (1956)	0·60–1·32
Meade (see Meade and Priestley, 1956)	0·77–1·21

Observations have been presented by Holland (1953) for two stacks at the Oak Ridge Laboratories of the United States Atomic Energy Commission, and for a stack at the Watts Bar Steam Plant of the Tennessee Valley Authority.   Apparently the estimates of the plume height were obtained from photographs of the smoke plumes from the stacks. No discussion of the quality of the estimates is given other than the statement that the Watts Bar observations were made more carefully. As there is no definite statement to the contrary, the implication may be that the recorded heights represented the maximum rise of the plume (z_{max}), but this implication has since been questioned (see Hawkins and Nonhebel, 1955, and the discussion on Bosanquet's 1957 paper). According to Holland's presentation of the data against wind speed the results show very wide scatter, though a trend for plume height to decrease with increasing wind speed is discernible. Holland's analysis of the data was guided by a wind-tunnel formula, which may be written

$$uz_{max} = 3w_0 R_0 \qquad (6.1)$$

where w_0 and R_0 are the efflux velocity and radius respectively. This formula refers to a plume with forced efflux velocity only. The values obtained by Holland of the product uz_{max}, for groupings of the data according to wind speed, are given in Table 6.III with other details relevant to the analysis.

Table 6.III

Observations of maximum plume rise.   (After Holland 1953)

Stack	X–10 Pile	X–10 Steam Plant	Watts Bar Steam Plant
Height of stack (ft)	200	180	160
Orifice diameter (ft)	$5\frac{3}{4}$	9	14
Exit velocity (miles/hr)	45	5	34
Exit temperature (°F)	180	400	350
Volume-emission-rate (cu.ft/min)	110,000	27,200	300,000
Heat-emission-rate Q_H (10^5 cal/sec)	8·3	7·1	66
uz_{max} in (miles/hr) × ft			
for u 1–6 miles/hr	610 (4)	483 (19)	2250 (69)
7–15 miles/hr	780 (4)	441 (14)	3732 (24)
16–21 miles/hr	417 (3)		
Mean	620 (11)	452 (34)	2632 (93)
Standard deviation	410	324	2950
$3w_0 R_0$ (miles/hr) × ft	390	68	720
$uz_{max} - 3w_0 R_0$	230	384	1912
$3 \times 10^{-4}\, Q_H$ cal/sec	249	213	1980

Note:

$$\left. \begin{array}{l} uz_{max} = u\Delta h \\ 3w_0 R_0 = 1{\cdot}5vd \end{array} \right\} \text{ in Holland's notation}$$

Figures in brackets are numbers of observations.

In comparison with the scatter of uz_{max} (represented by the standard deviation) the systematic variation with wind speed is small, but the mean values for each stack are clearly different from the product $3w_0R_0$. As the difference between the two could be expected to depend on the buoyancy of the plume, this difference was plotted against the rate of emission of heat, Q_H, and found to fit approximately the relation

$$uz_{max} - 3w_0R_0 = 3 \times 10^{-4}Q_H \qquad (6.2)$$

where z and R_0 are in ft., w_0 in miles/hr, and Q_H in cal/sec. As can be seen from Table 6.III the agreement is good for the X-10 pile and the Watts Bar Steam Plant, but poor for the X-10 steam plant, a result which Holland states could be due to a greater uncertainty in the values of Q_H and w_0 for this plant. In the original discussion it is also pointed out that uz_{max} is larger in lapse than in inversion conditions, and it is suggested that for these conditions the average value should be corrected by respectively adding or substracting ten to twenty per cent. Holland also gives values of plume rise calculated from the formula due to Bosanquet *et al.* These are consistently higher than the observed values, in contrast to the comparison with Bosanquet *et al.*'s own observations in Table 6.II where the formula tends to underestimate the incomplete rise of plume.

Thomas (1954) has reported observations at a steam plant, which are stated to refer to the maximum rise, and has analyzed them by the method used by Holland. In this case the coefficient multiplying Q_H in Eq. (6.2) was found to be $6 \cdot 0 \times 10^{-4}$, that is, exactly twice that found by Holland. Since the buoyancy term will often overshadow the efflux velocity term, this means that Thomas's empirical formula will often give nearly twice the plume rise obtained from Holland's formula.

The rise of the plume of cooling air discharged from the chimney of the Harwell reactor BEPO has been investigated by Stewart, Gale and Crooks (1954, 1958). Although again the maximum height of rise was not reached within the distances of observation from the chimney, the measurement are of unique interest in that the height of the invisible plume was accurately fixed by exploring the vertical distribution of the radioactive argon present in the effluent. Other details of the investigation are given in 6.3, and it suffices to note here that the internal diameter of the chimney exit was 3·5 m, and that the cooling air emerged at a height of 60 m, with a speed of 10 m/sec and a temperature of 50°C above the ambient air. Observations made when the lapse rate was close to the dry adiabatic were separated into three groups according to the wind speed at a height of 35 m. These are shown plotted against distance in Fig. 6.1, with calculated values derived from Bosanquet *et al.*'s formula for plume rise. At 700 m

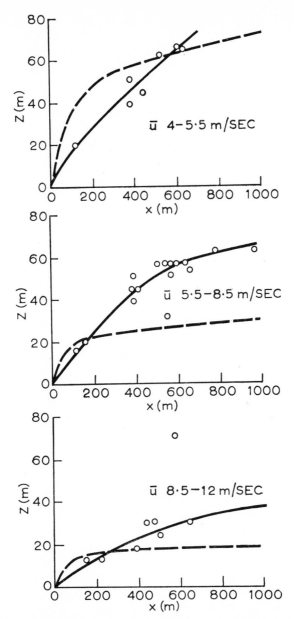

FIG. 6.1   Rise of the effluent plume (z) at distance x from the stack of the BEPO reactor at the Atomic Energy Research Establishment, Harwell.   Dotted curves represent values calculated from Bosanquet *et al.*'s formula.   (Stewart *et al.*, 1954) (*from A.E.R.E. HP/R* 1452, *United Kingdom Atomic Energy Authority*.   Copyright Reserved)

down-wind, near the maximum distance of observation, the agreement between the observed and calculated values is good at the lower wind speeds, but the calcaulated values are low at the higher wind speeds. Stewart *et al.*'s observations also included some in unstable and stable conditions. In both conditions there was a high degree of scatter in the results and, apart from noting the fact that the plume heights in unstable conditions were up to a hundred per cent higher than those at similar wind speeds in adiabatic conditions, no general conclusions were drawn.

Experiments on a small scale have been reported by Ball (1958), and compared with Sutton's and Priestley's formulae. Oil burners of the type used in orchard heating, with a heat output of about 10kW, were employed. The plume of smoke rising from a compact group of four of these burners was observed from a position some distance away across wind, and estimates were made of the average height reached by the centreline of the plume, over a period of two or three minutes at fixed distances of 30 ft and 60 ft down-wind. At greater distances the smoke became too diffuse for reliable estimates to be made. The results are shown in Fig. 6.2, with theoretical curves derived from Sutton's treatment and Priestley's 'first phase' treatment. Despite the scatter in the observations there is an unmistakable indication of a decrease of plume height with wind speed, and the average behaviour close to the source is evidently represented to a good approximation by both theories.

On the whole, however, the present position in the study of rising plumes is far from satisfactory. The available observations which have been summarized here are especially inadequate in the sense that most are known or suspected to refer to the incomplete ascent of a plume. The greatest down-wind distance at which measurements have been made is about 1000 m, in the case of the work reported by Stewart *et al.* In this case the plume was evidently still rising, and it is also suggested by observations of neutral balloons released in a chimney effluent (see Lucas, Spurr and Williams, 1957) that the plume from a power station may still be rising thousands of metres down-wind. Another difficulty is the wide scatter of the data, a feature which is particularly evident in the relation between the Oak Ridge measurements and wind speed. This is presumably a reflection of the fact that ultimately (i.e. in Priestley's second phase) the upward motion of the plume must become sensitively dependent on the lapse rate of temperature and the intensity of atmospheric turbulence, features which are notoriously variable in time and space. Finally, it should be remembered that the treatments and the observations have tended to be concerned with idealized conditions of airflow, and with average or normal meteorological conditions, whereas the severe air pollution problems

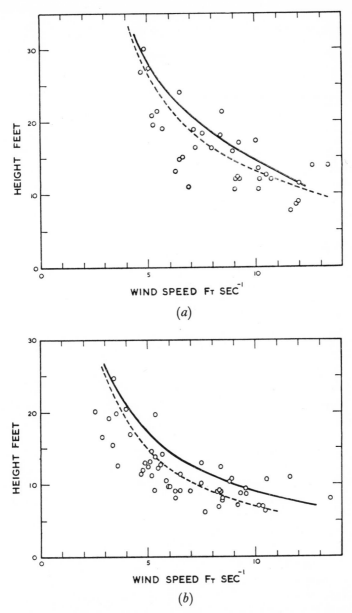

FIG. 6.2   Rise of smoke-plume at short distances from a hot source on the ground, as a function of wind speed. (a) 60 ft down-wind; (b) 30 ft down-wind; ——— Sutton's formula; – – – – Priestley's formula.   (Ball, 1958)

arise more especially in urban areas with abnormal conditions of light wind.

The net effect of wind speed on the concentration produced by a chimney plume

Both Holland (1953) and Best (1957) have drawn attention to the total effect of a change of wind speed on the feature which is of ultimate practical interest, namely the concentration of effluent at ground level.   There are now two opposing effects; on the one hand an increase of wind speed introduces further dilution of the effluent, while on the other hand the effective height of the source is reduced and the concentration at ground level tends to be increased.

Following Best's more general argument, with a slight change of notation, if the cross-wind and vertical spread of the plume are assumed to follow the same law of variation with distance, then from Eq. (5.24) say,

$$\chi_{max} = \frac{A}{u(H + z_{max})^2} \qquad (6.3)$$

where H is now the height at which the plume emerges and z_{max} is the complete rise of the plume.   For a given source strength, and a given ratio of cross-wind and vertical spread, A is a constant.   If z_{max} is now supposed to decrease with wind speed according to a simple power-law,

$$z_{max} = B/u^p \qquad (6.4)$$

it follows that the maximum concentration at ground-level will not decrease monotonically with wind speed, but will have a maximum value when

$$u^p = B(2p-1)/H \qquad (6.5)$$

and

$$z_{max} = H/(2p-1) \qquad (6.6)$$

This *absolute* maximum value, now taken with respect to both distance and wind speed, will be

$$\chi_{abs.\ max} = \frac{A}{B^{1/p}} \frac{1}{H^{(2-1/p)}} \frac{(2p-1)^{(2-1/p)}}{4p^2} \qquad (6.7)$$

It should be remembered that in the above equation a mean value of concentration over some interval of time is implied, and that no account is taken of the fluctuations of concentration about this value.   With this qualification the equation may be used either to estimate $\chi_{abs.\ max}$, or to estimate the minimum stack-height H which may be used if a specified threshold value of the effluent concentration is not to be exceeded.

Best (*loc. cit.*) has used Eq. (6.7) to evaluate the absolute maximum ground-level concentration for a range of conditions of plume release, using values of B and p according to Sutton, Bosanquet *et al.* and Holland, with the A in Eq. (6.3) as in Sutton's diffusion formula [Eq. (5.23)].

In Sutton's and Holland's formulae for plume rise the values of p are given explicitly as 3 and 1 respectively. As already noted Bosanquet *et al.*'s formula contains functions of u which are different in the terms representing efflux velocity and buoyancy, but numerical examples calculated by Best indicate that the over-all effective value of p is often near 2. The result emerges that for waste-heat outputs appropriate to power-stations of 2 and 2000 MW the values of $\chi_{\text{abs. max}}$ based on Sutton's and Bosanquet *et al.*'s formulae for z_{max} are remarkably similar. In other words Sutton's and Bosanquet *et al.*'s treatments both give much the same *minimum* value of $\bar{u}(H + z_{\text{max}})^2$. Similar comparison of Sutton's and Holland's formulae showed greater discrepancy. Of the three formulae, that due to Holland, better known as the Oak Ridge formula, has the merit of being simpler for evaluation, and it is noteworthy that the report of the Committee on Air Pollution (1954) recommended that the Oak Ridge version should be adopted for practical use. In this case Eq. (6.7) reduces to the simple form

$$\chi_{\text{max}} = A/4BH \qquad (6.8)$$

the values of A and B being defined through (6.3) and (6.4).

There is a different aspect of the influence of wind speed which has not so far been taken into account. The maximum concentration occurs when the vertical spread attains a certain magnitude in relation to the effective height of the source [see Eq. (5.21)]. Wind speed has commonly been assumed not to have any effect on the spread of a plume, in which case an increase of wind speed would be expected to reduce the distance at which the maximum concentration occurs, simply in accordance with the inverse influence on the effective height of the plumes. However, observations at heights in the range 150–1500 m, in fair weather, have shown a decrease of the intensity of the vertical component of turbulence (as represented by the standard deviation of wind inclination) with increase of wind speed (see 2.8). Since the rate of vertical spread of the plume will be in proportion to the intensity of turbulence, a reduction in effective height of source due to increase in wind speed might be offset to some extent by a decrease in vertical spread, and vice versa. The net effect has yet to be quantitatively assessed, and the possibility exists that the earlier considerations of the practical effect of changes in wind speed will require modification.

6.2   Deposition of airborne material

Deposition of airborne material on the ground may occur in three main ways, viz: general sedimentation of particles or droplets; retention at the ground surface by processes such as impaction and absorption, with subsequent downward turbulent transport to the *sink* thereby formed; and washout of the material in association with rain or other forms of precipitation.   In depleting the cloud of material, all three mechanisms ultimately hasten the reduction of airborne concentration otherwise occurring by diffusion, but the associated contamination of the ground surface and, in the case of sedimentation, the possibility of increasing the concentration close to a source, represent additional problems which may have practical importance.   As the rate of sedimentation of particulate material is determined by the terminal velocities of the particles it is clear that this mechanism can be important only for relatively large or dense particles.   The theoretical terminal velocity (v_s) in air of a spherical particle of diameter (d) 1 μ and density (ρ) 5 g/cc is 0·016 cm/sec.   For a Reynolds number (vd/ν) less than about 0·5, v_s is proportional to ρd^2.   Thus for very finely divided particulate material, as well as for gases and vapours, effective deposition must depend on the other processes.   The theoretical treatment of the effect of sedimentation and of collection at the ground, in proper association with the atmospheric diffusion process, is difficult, and practical applications have so far depended on relatively crude adaptations of the solutions for non-depositing materials.

Sedimentation

The simplest basis for the treatment of a sedimenting cloud or plume is to be found in the classical studies of Wilhelm Schmidt (1925).   In his treatment of the travel of spores and seeds Schmidt used a solution for constant eddy diffusivity, and allowed for the settling of the particles by in effect substituting $z + v_s x/u$ for z in the exponential term for the vertical distribution.   This is equivalent to adopting the distribution for the non-depositing cloud, and then tilting the cloud downwards at an angle to the horizontal of $\tan^{-1} v_s/\bar{u}$, the ground now being assumed to act as a permeable surface, and to retain all material passing through it.   The weakness of this method lies not so much in the implication that a particle which reaches the ground remains there, this is probably true for heavy particles at least, except in strong winds, but in the separation of the concurrent processes of diffusion and settling (strictly, the rate of diffusion should be regarded as a function of settling velocity—see 3.7).   Developments which retain this independence of diffusion and settling, but which use the later treatment of diffusion for an elevated source, and embody other refinements, have been given by Baron, Gerhard and Johnstone (1949) and by Csanady (1955, 1957, 1958).

Baron *et al.* take Sutton's expression for the distribution from a continuous point source at height H, as follows:

$$\chi(x, y, z) = \frac{Q}{\pi C_y C_z \bar{u} x^{2-n}} \exp\left\{\frac{-y^2}{C_y^2 x^{2-n}}\right\} \left[\exp\left\{-\frac{(z-H)^2}{C_z^2 x^{2-n}}\right\}\right.$$
$$\left. + \exp\left\{-\frac{(z+H)^2}{C_z^2 x^{2-n}}\right\}\right] \quad (6.9)$$

For the ground level distribution ($z = 0$) this equation reduces to Eq. (5.16). To allow for the settling of the plume z is replaced by $z + v_s x/\bar{u}$, and to allow for the progressive depletion of the plume at the ground the third exponential term, which in Sutton's treatment represents the effect of the *image* of the source in the ground is multiplied by a factor α (< 1). It is assumed that the local rate of deposition is $v_s \chi(x, y, 0)$, and α can then be evaluated by applying the continuity condition at distance x_1, i.e.

$$\int_0^{x_1} \int_{-\infty}^{+\infty} v_s \chi(x, y, 0) \, dy \, dx + \int_0^{\infty} \int_{-\infty}^{+\infty} \bar{u} \chi(x_1, y, z) \, dy, \, dz = Q \quad (6.10)$$

and solving numerically with certain approximations. The results are given in the form of theoretical curves showing deposition and axial concentration for a range of particle size. Apart from difficulties which arise in the interpretation of the quantity α, and in the subsequent development of the equations, the full implication of the z-coordinate transformation is not clear. In terms of *real* and *image* sources, the effects of which are represented respectively in the second and third exponential terms, the transformation is equivalent to tilting *both* plumes downward with increasing x. In view of these difficulties, and in the absence of confirmatory experimental data, the accuracy of the results is unknown.

Csanady's analysis begins (1955) with Sutton's equation, and is later (1957) applied to the general form, represented in Eq. (5.17), in terms of the standard deviations of the lateral and vertical distributions in the plume. Allowance for settling of the plume in these cases is made by replacing H by $H - v_s x/\bar{u}$, which represents downward and upward movement of the *real* and *image* sources respectively at rate v_s. It is assumed that the true rate of deposition is $v_s \chi(x, y, 0)$ but pointed out that this is not the same as assuming that all particles reaching the ground are retained, i.e. that the image term can be completely neglected. The latter assumption implies that the effective settling velocity of the particles is the sum of v_s and the rate of spread of the particles from the plume axis.   Csanady allows for deposition by retaining the image terms multiplied by a factor α_0, which is a complex function of distance.

The net result for the concentration and rate of deposition per unit area D at ground level is

$$\chi = \frac{D}{v_s} = \frac{Q(1+\alpha_0)}{2\pi\sigma_y\sigma_z\bar{u}} \exp\left\{-\frac{y^2}{2\sigma_y{}^2} - \frac{(H - v_s x/\bar{u})^2}{2\sigma_z{}^2}\right\} \qquad (6.11)$$

$$\alpha_0 = \frac{(H\bar{u} - v_s x)\sigma'_z/\sigma_z - \bar{u}H'}{2v_s + (H\bar{u} - v_s x)\sigma'_z/\sigma_z - \bar{u}H'} \qquad (6.12)$$

where the primes on σ_z and H denote differentiation with regard to x.   The inclusion of the H' term is to allow for thermal rise of the plume.   Csanady (1957) gives a chart for α_0 when $H' = 0$ (i.e. no thermal rise), and a chart for correcting the value when H' is finite.   In the same paper he discusses the validity of these equations and argues that in practice it should be valid to adopt them for the limits

$$0.25 \geqslant v_s/\bar{u} \geqslant 0.01$$

while in the last paper of the series (1958) he considers the application to the emission of dust with a continuous distribution of particle size, and the use of statistics of wind speed and direction in assessing the average deposition at a fixed position.

A formula for the estimation of the average rate of dust deposition has also been given by Bosanquet, Carey and Halton (1950).   In the present notation this is

$$D = 0.0032Qb \frac{(20H/x)^{m+2}}{H^2\Gamma(m)} \exp(-20H/x) \qquad (6.13)$$

where b is the fraction of time the wind is in a 45-degree sector (from the source) enclosing the ground position involved, and $m = 20v_s/\bar{u}$.   A chart for evaluation of the expression is given in the original paper.   Although the principle followed is evidently the usual one of tilting the plume downward to allow for the settling velocities, the details of the derivation are not given in the paper, and for these the reader is referred to unpublished appendices.   There are obvious similarities between the formula and an earlier formula given without formal proof by Bosanquet and Pearson (1936), and the numerical value of 20 presumably corresponds to $1/p$ in that equation, where p has the significance discussed in 5.3 and Table 5.II. The Bosanquet et al. formula is the only one for which experimental checks have so far been reported.   In the original paper the results of observations in three tests, at distances up to about 1500 m from the chimney, are given in the form of rates of deposition on the axes of the plumes. Values calculated from the formula compare reasonably well with the observations quoted, except close in to the source in one test, where the calculated value is much too low.

As already noted, the preceding formulae suffer from the disadvantage that they do not properly represent the *concurrent* processes of diffusive spread and settling. In the case of vertical spread this combination of processes can be formally represented by adding the term $v_s \chi(x, z)$ to the eddy flux, so that the two-dimensional equation (3.18) becomes

$$\bar{u} \frac{\partial \chi}{\partial x} = \frac{\partial}{\partial z} \left(K_z \frac{\partial \chi}{\partial z} \right) + v_s \frac{\partial \chi}{\partial z} \qquad (6.14)$$

Rounds (1955) has given a solution of this equation for a cross-wind line source of infinite extent, at height H, when v_s is of arbitrary magnitude, K_z is $ku_* z$ [see Eq. (3.8), which applies in neutral conditions of atmospheric stability], and for tractability $\bar{u}$ is taken proportional to z^α, as in Calder's form [Eq. (3.22)]. In the form given by Godson (1958), the expression for the concentration $\chi(x, 0)$ at ground level, hence for D/v_s, for a source emitting at rate Q per unit length, is

$$\frac{\chi(x, 0)}{Q} = \frac{\gamma}{H\bar{u}_H} \frac{\exp(-A/x)}{\Gamma(1-p)} \left(\frac{x}{A} \right)^{p-1} \qquad (6.15)$$

where

$$p = -\frac{v_s}{ku_* \gamma}, \quad \gamma = 1 + \alpha, \quad A = \frac{H^2 \bar{u}_H}{\gamma^2 K_H}$$

the subscript H referring to values at height H.

For conditions of stability other than neutral, with K_z say expressed as a power of z different from unity, a solution of Eq. (6.14) has yet to be given. Godson (1958) has put forward an approximate generalization of Rounds' solution by writing

$$K_z = \epsilon k u_* z \qquad (6.16)$$

and assigning to ϵ a value such that the mean K_z from the ground to the height of the source is equal to the mean value given by Deacon's Eq. (3.12). The result in Eq. (6.15) then applies approximately in non-neutral conditions when

$$p = -\frac{v_s}{\epsilon k u_* \gamma}, \quad \gamma = 1 + \alpha, \quad A = \frac{H\bar{u}_H}{\gamma^2 \epsilon k u_*} \qquad (6.17)$$

16—A.D.

The quantity ϵ is given by

$$\epsilon = \frac{2}{1+\beta} \left(\frac{z_0}{H}\right)^{1-\beta}$$

and the quantity α by equating the values of $\bar{u}_H/\bar{u}$ according to the simple power-law and Deacon's form in Eq. (3.12),

i.e. $$1+\alpha = \frac{1-(z_0/H)^{1-\beta}}{1/(2-\beta)-(z_0/H)^{1-\beta}}, \quad \beta \neq 1 \tag{6.18}$$

Godson has also adapted a form of Sutton's formula [similar to Eq. (6.9) but with distributions different from Gaussian]. Instead of the single *image* source usually invoked to represent the effect of the ground, Godson introduces a vertical line source extending below the surface, for the case of an elevated source of gaseous material. An expression for the strength of the line source is obtained by applying the continuity condition, Eq. (6.10), or alternatively by setting $\partial\chi/\partial z = 0$ at $z = 0$ (so expressing the fact that the net turbulent flux at $z = 0$ vanishes). The resulting expression can be solved numerically, and Godson shows that it leads to rates of deposition which are appreciably different from those given by Eq. (6.15), even though the two approaches are made equivalent by setting Sutton's n equal to zero, and taking values of K such that Sutton's formula satisfies the two-dimensional equation of diffusion.

The preceding considerations bring out certain features which in a qualitative sense are entirely expected on any rational grounds. Thus, a decrease in the rate of vertical spreading of the cloud leads to higher rates of deposition over a narrower band of down-wind distance. Also, decrease in the height of emission, or increase in particle size (i.e. in v_s), both bring higher rates of deposition closer in to the source. However, the verification of the finer points of the various solutions, and the assessment of their relative practical merits, will require observations of a critical nature. On the theoretical side also the methods require further attention, especially for very large and very small particles. In the former case the outstanding difficulty is that of taking into account the effect of the settling process on the rate of turbulent dispersion, an effect which is completely disregarded in the foregoing treatments. Reference has been made to this aspect in 3.7. Theoretically the turbulent spread of particles decreases with increasing v_s, especially for a cluster of particles as distinct from the average distribution formed by a continuous plume. The implication in the present context is that for large particles the maximum rate of deposition down-wind of a source will be even greater than originally supposed, especially in the instantaneous or short-term sense, but here again the quantitative indications require confirmatory observation.

Retention of small particles and gases at the ground

Turning to the case of the retention of very small particles at the ground surface, the first fundamentally important step was the recognition of the possibility that the rate of deposition might be greater than that provided by the settling of the particles at the appropriate terminal velocity. In the context of atmospheric diffusion this seems first to have been considered by Gregory (1945) in an analysis of data on the travel of spores. Gregory used observations made by Stepanov of the deposition of spores artificially released from a point source over a lawn. The deposits were collected on glass slides, coated with glycerine jelly, distributed on the ground around the source on arcs of radii up to 40 m. It was found that the observed variation of deposition with distance was consistent with a modification of Sutton's treatment of diffusion from a point source at ground-level. Gregory's modification amounts to assuming that the shape of the vertical distribution in the plume is unaltered, but that material is deposited at a rate proportional to the local ground-level concentration. As noted later this is equivalent to replacing the original source strength by an effective magnitude which decays exponentially with distance of travel down-wind. In his analysis Gregory introduces a deposition coefficient p which is equivalent to $D/\bar{u}\chi$ in the present notation. The ratio D/χ, which has the dimensions of velocity, and is the equivalent rate of settling of the cloud to give the same rate of deposition, was later given the name *deposition velocity* by Chamberlain (1953). Gregory's estimate of the value of p was 0·05, for wind speeds which were not clearly specified, but which were unlikely to be less than 1 m/sec, implying that the deposition velocity was about 5 cm/sec, whereas the terminal velocity of the spores employed was known to be about 1 cm/sec.

In view of the necessarily indirect nature of Gregory's estimate, the implication that in turbulent air light particles may be deposited more rapidly than in accordance with their terminal velocities was not decisive. Moreover, preliminary attempts to measure the deposition of *lycopodium* spores in the field (Chamberlain, 1953) failed to provide any support for the idea. However, for much smaller particles supporting evidence has since been quoted by Chamberlain (1961, see later in this section).

The most significant development of the concept of deposition velocity has occurred for the case of a vapour or gas which is strongly absorbed at the boundary. As Chamberlain (1953) has pointed out, it may then be valid to regard the boundary as a perfect *sink*, so that the pressure at the surface of the absorbed gas or vapour is effectively zero, and to calculate the distribution in the air by the familiar treatments of turbulent transport.   This is easily done in an approximate way in the so-called one-dimensional case, i.e. for a horizontally uniform distribution which is constant with time.   If, following the Reynolds analogy, it is assumed that the ratio of the vertical flux to the vertical gradient is the same for the gas or vapour as for momentum, and that the boundary conditions are the same, so that the vertical profiles of concentration and wind speed are entirely identical in shape, the ratio of flux to concentration at a given height will also be the same.   It then follows that the deposition velocity is

$$v_d = \frac{D}{\chi_z} = \frac{\tau}{\rho \bar{u}_z} = \frac{u_*^2}{\bar{u}_z} \qquad (6.19)$$

since τ and $\rho \bar{u}$ represent the flux and *concentration* of momentum.

Chamberlain and Chadwick (1953) have published an account of field experiments on the deposition of iodine-131.   In addition to measuring the deposition on grass, at several positions 15 or 20 m down-wind of the source, the concentrations in the air above were measured by drawing the air through caustic soda, and also the wind profile was measured for the determination of u_* through Eq. (3.5).   Release of the source of radio-iodine was maintained over a period of about twenty minutes in each case, and the velocity of deposition was actually obtained from the ratio of the *total deposit* per unit area to the *dosage* in the air, interpolated for the appropriate position.   Results given in the paper are summarized in the first five columns of Table 6.IV, and magnitudes of $u_*^2/\bar{u}$ computed from the specified values of u_* and $\bar{u}$ at a height of 1 m are given in the last column. The ratio of the velocity of deposition to $u_*^2/\bar{u}$ averages about 0·7.   The

Table 6.IV

Velocity of deposition of radioiodine on grass.   (After Chamberlain and Chadwick, 1953)

Trial	G.M.T.	Date	$\bar{u}$ at 1 m cm/sec	Velocity of deposition cm/sec	$\dfrac{u_*^2}{\bar{u}}$
1	1620	8.5.49	420	1·91 ± 0·32†	5·5
2	1500	8.8.50	372	2·65 ± 0·50	3·3
3	1100	3.7.51	442	1·79 ± 0·21	5·1
4	1500	8.8.51	310	3·75 ± 0·19	4·7
5	2000	8.8.51	138	1·72 ± 0·27	1·6

† Standard error derived from four determinations.

values of deposition velocity and $u_*^2/\bar{u}$ are not precisely comparable, since the former is based on concentrations measured at a height of 25 cm, and the latter on wind speeds at a height of 100 cm. A rough estimate of the correction required may be made by extrapolating from the wind speeds given for heights of 2 m and 1 m, and this suggests that the true average ratio would probably be near 0·5. It should also be remembered that the observations of iodine distribution refer to a position close to a source, where the concentration would not be independent of distance from the source as assumed in the above theoretical argument. With these features in mind, the agreement is surprisingly good, especially when finally it is noted that auxiliary wind-tunnel experiments, on the absorption of radio-iodine by filter paper and the leaves of growing plants exposed in a similar way, indicated that the leaves were not acting as a perfect sink, as was also assumed in the theoretical argument.

Further discussion of these experiments, and of two additional experiments in which the measurements were carried out at greater distances (50 and 100 m) down-wind of the source, has been given by Chamberlain (1961). In these additional experiments the iodine-131 was released as a vapour from the beginning, whereas in the preceding experiments it had been released in the form of an atomized solution in carbon tetrachloride. The consistency of the two sets of results is indicative that the persistence of droplets could not have been an important factor in the process of deposition. In the theoretical considerations of this later paper Chamberlain uses a more elaborate argument than that leading to Eq. (6.19). Assuming (following Sheppard, 1958) that the vertical flux is more correctly written as $(ku_*z + D)\partial\chi/\partial z$, where D is molecular diffusivity, the expression derived for the deposition velocity is

$$v_d = ku_*/\log_e (ku_*z_1D^{-1}) \qquad (6.20)$$

where z_1 is the reference height at which the concentration is measured. This expression gives values of v_d less (by a factor of approximately 2) than those according to Eq. (6.19), and so provides even closer agreement with the observations. However, in view of the earlier qualifications concerning the short distance of travel, and the actual adsorptive behaviour of leaves in the laboratory, the significance of this improved agreement is questionable.

Returning to the process of deposition of small particles as distinct from readily adsorbed vapours, it is recalled that results obtained with *lycopodium* spores failed to establish any substantial increase of deposition above that attributable to sedimentation. However, such an increase has since been demonstrated for the particles of sub-micron size which carry the fission products produced in high-altitude nuclear bomb explosions.   In this case Chamberlain (1961) concludes that particles of terminal velocity 10^{-4} cm/sec or less may have deposition velocities of the order of 10^{-2}– 10^{-1} cm/sec.   A complete understanding of the physical processes by which such deposition velocities are achieved has yet to be provided. Discussion of various processes has been given by Chamberlain (*loc. cit.*).

Reference has already been made to the consequences of assuming that the rate of deposition is proportional to the concentration at ground-level, and that the shape of the vertical distribution of material is unaltered by the process of deposition.   Since it is obviously reasonable to assume that lateral spread is unaffected by deposition the point can be conveniently analysed for the two-dimensional case, i.e. for the cross-wind line source of infinite extent, when the appropriate continuity condition [the two-dimensional form of Eq. (6.10)] is

$$\int_0^{x_1} \chi(x, 0)v_d \, dx = Q - \int_0^{\infty} \chi(x_1, z)\bar{u} \, dz \qquad (6.21)$$

The integral on the right-hand side can be regarded as an effective (reduced) source strength $Q(x)$ and on differentiating (6.21)

$$\frac{dQ(x)}{dx} = -\chi(x, 0)v_d$$

With the assumption that the shape of the vertical distribution is unaltered by deposition $\chi(x, 0)$ is proportional to $Q(x)$, and therefore $Q(x)$ diminishes exponentially.   Chamberlain (1953) has given the result appropriate to Sutton's formula for a ground-level source, i.e.

$$Q(x) = Q(0) \exp\left[-\frac{4v_d x^{n/2}}{n\bar{u}\pi^{1/2}C_z} \right] \qquad (6.22)$$

In this case the concentration from a depositing source is given by replacing Q in Sutton's formula by $Q(x)$, and the rate of deposition per unit area is equal to this concentration (at ground level) multiplied by the deposition velocity.   For the case of an elevated source at height H Chamberlain has given the following expression for the effective source strength $Q(x)$ to be used with Sutton's formula [Eq. (5.16)]

$$\log_e \frac{Q(x)}{Q(0)} = \frac{b}{m} \left(-\frac{e^{-\xi}}{\xi^m} + \Gamma_\infty(-m+1) - \Gamma_\xi(-m+1) \right) \qquad (6.23)$$

where $m = \dfrac{n}{4-2n}, \quad b = \dfrac{2v_d}{\bar{u}C_z\pi^{1/2}(2-n)} \left(\dfrac{h}{C_z}\right)^{2m}, \quad \xi = \dfrac{H^2}{x^{2-n}C_z^2}$

The assumption that the form of the vertical distribution is unaffected by the deposition process is an approximation which may be expected to be reasonable only when the deposition velocity is small compared with the rate of vertical spread of the cloud of airborne material. Thus, in neutral conditions in the lower atmosphere, when for a ground level source $d\sigma_z/dt \simeq 0\cdot1\bar{u}$, it should be permissible to use the above formulae for deposition velocities up to say $0\cdot01\bar{u}$. The latter value is similar to the approximate theoretical deposition velocity for grassland which is acting as a perfect sink [$u_* \simeq 50$ cm/sec, for $\bar{u} = 500$ cm/sec over long grass, in Eq. (6.19)].

In more precise terms, however, a deposition which is provided solely by downward turbulent transport requires an increase of concentration with height near the ground, and this offers a possible method of indirectly measuring deposition. At long distance from a source the rate of deposition $v_d\chi$ may also be written as $K\partial\chi/\partial z$, and with a K at a height of 2 m 5×10^3 cm²/sec, typical of long grass, and the 'perfect sink' value of 5 cm/sec for v_d, the quantity $\dfrac{1}{\chi}\dfrac{\partial\chi}{\partial z}$ would be 10^{-3}. Thus, even with such a substantial rate of deposition, the increase in concentration between, say, 1·5 and 2·5 m would only be about ten per cent. This means that measurement of the vertical profile of concentration would have to be made with great precision, and a satisfactory demonstration of measuring deposition in this way has yet to be given. On the other hand it should be remembered that the convenient *direct* measurement using artificial collecting surfaces, such as filter papers on flat plates lying on the ground, gives deposition rates which are of questionable relevance to natural surfaces. For sub-micron particles a small number of experiments by Megaw and Chadwick (see Chamberlain, 1961) indicated deposition velocities on grass three times those on horizontal surfaces of filter papers.

Washout in rain

The collection of suspended particles by falling drops is an aspect of the problem of impaction which has received particular attention, both with regard to the physics of aerosols [see Green and Lane (1957)] and the coalescence and growth of raindrops [see Mason (1957)]. In general only a fraction of the particles in the path of a drop will collide with it, and the remainder will be swept clear in the stream-lines around the drop. A theory of the process has been developed mainly by Langmuir, and this specifies the above fraction as a function of the terminal velocities of the raindrop and particle. The fraction is alternatively referred to as *collection* efficiency or *collision* efficiency; the latter term is to be preferred since collision does not necessarily imply retention of the particle.

Disregarding for the moment the distinction between collection and collision the rate of removal of particles from the air by rain drops may be expressed in an approximate way as follows.   Considering drops of radius between s and $s + ds$, let the number per unit volume of air be N_s and the terminal velocity V_s.   Since the number of drops which fall through a cube of unit volume in one second is $N_s V_s$, then the proportion of the unit volume which is actually swept is $\pi s^2 N_s V_s$, and if the collection efficiency for particles of radius r is $E_{(r,s)}$, the fraction of particles removed in one second by the whole spectrum of raindrops will be

$$\Lambda = \int_{s=0}^{s=\text{max}} \pi s^2 N_s V_s E_{(r,s)} \; ds \qquad (6.24)$$

Using Langmuir's theoretical values for $E_{(r,s)}$ and Best's tables of the size distribution of raindrops for various rates of rainfall, Chamberlain (1953) has evaluated (6.24) and produced a series of curves giving the *washout coefficient* Λ as a function of rate of rainfall for various terminal velocities of particles (see Fig. 6.3).

Having estimated the values of Λ the modification of airborne concentration and rate of deposition follow simply for the case of wind speed constant with height.   As before the analysis can be carried out for a cross-wind line source of infinite extent, and the same result applied to a point source.   At any position x down-wind of the source the rate of deposition per unit area, by rain which has fallen through the whole depth of the particulate cloud, will be

$$\Lambda \int_0^\infty \chi(x, z) \; dz = \frac{\Lambda Q(x)}{\bar{u}} = -\frac{dQ(x)}{dx} \qquad (6.25)$$

where $Q(x)$ is the reduced source strength effective at distance x.   From this

$$Q(x) = Q(0) \exp - \frac{\Lambda x}{\bar{u}} \qquad (6.26)$$

where $Q(0)$ is the original source strength, and substitution of $Q(x)$ for Q in the diffusion formulae gives the airborne concentration as modified by washout.   For further details the papers by Chamberlain (1953) and U.S. Weather Bureau (1955) should be consulted.

The result for depletion by rain is similar in form to that given in Eq. (6.22) for *dry* deposition at a rate proportional to the ground-level concentration, but in the present case the derivation is less open to question since it is reasonable to assume that the collection of particles by rain falling right through the plume would not affect the *shape* of the vertical distribution.

Field measurements of the washout of *lycopodium* spores released from an artificial source have been described by May (1958), and the results

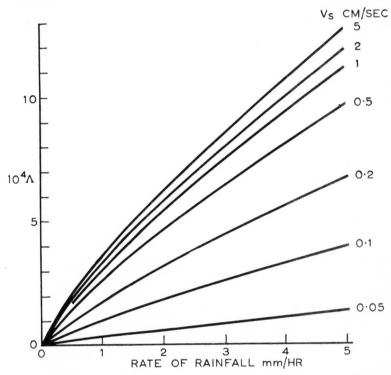

FIG. 6.3   Washout coefficient, Eq (6.24), as a function of rate of rainfall, for particles of terminal velocity v_s as indicated. (Chamberlain, 1953) (from *A.E.R.E. HP/R* 1261, *United Kingdom Atomic Energy Authority.* Copyright Reserved)

used to determine the effective value of Λ for comparison with the theoretical values calculated by Chamberlain.   Spores marked with a radioactive tracer were released from a height of 3·3 m, and the rain was collected in small basins set out around the source on a circle of 10 m radius. After a number of experiments had been carried out it was realized that the assumption of negligible deposition by processes other than washout was unjustified, and thereafter *dry* deposition was also measured in adjacent basins shielded from rain.   The results of the subsequent five experiments are summarized in Table 6.V, with the theoretical values of Λ.   May discusses the errors which might have arisen from the electrostatic collection of the spores by raindrops, and also from the fact that the smallest raindrops affecting the plume of *lycopodium* spores probably did not reach the ground within the sampling distance.   Estimates are given of the possible total error due to these two effects, in terms of wind speed and rate of rainfall, as a percentage of the theoretical value of Λ.   For the conditions in Table 6.V these possible errors range from 0 to +20 per cent.   Furthermore, Langmuir's values of collection efficiency, as used in calculating Λ, neglect the finite size of the particles.   A correction for this on lines suggested by Mason (1957, Appendix A) increases the theoretical value of Λ by an amount which depends on the rate of rainfall, but which is always less than 10 per cent for the cases in Table 6.V.   From these data May concludes that the calculated values are substantially correct.

Table 6.V

Measurements of washout coefficient Λ for *lycopodium* spores.   (After May, 1958)

Date	$\bar{u}$ cm/sec	Rate of rainfall mm/hr	Type of rain	Λ 10^{-4}/sec	
				Observed	Theoretical
16.8.56	320	3·91	frontal	10·2	9·7
27.9.56	543	1·12	frontal	4·2	3·6
25.10.56	845	14·1	heavy frontal	30·8	26·8
11.12.56	334	1·01	frontal	3·2	3·2
31.12.56	332	3·64	continuous rain of showery type	8·9	9·2

Although these experiments represent only a very limited test of the theoretical understanding of the washout process, they suggest that useful estimates of deposition in rain may now be made.   The relatively powerful depositing action of rain, in relation to the dry deposition of particles, is immediately obvious from the following simple example.   If material is distributed uniformly with height over a height h, then in Eq. (6.25) $Q(x) = \bar{u}h\chi$, where χ is the concentration of material in the air at the distance x.   The rate of deposition is $\Lambda h\chi$, and the equivalent deposition velocity as defined in the previous section is Λh.   For particles of terminal velocity 0·1 cm/sec, and rainfall at a rate of say 1 mm/hr, Fig. 6.3 gives $\Lambda = 10^{-4}$, and with $h = 1000$ m this would correspond to a deposition velocity of 10 cm/sec.

It should, however, be borne in mind that calculations made on the above lines may lead to over-estimation of the washout, since they assume collision to imply collection.   This clearly may not be true if, for example, there is a high interfacial tension between the water and the material of the particle, that is, if the particle is not easily wettable.   In this case, on collision the particle may fail to penetrate the surface of the drop, and may immediately or subsequently become detached.   A discussion of this feature, including the results of some field measurements with non-wettable and wettable fluorescent powders, has been given by McCully *et al.* (1956). Particles were released in rain from an aircraft flying across wind at a height of 500 ft, and the rain was collected on a cross-wind line 4000 ft down-wind.   The results indicated that the collection efficiencies for the non-wettable dust were well below the theoretical collision efficiencies.   A theoretical discussion by Pemberton (1961) has suggested that in the case of particles of median diameter 2μ, and a rainfall intensity of 2·5 mm/hr, the fraction of non-wettable material removed in a few hours may be only about 25 per cent, as compared with about 90 per cent of wettable material.

The above considerations have referred only to the collection of *particulate* materials by raindrops *falling through* the cloud of material.   In a discussion of the washout of radioactive debris Greenfield (1957) has considered the mechanism of the collection of very small particles by cloud droplets, and the subsequent deposition of these droplets as rain, but his calculations for assumed typical conditions indicate that the bulk of the deposition was provided by the direct process of collection of particles by falling drops.   This was presumably a consequence of assuming a mean particle diameter of 2μ, but it would appear (see Chamberlain 1961) that effective washout of sub-micron particles must depend on other processes such as the one suggested by Greenfield.   Another feature which presents some difficulty is the washout of soluble gases and vapours.   Chamberlain (1953, 1961) has treated this problem on the assumption that the vapour pressure of gas dissolved in the drop can be neglected, in which case the analysis is exactly analogous to that of the evaporation of falling drops into a vapour-free atmosphere.   Using results obtained for the latter by Ranz and Marshall, an expression is derived for the effective value of the washout coefficient.   It is noteworthy that the values for sulphur dioxide and iodine vapour lie mostly between those for the washout of particles of terminal velocity 0·05 and 0·1 cm/sec.   No critical test of these results has yet been possible; the most that can be said is that the theoretical effect is consistent in order of magnitude with the amounts of SO_2 collected in the deposit gauges used in air pollution surveys in Britain.

6.3   Studies of the distribution of effluent in the neighbourhood of single stacks

Several surveys of the distribution of effluent concentration down-wind of single chimney stacks are now on record, with some analysis in terms of diffusion formulae and meteorological data.   The data from those which appear to be concerned with relatively straightforward circumstances of weather and terrain are now examined in close comparison and in relation to the previous discussions of diffusion in idealized conditions.   Hewson's (1945) well-known study is concerned with the special effects arising in a deep valley, with stable stratification of the air, and this is more appropriately discussed in a later section.

The nature of the surveys

Thomas, Hill and Abersold (1949) have analysed data derived from long records of the concentration of sulphur dioxide at positions in the vicinity of four smelters in the United States.   In each case records were available from one or more automatic sampling instruments.   Localities, stack heights and distances of recorders from the site were as follows:

	Stack height (ft)	Sampling distance (miles)
Selby, California	146, later 605	2·6
Tacoma, Washington	573	2·9
Garfield, Utah	407	5, 6, 6·5
El Paso, Texas	225, 400	0·13, 0·43, 1·5

Concentrations averaged over 30 min were provided by all recorders, while the Tacoma and El Paso recorders also gave values averaged over 1–2 min.

Gosline's (1952) analysis is concerned with a planned survey of the concentration of oxides of nitrogen emitted from a stack 80 ft high.   The measurements were made by stationing a mobile direct-reading gas-analyser at one of two standard distances from the stack (400 or 800 ft), on a bearing which was judged to be directly down-wind.   Readings were taken every ten seconds for some period while the wind remained in the required general direction.

The extensive field studies at the Atomic Energy Commission site at Oak Ridge, Tennessee (Holland, 1953), included a special three-day series of measurements of the gamma-radiation, and the total gamma- and beta-radiation, at ground positions 1·0, 3·1 and 5·4 miles down-wind of the reactor.   Averages over periods of fifteen minutes were obtained, and used to derive the intensity due to beta-radiation alone, this being converted to local concentration of argon-41.   There were difficulties in making proper allowance for background levels of radiation, and in converting from radiation intensity to local concentration, which precluded a high degree of accuracy in the final results.

Stewart, Gale and Crooks (1954, 1958) have described a detailed survey of the distribution of the argon-41 contained in the cooling air of the BEPO reactor at Harwell, using a differential method in order to obtain the response to beta-radiation alone.   A direct calibration was performed by enclosing the instrument in a large balloon containing chimney gases in known dilution.   The survey was particularly notable in that, by using an array of instruments mounted at intervals on the cable of a captive balloon, the vertical distribution was explored at distances up to 1000 m down-wind of the stack.   At ground level the measurements covered a range of 10,000 m down-wind, but those beyond 3000 m had to be based on the gamma-radiation measurements alone, since the beta-radiation was then too low for satisfactory measurements.   In the vertical surveys the sampling duration was usually between 10 and 30 min, though a few shorter observations were made, while in the ground surveys the sampling time ranged from 15 to 60 min.

The distribution of sulphur dioxide from a power station chimney has also been considered in studies by Stratmann (1956) and by Meade and Pasquill (1958).   Stratmann's data were obtained from surveys with a mobile sampler, operated at selected positions within a radius of about 4000 m from the stack.   The measurements referred to an average over about ten minutes, and were obtained between 8 a.m. and 2 p.m. on fifty-seven days.   Meade and Pasquill used long-term average data for a relatively isolated power station at Staythorpe, Nottinghamshire.   In this case the measurements were made with the 'lead peroxide candle' method widely used in routine surveys, in which the candle is exposed for one month and then analysed for the amount of sulphur dioxide absorbed.   Data for fourteen observing sites, averaged over a five-month season (May–September or November–March) were available for six seasons during the period November 1951 to September 1954.

The original analysis in terms of current diffusion formulae

The main analysis for all except the last of the studies enumerated above was based on one or both of the formulae developed by Sutton [Eq. (5.16)] and Bosanquet and Pearson [Eq. (5.15)].   In the case of Meade and Pasquill's analysis an integrated form of Eq. (5.17) was used, and the final results converted into the terms of Eq. (5.16) for comparison with previous data.

Thomas *et al.*'s method of analysis was to derive values of the quantity $\chi \bar{u}/Q$ from the records of average concentration over 30-min or 1–2-min periods. Values of $(\chi \bar{u}/Q)_{max}$ and of $(\chi_{max} \bar{u}/Q)$, which were not usually the same, were extracted over periods of one month or one year. These were compared with the peak values derived from the formulae by plotting the data on a composite diagram, with scales adjusted so that in effect $\chi \bar{u} H^2/Q$ was plotted against $x/H^{2/(2-n)}$. Curves appropriate to the formulae were constructed for the nominal values $p = C_z \equiv q = C_y = 0.05$ or 0.07, and $n = 0, 0.25, 0.33$ or 0.50. The units of C are presumably $m^{n/2}$, whereas p and q are non-dimensional. From the general trend of the points Thomas *et al.* were able to conclude that there was good agreement between the data for tall stacks and Eq. (5.15), or Eq. (5.16) with $n = 0$. For the short stacks it was concluded that values of n up to 0.25, with values of C in the range 0.05 to 0.10 would be required to fit the data. These results, although obviously useful in a practical way, need to be considered with some caution as far as verification of the formulae is concerned. In the first place the fitting in the above way to Eq. (5.16) does not determine a unique combination of n, C_y and C_z, and it is clear that equivalent fitting to the data could be achieved by using larger values of C with larger values of n. Secondly, the theoretical estimates apparently do not include any correction for the effective height of the plume as distinct from the height of release. As the winds on the occasions of the maximum concentration were usually fairly light it might be expected that plume-rise would be an important factor. This is strongly supported by Thomas *et al.*'s statement that on occasions of low wind speed the maximum value of χ did not always yield the maximum value of $\chi \bar{u}/Q$, which implies that increase of χ as a result of smaller dilution was being offset by increased rise of the plume (the combined effect of these two variations has already been discussed in 6.1).

Gosline also used nominal values of the diffusion parameters in comparing the formulae with average (presumed axial) concentration over thirty minutes or more. The data were grouped into neutral and unstable categories, and also according as the wind speed was in the ranges 0–6, 7–13 miles/hr. It was concluded that reasonable agreement could be obtained. The conclusion is again subject to some reservation in the sense that no correction for plume rise is stated, and it is noteworthy that at the 400 ft distance in 'unstable' conditions the concentration for the higher wind speed group was *greater* than that for the lower wind speed group. This could have arisen from a decrease of plume rise with increase of wind speed, though other factors may have been involved.

Holland used nominal values of n (Eq. 5.16) as stated by Sutton for neutral, moderate inversion and strong inversion conditions of temperature gradient, with values of C calculated from Sutton's analytical expression for this parameter, using locally observed values of gustiness $[(\overline{u'^2})^{1/2}/u]$. The value of C_z was presumably taken equal to C_y. The values of n and C_y were

	$T_{183\ ft} - T_{5\ ft}(°F)$	n	$C_y(m^{n/2})$
Neutral	-1 and 0	0·25	0·095–0·14
Moderate inversion	$+1$ to $+5$	0·33	0·052–0·077
Strong inversion	> 6	0·50	0·029–0·074

the range of C_y being associated with a range of wind speeds.   Using estimates of plume rise based on the direct observations discussed in 6.1, and correcting for radioactive decay, values of axial concentration of argon-41 were calculated from Eq. (5.16) for each of the three distances involved, and for a suitable range of wind speeds.   From an integrated (with respect to y) form of Eq. (5.16) values of the average concentration over a 20° arc centred on the plume axis were also calculated.   The concentrations derived from the argon measurements (in wind directions within $\pm 10°$ of the bearing of the reactor) were plotted against wind speed and compared with the theoretical axial and average values.   From the rather scattered data Holland concluded that the theoretical axial value was a rough upper limit to the 15-min average concentrations, and that the theoretical averages over a 20° arc approximated to the observations within the error of measurement.   Detailed examination of the graphical comparisons show that the biggest discrepancy occurs in conditions of strong inversion, when appreciable concentrations were observed, while the theoretical calculations indicated that the plume had not spread to ground level to any effective extent.   This appearance of effluent at ground level, at a distance which is within twenty times the effective plume height as estimated by Holland, is in contrast with the findings over less rugged terrain at Brookhaven (see Smith, 1951b), where in inversion conditions no oil-smoke was ever found at ground level within a distance of 350 times the height of release.

The procedure followed by Stewart *et al.* in analysing their surveys of argon-41 was to make use of the observations to calculate effective values of C_y and C_z in Eq. (5.16), assuming n to have the value $\frac{1}{4}$ in all conditions. This had the advantage of simplifying the analysis considerably without, in their view, introducing discrepancies which were likely to be significant in relation to the scatter of the experimental data.   When the cross-wind and vertical distributions of concentrations were observed, values of the parameters were obtained directly from the basic relationships for σ_y and σ_z

(see Table 5.II).   Otherwise they were obtained indirectly from Eq. (5.10); e.g. in the case of the conditions near the plume height C_z was obtained directly from the observation of the vertical distribution and hence of σ_z. Substitution of this value of σ_z with the observed value of axial concentration in Eq. (5.10) (with $y = z = 0$) then gave σ_y and hence C_y.   The values of C_y and C_z show an interesting pattern in relation to position.   From the vertical surveys, within 1000 m of the stack, the average C_z ranges from $0 \cdot 11$ m$^{1/8}$ in inversion conditions to $0 \cdot 25$ in lapse conditions, and is systematically greater than C_y.   This difference is considered not to be a reflection of a difference in the vertical and lateral structure of atmospheric turbulence, but to be a result of variations in plume rise associated with fluctuations in wind speed.   On the other hand the values of C_y and C_z obtained from the ground surveys at 6000 to 10,000 m are very similar, and near to $0 \cdot 16$ in neutral and lapse conditions.   However, C_y from ground surveys shows a systematic increase as the perimeter of the site buildings is approached, evidently due to the turbulence generated by the buildings, and close in to the perimeter an average value of $0 \cdot 46$ m$^{1/8}$ is attained in adiabatic and lapse conditions.

In Stratmann's analysis of the sulphur dioxide surveys the average values in the so-called zone of influence, a 45° sector on the down-wind side of the stack, were determined, and the increase above background as observed on the up-wind side was compared with theoretical values derived from Sutton's formula.   Parameters suggested by Thomas *et al.*'s analysis, i.e. $n = 0$, $C_y = C_z = 0 \cdot 07$ were employed.   The agreement was considered to be good, but clearly an equally good agreement could have been obtained with, say, $n = \frac{1}{4}$ and larger values of C_y and C_z.   Since $\sigma_z = \frac{1}{\sqrt{2}} C_z x^{1-n/2}$ it follows that to produce the same vertical spread at a given distance alternative combinations of n and C must satisfy the relation

$$C_2/C_1 = x^{(n_2-n_1)/2}$$

Thus, working in units of metres, similar agreement would be obtained at $x = 2000$ m (near the position of maximum ground-level concentration in Stratmann's data) by

$$n = 0 \quad C = 0 \cdot 07$$
or $$n = \tfrac{1}{4} \quad C = (2000)^{1/8} \times 0 \cdot 07 = 0 \cdot 18 \text{ m}^{1/8}$$

It is also to be remembered that Stratmann's analysis presumably used a plume height equal to the stack height, and on that account the implied values of C are probably too low.   Meade and Pasquill's analysis of the long-term distribution of sulphur dioxide around a power station, certain special aspects of which are discussed in detail below, gave equivalent values of C_z (with $n=\frac{1}{4}$) equal to 0·21 m$^{1/8}$ in winter and 0·35 m$^{1/8}$ in summer.

The long-term distribution around a single source

Routine surveys of sulphur dioxide in the neighbourhood of power stations in the United Kingdom provide estimates of average concentration over appreciable periods. As a result of the wide variations in wind direction which normally occur, the long-term average concentration at any site, due to the power station itself, may be quite low. As this concentration is superimposed on a background which may be relatively high and variable, the examination of the influence of the power station, in relation say to the amount of coal consumed, becomes a very difficult matter. The analysis carried out by Meade and Pasquill (1958) was aimed particularly at overcoming this difficulty.

The mathematical basis was provided by the general form of equation for distribution from an elevated point source, assuming Gaussian distribution in the vertical and lateral sections of the plume [Eq. (5.17)]. As the plume may normally be assumed to be instantaneously narrow in the lateral (cross-wind) direction the integral of concentration around an arc of radius x from the source is to a sufficient approximation equal to $\int_{-\infty}^{+\infty} \chi(x, y) \, dy$. From this it immediately follows that the long-term average concentration on a circle of radius x is

$$\bar{\chi} \,(\text{circle}) = \frac{1}{2\pi x} g(H, x) \frac{Q}{\bar{u}} \tag{6.27}$$

where

$$g(H, x) = \frac{\sqrt{2}}{\sigma_z \sqrt{\pi}} \exp \frac{(-H^2)}{(2\sigma_z{}^2)} \tag{6.28}$$

and the long-term average concentration over an octant of the circle

$$\bar{\chi} \,(\text{octant}) = \frac{f(\theta)}{12\cdot 5} \cdot \frac{1}{2\pi x} \cdot g(H, x) \frac{Q}{\bar{u}} \tag{6.29}$$

where $f(\theta)$ is the percentage frequency of wind directions affecting the octant. With a background pollution of concentration a the total pollution p averaged over any octant around a power station discharging sulphur dioxide at a rate S should therefore be related to wind speed, wind direction and rate of discharge, by the form

$$p = a + b\frac{f(\theta)S}{\bar{u}} \tag{6.30}$$

17—A.D.

When S is in tons of sulphur dioxide per month, $\bar{u}$ in knots, x in yards, p and a in mg SO_3 per day per 100 cm² (as derived from the lead-peroxide candle measurement), and using an empirical relationship between concentration of SO_2 and deposition on the lead peroxide candle.

$$b = \frac{8\cdot5 \times 10^3}{x} g(H, x) \tag{6.31}$$

with $g(H, x)$ still in c.g.s. units.

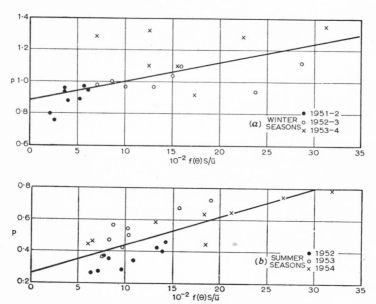

Fig. 6.4   Average sulphur pollution, p, at 1500 yd from a power station, as a function of wind direction frequency, $f(\theta)$, wind speed $\bar{u}$, and rate of emission, S. (a) Winter season; (b) Summer season. p is in mg SO_3 per month, $\bar{u}$ in knots, $f(\theta)$ is the percentage frequency in a prescribed octant.   The lines represent the equations

(a) $p = 0\cdot89 + 1\cdot16 \times 10^{-4} f(\theta)S/\bar{u}$
(b) $p = 0\cdot26 + 1\cdot76 \times 10^{-4} f(\theta)S/\bar{u}$

(Meade and Pasquill, 1958)

From routine wind records, obtained at the meteorological station nearest to the power station at Staythorpe, values of $f(\theta)/\bar{u}$ were obtained for octants 0–45°, 45–90° etc., for each of the six five-month seasons. Pollution diagrams showing average values over each season, at fourteen observation sites, were constructed.   Smooth isopleths of pollution were drawn in, and used to estimate the average pollution p on each 45° arc at a radius x of 1500 yds.   With these data, and the estimated rates of emission of sulphur dioxide, the relation between p and $f(\theta)S/\bar{u}$ was as shown in Fig. 6.4.   An approximation to a linear relation, as in Eq. (6.29), is fairly obvious, despite the scatter of the points, and the regression equations obtained by the method of least squares (shown on the diagrams) were found to be statistically significant.   Moreover, the values of the constant a were in good agreement with the seasonal background values of pollution observed at Staythorpe before the power station began to function.   From the variations in S from year to year it was fairly evident that the systematic relation between p and $f(\theta)S/\bar{u}$ could be taken to indicate a systematic effect of changes in output, and in this sense the analysis was able to demonstrate a feature which had apparently been unrecognizable from the overall average pollution in the area around the power station.

Empirical generalizations

The analyses which have just been discussed show that in a broad sense the diffusion formulae represented in Eq. (5.15) and (5.16) may be employed to represent the observed distributions from stack sources, provided some empirical adjustment of the parameters is allowed.   For some purposes, it would be just as useful, and less open to misinterpretation, to represent the data in a more directly empirical way.   Furthermore, by expressing the data in the basic form of the dimensions of vertical and cross-wind spread, either directly from the observations, or by interpretation of incomplete measurements through a general form such as Eq. (5.10), the results will be more easily and directly correlated with the developments which are emerging from the application of the statistical ideas of turbulence (see concluding discussion of Chapter 4).

Estimates of the vertical spread are obtainable from the existing data as follows.   Thomas *et al.* conclude that for tall stacks the effective values of the parameters in Eq. (5.16) are $n=0$, $C_y = C_z = 0.05$.   Using the corresponding relation between σ and x (Table 5.II) an effective value of σ_z may be derived, and this may be said to be most reliable for distances of the order of those at which the ground concentration was near the maximum (with respect to distance).   The conclusion regarding shorter stacks may be similarly used.   Gosline's paper gives averaged data for the near-axial ground-level concentrations at distances of five and ten stack-heights (his Table E), from the ratio of which, assuming as an approximation $\sigma_y \propto x$ and $\sigma_z \propto x$ over this range, σ_z/x may easily be derived through Eq. (5.17) with $y=0$.   Stratmann's data include some examples of the variation of axial concentration with distance from the stack, showing a maximum value in neutral conditions at about 2000 m down-wind.   This fact can be used with Eq. (5.21) to obtain an estimate of σ_z.   Estimates from the previous three sources of data will be *underestimates* in the sense that the actual stack heights are involved, in the absence of data on the plume rise.   Holland's analysis justifies effective values of C_z ($= C_y$ in his application), with nominal values of n and empirical estimates of H, from which σ_z may again be deduced using the implied relation between σ and x (Table 5.II).   From Stewart *et al.*'s paper direct observations are available for distances up to 1000 m, and beyond this, up to 10,000 m, effective values of C_z are given (for $n = \frac{1}{4}$), from which again σ_z can be deduced.   The Staythorpe analysis (Fig. 6.4) gives values of b in Eq. (6.30), which may be used with a graphical solution of Eq. (6.28) to derive σ_z at a distance of 1500 yd.

Table 6.VI

Collected data on the magnitude of σ_z/x for plumes from stacks, at distances < 10,000 m

Source of data	Assumed plume height (m)	Order of distance (m)	Conditions	$100\sigma_z/x$
Thomas *et al.* (1949)	100–200†	3000	Unspecified	3
Gosline (1952)	25†	200	Unstable	10
			Neutral	7
Holland (1953)	100	2000	Neutral	3
		5000	Mod. inversion	0·5
Stewart *et al.* (1954)	120	1000	Lapse	9‡
			Neutral	7‡
			Inversion	4‡
		8000	Lapse and neutral	4
			Inversion	< 1
Stratmann (1956)	150†	2000	Neutral	5
Meade and Pasquill (1958)	150	1500	Summer average	11
			Winter average	6

† Figures are *stack* heights, hence for these in particular the value of σ_z/x may be underestimates.

‡ These are measured values, the remainder have all been estimated indirectly as indicated in the text.

Estimates of σ_z/x which have now been obtained in the above manner are collected in Table 6.VI.   It is to be remembered that as regards the indirect estimates the only important assumptions concerning the character of the diffusion are that the distribution in the vertical is Gaussian, and, in the interpretation of Thomas *et al*'s and Holland's data, that lateral and vertical spread are equal.   Apart from the large value from Stewart *et al.*'s data in inversion conditions, at relatively short range, the data on σ_z/x and its variation with stability are consistent in a broad way. The suggestion that the vertical spread immediately down-wind of the stack contains an important contribution from the fluctuations in the plume rise has already been mentioned. While the smaller value estimated indirectly for longer range in inversion conditions is in keeping with this suggestion, it is also possible that this diminution is partly a consequence of an absence of low-frequency components, which has been found (2.2) to be a feature of the spectrum of the vertical component in inversion conditions. There is also some suggestion that in general σ_z/x tends to be smaller at the greater distances, as indeed would be expected except perhaps in unstable conditions, but the effect is probably not worth considering when using the results to form rough estimates of the effect of elevated releases on concentration at ground-level. In this context the overall indication is that in the absence of vigorous convection, or marked stabilization of the atmosphere, the values of σ_z/x for plumes at a height of 100–200 m, for distances of a few thousand metres, will be near 0·05. Evidently this may be expected to be doubled at least in convective conditions, and to be reduced to less than 0·01 in conditions of moderate stabilization. In round figures, the distances in effective stack-heights at which maximum ground-level concentration would be expected [see Eq. (5.21)] are therefore $\leqslant 7$, 15 and $\geqslant 70$ in convective, neutral and stable conditions respectively.

Additional data in stable conditions, and at longer distances from the chimney, have been summarized by Leonard (1959). These are based on unpublished observations of plumes of sulphur dioxide from large power plants. Cloud dimensions are given from which the equivalent values of σ_z/x at 1, 10 and 100 km are respectively 0·04, 0·007 and 0·001, in fair agreement with the general trend already indicated.

It is of interest to compare the foregoing generalizations with the independent tentative estimates of vertical spread quoted in 5.4 (Fig. 5.7). Assuming a Gaussian distribution, the values of h given there should be compared with approximately twice the present values of σ_z. In neutral and stable conditions the respective values are reasonably consistent, but those in Fig. 5.7 show a much greater increase as a result of instability in the atmosphere.

Stewart *et al.*'s suggestion that the total vertical spread was due partly to fluctuations in plume rise arose principally from the fact that their observations would otherwise have implied a rate of turbulent mixing in the vertical greater than that in the cross-wind direction, which is contrary to usual assumption. Independent support for their conclusion is provided by the smoke-puff observations, referred to in 4.4, which were carried out on an airfield immediately south of the site over which the stack effluent was measured. From a large number of day-time observations, taken in three series during 1951 and 1952 the following averages were obtained for the ratio (evaluated over 15-min periods) of the standard deviation of the fluctuations of direction (θ) and inclination (ϕ) of the wind.

Height above ground (ft)   100   300   500
$\sigma_\theta/\sigma_\phi$ 1·50   1·25   1·06

The BEPO plume was usually at a height between 300 and 500 ft, and for these heights the smoke-puff data indicate that the vertical component of turbulence was somewhat less than the cross-wind component.

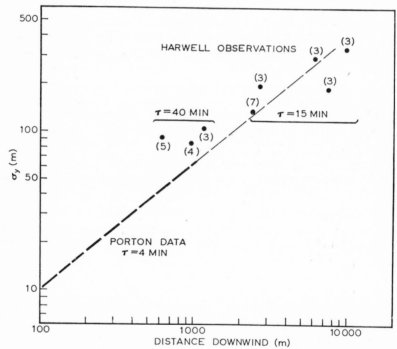

Fig. 6.5   Standard deviation (σ_y) of the cross-wind distribution produced by the BEPO plume at ground level, compared with Porton data for a ground level source in neutral conditions over open downland. The points are averages for the number of observations given in parentheses (from Stewart *et al.*, 1954). τ is the time of release or of sampling

The variation of cross-wind spread with distance down-wind of the BEPO chimney at Harwell, where the site buildings extended to about 400 m down-wind of the stack, is shown in Fig. 6.5. The points are averages for groups of values, at the same or similar distances, obtained from Tables V and VIII of Stewart *et al.*'s 1954 paper. Plotted on the same diagram is a line representing the general variation observed in the early Porton observations in neutral conditions over open country (namely $\sigma_y \simeq 10$ m at $x = 100$ m, and $\sigma_y \propto x^{0.8}$ in the range 100–1000 m, see 4.3). At 1000 m the Harwell results are above the Porton line, but at 10,000 m they show a tendency to be below the extrapolated position of the line. Interpretation of these results is complicated by the different sampling times (τ) involved, but since the Porton data on cross-wind spread from 4-min and 30-min releases indicated an increase due to the greater sampling time of only 30 per cent, it seems unlikely that the disposition of the data on Fig. 6.5 could be entirely due to variation in sampling time. The most reasonable conclusion is that already drawn by Stewart *et al.*, namely that the results show the influence of the turbulence generated by the site buildings, to a degree which decreases with increasing distance from the site.

The data on sulphur dioxide plumes in stable conditions, summarized by Leonard (1959), include lateral dimensions for which the equivalent values of σ_y at 1, 10 and 100 km are roughly 70, 500 and 3500 m. These values are very similar to those for neutral conditions in Fig. 6.5, but are only about one-third of those in Fig. 4.12 ($2Y_0 = 4.3\sigma_y$ for a Gaussian distribution), which refer mainly to day-time unstable conditions.

With regard to the absolute magnitude of effluent concentration, the main interest is in the maximum value. According to the idealized treatment in 5.3 [see Eq. (5.22) *et seq.*] $\chi_{max}\bar{u}H^2/Q$ depends only on the ratio of the vertical and cross-wind spread, and on the shape assumed for the distributions. On the customary assumption of Gaussian shape

$$\frac{\chi_{max}\bar{u}H^2}{Q} = \frac{2\sigma_z}{e\pi\sigma_y} = \frac{0.24\sigma_z}{\sigma_y}$$

and σ_z/σ_y may usually be expected to be less than 1.0, though not greatly so except in stable conditions or at long distances from the source. Chamberlain (1961a) has collected the values of $\chi_{max}\bar{u}H^2/Q$ provided by the data of Thomas *et al.*, Holland, and Stewart *et al.*, and by the oil-fog measurements at the Brookhaven National Laboratory, reported by M. E. Smith. The values range from 0.02 to 0.28, but the low values (from Thomas *et al.*'s data) are attributed to the use of release-height for H (instead of actual plume-height), and to the possibility that the measured concentrations (at fixed positions) would not necessarily represent the maxima with respect to distance. With this qualification it appears that the observations of $\chi_{max}\bar{u}H^2/Q$ are roughly as indicated by the idealized treatment.

Data on the fluctuation of effluent concentration have been collected by Gifford (1960). These show that at ground-level near tall stacks the short-term peak concentration may be 50–100 times the value averaged over tens of minutes. With increasing distance from the stack the peak-to-average ratio decreases systematically to values in the region of two at about 50 stack-heights. This trend in the ratio is consistent with the theoretical lower limit of unity [see Eq. (3.96) *et seq.*].

6.4   Factors in the incidence of air pollution

In view of the many complexities which arise in the dispersion of windborne material, quantitative discussion has been largely confined to relatively simple circumstances. In particular these are the circumstances involving a well-defined source, and conditions of flat terrain and steady airflow which lead to a simple distribution of material, of the sort which has been discussed in previous chapters. It is obvious from experience, however, that the development of the most intolerable levels of air pollution is determined by meteorological and topographical conditions in which the air movement is inadequate for effective dispersal.

Persistent anticyclones, with their very light winds and subsidence inversions, present specially effective conditions for the accumulation of atmospheric pollutants. An account of some well-known examples has been given by Jalu (1955), and a brief discussion of those occurring in Great Britain in the winter of 1958–9 has been given by Meade (1959). Forecasting the imminence of severe widespread pollution is largely a matter of forecasting the incidence of stagnating anticyclones. This has been recognized, for example, in an experimental system of forecasting 'air pollution potential', which has been formulated and tested in a preliminary way by Niemeyer (1960) for areas in the eastern U.S.A.

In stagnant conditions, whether these arise from the weather situation or from sheltering, the concepts and formulae which have been presented earlier obviously cannot be applied. Furthermore, there are many other conditions in which an application in detail or with implied precision would be unwarranted. Nevertheless, there are aspects for which qualitative or semi-quantitative discussion may be useful, and some of these are now considered.

The effects of surface features

The geometry of the surface over which the air-stream passes may be important either in causing a deflection of the air-stream, or in modifying the rate of mixing and consequent dilution of the material carried with it.

Appreciable deflection and disturbance of the air-stream may occur in the vicinity of a chimney stack, with undesirable effects on the plume of discharged effluent, and with the object of avoiding these certain rules are adopted by engineers when considering the siting of a stack.   A general account in relation to power station chimneys has been given by Hawkins and Nonhebel (1955).   There are two separate effects, known as *down-draught* and *down-wash*, both of which may be effective in bringing effluent near to ground level before substantial dilution can occur.   Down-draught, which is simply the downward trend of the flow on the lee side of the building carrying the chimney, is usually considered to affect a height equal to about twice the height of the building, and a down-wind distance of about six times the height of the building.   Down-wash is produced by the vortices shed from the lee side of the chimney itself, and as a result effluent may be drawn down into the regions affected by down-draught, and so deflected to ground-level.   The measures for eliminating or minimizing these effects are firstly the choice of a sufficiently high chimney, and secondly the imparting of sufficiently large efflux velocity to the effluent.   The well-known rule is that the chimney should extend to two and a half times the height of adjacent buildings, and for efflux velocity the figures quoted by Hawkins and Nonhebel correspond to approximately 1·3 times the wind velocity.

An increase in the spread and dilution of a pollutant may be expected as a result of the incidence of additional surface irregularities, especially when the wind is strong and vigorous turbulence is generated locally.   The statistical effect arising from trees, small buildings and variations in contour has been well demonstrated in Cramer's observations of turbulence and diffusion at Round Hill Observatory, Massachusetts.   These observations have already been noted in 4.3, and the point to be recalled here is that the cross-wind spread of a plume and the standard deviation σ_A of the wind direction fall into line with the smaller magnitudes of diffusion and turbulence observed over the much smoother site at O'Neill, Nebraska.   Cramer (1957) has tabulated estimates of σ_A, and of the corresponding quantity for wind inclination, σ_E, for these two sites.   The ratio of σ_A on the rough site to that on the smooth site shows a fairly distinct trend with atmospheric stability, with a maximum of about 1·8 in near-neutral and moderately stable conditions and a reduction to about 1·2 in extremely unstable or extremely stable conditions.   This is as might be expected, namely an additional contribution of mechanical turbulence from the rougher features, but of an extent which is less noticeable when the turbulence is already augmented by thermal instability or when it is greatly suppressed by thermal stability.   The values of σ_E are also higher on the rougher site, but by a factor in the region of only 1·3 for most conditions, and about 1·5 in the extremely stable conditions, though the latter figure is of doubtful significance in view of the small values of σ_E over both sites in such conditions.

Local increases in mechanical turbulence will presumably appear in the turbulence spectrum at wave-numbers related to the size and nature of the surface irregularities. The proportionate increase in the total intensity of turbulence should therefore depend on the sampling duration (see 1.4) of the observations. Cramer's data are for a sampling duration of about ten minutes. The diffusion data quoted by Cramer make it clear that the additional mechanical turbulence then involved was fully effective in increasing the diffusion at distances in the region of 100 m. This increase would not however be expected to persist indefinitely with increasing distance from the source, when the spread of the plume becomes large compared with the disturbances produced by the surface irregularities.

For the case of more rugged terrain a survey of the air-flow in relation to dispersion processes was carried out at the United States Atomic Energy Commission site at Oak Ridge, Tennessee (Holland, 1953). This site is located in a large valley running roughly NE–SW in the Southern Appalachians. The observations display typical régimes of valley and drainage winds, and include some interesting data on the vertical motions, as derived from double-theodolite observations on neutral balloons. A special analysis was made of flights with trajectories either down-valley or across-valley, in the latter case over a ridge rising 100 m above the release station to a parallel valley some 2 km to the north-west. During the day, and especially in very unstable conditions, the ridge appeared not to have any mechanical effect comparable with the thermal eddies of large vertical extent, which alone would quickly disperse any material released in the valley. At the other extreme, on clear nights with light winds, vertical flow within the valley was obviously dominated by the circulations generated by cooling of the valley slopes, and was virtually isolated from the general airflow above the ridge.

Some quantitative indications of diffusion in a valley are provided by Hewson's (1945) well-known systematic study of the effluent of the Trail smelter in the Columbia River valley, about seven miles north of the boundary between Canada and U.S.A. In this area the valley is about 2500 ft deep and 1–3 miles wide, and the 400-ft stacks of the plant are located on a site about 100 ft above the valley floor. Effluent from these stacks had apparently caused damage to crops and vegetation at distant points downstream. Continuous records of the concentration of sulphur dioxide in the air at places up to over thirty miles downstream had shown a striking diurnal pattern.   In the spring and summer especially, pronounced maxima tended to occur at about 8 a.m. at all places simultaneously. Moreover, the examples quoted by Hewson show maximum concentrations of similar magnitude at the different places, despite the fact that these places were at distances in the ratio of 4:1 and more.

The special investigations carried out by Hewson included an exploration of the three-dimensional distribution of effluent in the valley, using sampling instruments based on the ground and also some carried aloft by aeroplane or kite-balloon, and a detailed study of the air motion in the valley by numerous pilot balloon observations.   From these Hewson was able to build up the following general picture of the travel and dispersion of the effluent plume.   In the early morning hours, with light winds, the plume rose to about 500 ft above the tops of the stacks, and thereafter moved downstream within the valley without any appreciable spreading.   Apparently any air movements and circulations generated by the drainage of cold air down the valley side had no important effect, and the plume remained undisturbed until it became entrained in the cross-valley circulation set up by the heating of the valley sides.   As a result of this, effluent appeared relatively suddenly and at much the same time at all positions along a considerable length of the valley floor.   It also seemed possible that these 'fumigations' could result merely from the spread upwards of the usual convective régime, which occurs irrespective of the ground configuration.   Such fumigations have been recognized as a characteristic diurnal effect over more level country (see 6.1).   In any case it seemed that the result was to disperse the plume rapidly throughout the cross section of the valley, giving similar concentrations at various places, the approximately exponential reduction thereafter being a consequence of the progressive ventilation of the valley by the air-stream above.

As regards the build-up of the concentrations in stagnant conditions of airflow no detailed information is given in Hewson's paper, but there is a brief reference to such occurrences in winter, when high concentrations could persist for several days.   Some indication of the isolation of the air in a deep valley, from the dispersing action of the wind above it, is given by meteorological and smoke plume observations reported by Hosler, Pack and Harris (1959) for the United States reactor site at Shippingport, Pennsylvania.   It appeared that material released at the site was fairly rapidly spread within the valley, but that even in the absence of stable conditions it could be confined within the valley walls for periods as long as thirty minutes unless strong winds existed above.   The tragic incidents in the Meuse valley in Belgium in 1930, and at Donora in the U.S.A. in 1948, were clearly examples in which confinement of the valley air and pollutants was further protracted by the existence of a strong temperature inversion.

Urban distribution of pollution

A well-known systematic investigation of the distribution of smoke and sulphur. dioxide in and around a large industrial city was conducted in Leicester in 1937–9, under the supervision of the Atmospheric Pollution Research Committee of the Department of Scientific and Industrial Research. Over the period of three years regular daily and monthly observations were carried out with a variety of instruments at twelve stations, including one in the centre of the city and two in the surrounding country. For a description of these, and for full details of the results and analyses, the official report (Department of Scientific and Industrial Research, 1945) should be consulted; in the present context only a brief indication of the principal results and conclusions can be given.

The characteristic pattern of pollution was revealed in composite maps which were drawn of the concentrations of *native* Leicester smoke or sulphur dioxide. Native values were obtained by subtracting from the total pollution estimates of the *country* pollution, based on the measurements on the outskirts of the city. This process was carried out for summer and winter averages at each station, discriminated according to the eight standard wind directions, and according as the wind speed was in specified ranges. ,For each season and wind-speed range it was thus possible to draw eight contour maps representing the distribution, and the composite maps were obtained by, in effect, superimposing the individual maps with the wind directions coincident. This led to smoother distributions of pollution, which it appeared could be adequately represented by circular isopleths. With decrease of the level of pollution the centres of the isopleths were displaced systematically down-wind, but only slightly, and indeed one of the conclusions which was particularly emphasized was that the point of maximum concentration was never more than about half a mile from the centre of the city. For an area with a uniform distribution of equal sources it would be expected that pollution would build up steadily to a maximum at the down-wind edge, and the result at Leicester was evidently mainly a reflection of the concentration of sources of pollution in the central districts. Lucas (1958) has carried out calculations which demonstrate this effect for a hypothetical distribution of sources in which the effective rate of emission rises linearly from the perimeter to the centre of the city.

Two other features of the Leicester results are noteworthy here. The first is that the decrease of concentration with increase of wind speed was usually less than according to the theoretical inverse law, the departure from this being the more marked the greater the instability as indicated by temperature gradient, with the effect that in the most unstable conditions the variation with wind speed was of little practical consequence. In the light of the current ideas it seems that there were probably two main contributions to this effect: a decrease of wind speed would mean that the rise of effluent due to efflux velocity and buoyancy would be greater, as discussed in 6.1, and this elevating of the effective source would lead to lower concentrations; furthermore, the effect of stability on vertical mixing near the ground is known to be more clearly related to the Richardson Number, rather than to lapse rate alone (see 3.1), and this means that in unstable conditions any tendency for a reduction of wind speed to produce higher concentrations would be opposed by an increase in effective instability.   In general the total effect of wind speed on averaged levels of pollution will be complicated by the distribution of the main sources with height, and their variation with time of day.   This may explain why other estimates of the effect of wind speed on urban pollution give widely conflicting results (see World Meteorological Organisation 1958).

More recent measurements of urban air pollution have been reported by Pemberton *et al.* (1959), for Sheffield, which has more variations in elevation than Leicester.   A correlation with elevation is shown quite clearly in the average results for two winter seasons, in that the levels of both smoke and sulphur dioxide decrease almost tenfold with increase in elevation from 40 to 300 metres.   It is argued that this variation was partly a physical consequence of elevation, though it is also concluded that for smoke especially the most important factor was the variation in the local density of population.

The larger-scale distribution of air pollution

The measurement of *country* pollution, on the outskirts of Leicester, shows values which were correlated with wind direction, and evidently due to major sources of industrial pollution such as Birmingham and London, respectively 35 and 90 miles away.   More detailed analysis showed that the level of contribution from these distant sources was approximately proportional to the population of the district, and inversely proportional to the square of the distance.   The simplest interpretation, namely that the results are consistent with the maintenance of vertical and lateral spreading of the material, with a linear relation between spread and distances downwind, needs careful consideration for the distances involved.   In particular it should be remembered that the more recent basic investigations demonstrate that the vertical spread of material over long distances may be slowed up, or even effectively halted, at quite low heights in the atmosphere.

Furthermore, washout and deposition of the material would in theory contribute to the diminution of concentration with distance, and results discussed below suggest that this could have been important.

The quantitative relation between the average level of air pollution over a large area and the quantities of pollutant released has been examined by Meetham (1950, 1954), using the measurements made by local authorities over many years in Britain. These were used to draw maps of the average distribution of deposited matter, and of sulphur dioxide and smoke concentration in the surface air, and the results examined in relation to published estimates of the release of pollutants from the burning and other utilization of coal. The essential data and the results which follow are summarized in Table 6.VII. The data show two apparently inconsistent

Table 6.VII

Balance of smoke and sulphur dioxide pollution over Britain. (After Meetham, 1950, 1954)

	Smoke	SO_2	
Rate of emission m	2·3	5·0	10^6 tons/yr
Rate of deposition d (from deposit gauge)	0·8	0·7	10^6 tons/yr
Concentration in surface air	5·7	4·1	10^{-11} g/cc
Rate of loss over coast l	1·5	1·1†	10^6 tons/yr
Rate of deposition d		3·9†	10^6 tons/yr
'Life-time' t'‡	28	$8\frac{3}{4}$	hr
Effective height of diffusion $\bar{h}$	——212——		m

Notes:

   † From Eq. (6.32)

   ‡ From Eq. (6.33) with $\overline{T} = 12\frac{1}{2}$ hr

features, firstly that a release of sulphur dioxide approximately double that of smoke produces a concentration of sulphur dioxide which is actually *less* than the concentration of smoke, secondly that the measured deposition of sulphur dioxide is also less than that of smoke. Meetham points out that the measurements of deposition, which were made with standard deposit gauges, are very questionable, but accepting the results for smoke, as more representative than those for sulphur dioxide, he infers a deposition rate for the latter. The essence of the argument is as follows, where m, d, l are the total rates of emission, deposition and loss by blowing out to sea, and $\bar{\chi}_0$ is the average concentration in the surface air. For smoke

$$m_1 - d_1 = l_1$$

and it is assumed that

$$l_1 = a(\bar{\chi}_0)_1$$

where a is a constant.   For sulphur dioxide, only m_2 and $(\bar{\chi}_0)_2$ are accepted as known, but with the assumption of the same proportionality between l_2 and $(\bar{\chi}_0)_2$

$$d_2 = m_2 - l_2 = m_2 - l_1 \frac{(\bar{\chi}_0)_2}{(\bar{\chi}_0)_1} \qquad (6.32)$$

and d_2 and l_2 can be calculated.   The ratio d/m for sulphur dioxide is approximately double that for smoke, possibly implying that sulphur dioxide is removed more rapidly by deposition processes.   Moreover, the calculated deposition rate for sulphur dioxide is much greater than that measured by the deposit gauges, possibly implying that the mechanism of its deposition to natural surfaces is much more effective than is that to the deposit gauge.

Assuming that the reduction of material in the air as a result of deposition follows an exponential law, i.e.

$$l/m = \exp\left(-\frac{\bar{T}}{t'}\right) \qquad (6.33)$$

where $\bar{T}$ is the average time the material travels over the land and t' is a time-constant, Meetham estimates $\bar{T}$ from a consideration of average wind speed and distribution of wind direction over the country, and so obtains estimates of t', the 'life-time' in the air.   Meetham's calculations also involve the quantity $\bar{h}$, defined by

$$\int_0^\infty \bar{\chi}\,\mathrm{d}z = \bar{h}\bar{\chi}_0$$

which may be described as an effective height of vertical diffusion.   This quantity is not essential to the derivation of the 'life-time' t', but is derived by Meetham in the process, using a relation

$$l\bar{T} = \bar{\chi}_0 A\bar{h} \qquad (6.34)$$

which states that the amount blown out to sea in the time taken for the smoke to reach the coast is equal to the total average amount of material which exists in the atmosphere over the land at any instant (A = area of land).   From this equation Meetham obtains $\bar{h} = 212$ m.   Meetham has also expressed l in terms of the concentration at the coast and from this the implied value of $\bar{h}$ is approximately 170 m.

Meetham's data for sulphur dioxide have been used by Chamberlain (1961) to obtain the deposition velocity v_d ($=d/\chi_0$). Using the indirect estimate of d, i.e. $3\cdot9 \times 10^6$ tons/yr Chamberlain obtains $v_d = 1\cdot8$ cm/sec. The quantities v_d and t' in Eq. (6.33) are related in a complex way. For rough considerations, let the vertical spread from an elementary cross-wind line source, emitting at a total rate δm, be assumed to occur rapidly throughout the layer up to the height $\bar{h}$, with thereafter no further vertical spread. Concentration will be effectively constant with height, and

$$\frac{d}{dt}(\bar{h}\chi_0) = -v_d\chi_0$$

$$(\chi_0)_t = (\chi_0)_{t=0} \exp\left\{\frac{-v_d t}{h}\right\} \tag{6.35}$$

If t is the time taken for the material from the elementary source to reach the coast, this means that the rate of loss δl over the coast is given by

$$\frac{\delta l}{\delta m} = \frac{(\chi_0)_t}{(\chi_0)_{t=0}} = \exp\left\{\frac{-v_d t}{h}\right\} \tag{6.36}$$

The magnitude of l/m, appropriate to the whole country, will depend on the distribution of the elementary sources. If this is assumed to be uniform, then since $\int_0^{x'} \exp(-x)\,dx > x' \exp(-x'/2)$ it follows that

$$l/m > \exp\left(\frac{-v_d \bar{T}}{h}\right)$$

where $\bar{T}$ is the *average* time for the material to reach the coast, as used in Eq. (6.33). Accordingly

$$t' > \frac{\bar{h}}{v_d}$$

or, using Meetham's value of t' ($8\frac{3}{4}$ hr) and Chamberlain's value of v_d ($1\cdot8$ cm/sec),

$$\bar{h} < 570 \text{ m}$$

which is broadly consistent with Meetham's estimate.

The foregoing analysis has been based on measurements which may not be representative of the whole area concerned. Moreover, the measurements of the deposition of smoke, on which these interesting results finally hinge, are admitted to be the most questionable of the direct observations. Nothing more than a very rough fitting of the data and ideas can therefore

be expected at the present stage.   Even so, it may be thought that the estimates of $\bar{h}$, the effective height of diffusion, are rather small, bearing in
mind the evidence already discussed in 4.6 and 6.3 for the rate of vertical
spread.   It should be remembered, however, that an estimate of $\bar{h}$ based
as above on long-term averages of concentration and deposition is effectively being derived from a long-term average of $1/h$, and could therefore
be considerably less than the actual long-term average of h.   The results
have the further interest that the implied deposition velocity for sulphur
dioxide is greater than that for smoke by a factor $(3\cdot9/0\cdot8) \times (5\cdot7/4\cdot1)$, i.e.
approximately 7, whereas according to the deposit gauge it is only $1\cdot2$ times
that for smoke.   The suggestion that direct absorption of sulphur dioxide
at the surface of vegetation and other surfaces is an important mechanism
(Meetham, 1952) is supported by the fact that the apparent deposition
velocity is $1\cdot8$ cm/sec, since this is a reasonable fraction of values which
would be expected (see 6.2 and Table 6.IV) over a rough surface acting as
a perfect sink.   Finally, assuming that the deposit gauge gives essentially
the amount of sulphur dioxide washed out by rain, it is noteworthy that the
correct order of magnitude of washout is given by Chamberlain's (1961)
treatment referred to in 6.2.

Magnitude of pollution in smog

Some interesting indications of the magnitude of sulphur dioxide pollution in smog, in relation to the amount of sulphur dioxide emitted, are
provided by the case of the London smog of December 1952.   A brief
account of the general meteorological aspects of the situation has been
given by Absalom (1954).   The main feature was the maintenance over the
country of the almost stationary central region of an anticylcone, from
midnight 4–5 December to 9 December.   With little cloud, and very light
or calm surface winds, dense fog persisted over the London Basin throughout the period.   No information was available on the local temperature
inversion, but at Cardington 50 miles away, where there was little fog, the
inversion extended to heights between 500 and 1000 ft.   Wilkins (1954)
has described the data of mean daily air pollution which were available
from sites in the Greater London area.   The apparatus used at these sites
was the type in which air is drawn successively through an inverted funnel,
a filter paper, a solution of hydrogen peroxide and a flow-meter, and is
assumed to collect gaseous sulphur dioxide, and particles and droplets less
than about 20 μ in diameter.   Wilkins's figures show that the average
sulphur dioxide concentration, for the eleven sites which operated regularly,
rose from the normal figure of just over $0\cdot1$ parts per million (by volume)

18—A.D.

in the 24 hours ending noon on 4 December, to near 0·7 p.p.m. during the period ending noon on 8 December.

Assuming that the measured concentrations applied to the whole volume of air over the area of Greater London (500 square miles) to the top of the fog layer (approximately 300 ft), Wilkins pointed out that the rate of increase of approximately 0·2 p.p.m. per day was equivalent to a total daily accumulation of sulphur dioxide of about 70 tons.   This is only about 4 per cent of the estimated daily release of sulphur dioxide, implying a rate of removal of sulphur dioxide which may at first might seem surprising.   A rough analysis of the rate of removal of sulphur dioxide on this occasion has also been made by Meetham in his 1954 paper.   Meetham assumes a steady state, in which a sulphur dioxide concentration of 2·1 mg/cu.m (equivalent to 0·74 p.p.m. by volume) is maintained, with a release which in the absence of decay would be equivalent to an increase of concentration of 8·0 mg/cu.m per day, in the air to a height of 500 ft over an area of 450 square miles.   If the released sulphur dioxide decays exponentially with time after release, with a time-constant t' as in Eq. (6.33), these figures mean simply that $t' = 2·1/8·0$ days or approximately 6 hrs.   Alternatively, using the form in Eq. (6.35), with $h = 500$ ft, this corresponds to a deposition velocity v_d of 0·7 cm/sec.   Wilkins's figures give a maximum average concentration (0·7 p.p.m.) only $\frac{1}{8}$ of the increase which would have occurred per day had there been no decay.   The difference between this and the value of $\frac{1}{4}$ in Meetham's analysis is due mainly to taking $\bar{h} = 300$ ft, but also partly to taking a release of 2000 tons of sulphur dioxide per day and an area of 500 square miles, compared with respective figures of 1400 and 450 adopted by Meetham.   Again assuming a steady state $t' = 3$ hr and $v_d = 0·8$ cm/sec. In the model of diffusion and decay implied in these calculations the value of v_d is independent of the assumed value of h, and the small discrepancy between the values obtained from Meetham's and Wilkins's data is due to the differences in the estimates of the amount of sulphur dioxide released and of the area affected.

It is interesting to consider to what extent the apparent loss of sulphur dioxide could be due to a slow advection of air over the area.   For rough calculation assume the material to be released into a box 20 miles square and 500 ft (0·1 mile) high.   If the loss of sulphur dioxide is ascribed entirely to a flow of air out of the down-wind side of the box, the wind speed required would be 20/0·1 times the deposition velocities evaluated above, i.e. approximately 1·5 m/sec or 5 ft/sec.   According to data quoted by Lucas (1958) daily average surface wind speeds at Kew Observatory were 0·5, 0·5, 0·6 and 1·6 ft/sec for the period 5–8 December, i.e. an overall average of 0·8 ft/sec.   Unless, therefore, the height of the layer into which the sulphur dioxide was mixed has been seriously underestimated, it seems that clearance by advection could not have been an important factor.   A similar conclusion follows from the calculations made by Lucas (1958), using an integrated form of a simple line-source equation, in which vertical spread of the cloud is assumed to increase linearly with distance.

The considerable variations in space which are evident in the measurement of sulphur dioxide concentration, and the lack of precise knowledge about the air movement and mixing process, are such that the inferences drawn above must be regarded as very rough.   There is, however, a fairly convincing indication that in the presence of smog there is a mechanism, other than advection, which removes sulphur dioxide as affectively as it appears to be removed by deposition in normal weather.   Solution of the sulphur dioxide in fog droplets which are subsequently deposited is an obvious possibility to be considered, but the quantitative acceptability of this mechanism has yet to be demonstrated.

6.5   The travel and deposition of radioactive material

Some reference to the diffusion of radioactive gases has already been made in an earlier section of this chapter, but only with regard to the effects in the relatively close proximity of an atomic energy installation.   The outstanding aspect of the problems of radioactive contamination of the atmosphere and ground is the fact that minute quantities of material are capable of producing significant levels of contamination over enormous distances and areas.   For example, the total ground contamination of north-west England as a result of the accident at the Windscale Works in 1957 amounted to only a fraction of one gram of iodine-131.   There are features of medium-range and long-range diffusion involved in the latter incident, and in the travel of debris from atomic bombs, which it will be of interest to review here, but before dealing with these specific items some brief reference to the question of 'fall-out' is desirable.

Considerations of fall-out arise in connection with the short-term and long-term biological hazards presented by the debris of nuclear weapons. It is usual to recognize three stages, namely close-in, intermediate and delayed fall-out, which occur in periods of hours, weeks and months or years respectively (see Committee on Meteorological Aspects of the Effects of Atomic Radiation, 1956).   The last two stages are obviously influenced to a great degree by diffusion processes, but the action of these processes in close-in fall-out is probably of much less importance.   In this case (see Kellogg, Rapp and Greenfield, 1957, for a general account of the physical and meteorological aspects of close-in fall-out), the ground distribution of the relatively large particles of debris is assumed to be controlled principally by the action of the large-scale wind profile on the trajectories of the particles, which fall from various heights with various velocities. Basically using Kellogg *et al.*'s notation, this distribution is determined by writing the horizontal vector displacement $D(h_i, r)$ of a particle as

$$D(h_i, r) = \sum_{h_i}^{h=0} V(h) \, \Delta h / W(h, r) \qquad (6.37)$$

where $V(h)$ is the vector mean wind in a horizontal layer of depth Δh, and $W(h, r)$ is the rate of fall of the particle, the latter being dependent generally on height and particle radius r. The spread of the ground pattern is thus produced by the variation of wind direction in the height range within which the debris is originally distributed, in conjunction with the range of terminal velocities associated with the particles at each initial height. Neglect of the effects of diffusion of the falling particles will result in an underestimate of the dimensions of the area of ground contaminated, and hence an overestimate of the degree of contamination. Clearly, a correction could be applied by extending the dimensions of the area affected, in accordance with the best available estimates of diffusive spread, but, in comparison with the errors which will already exist from uncertainties in wind speed, rates of fall and initial distribution, such adjustments may often be of doubtful value.

The Windscale accident—October 1957

Discussions of the distribution of the radioactive contamination which occurred during the Windscale accident have been given in separate but complementary papers by Chamberlain (1959) and Crabtree (1959). During the accident some of the uranium fuel became white hot and fission products, notably iodine-131, escaped from the 120-m chimney stack. Measurements of the activity retained by the filter at the top of the stack, and of the activity in the air near ground-level locally, established the period of discharge and the broad variation of its rate. However, these measurements did not immediately provide an estimate of the total amount of radioactivity released, so that it was not possible to make the fullest use of the data in testing or developing ideas on medium-range diffusion. Indeed one of the practical interests, considered by Crabtree, is the reverse process of using the incomplete data on the large-scale distribution to estimate the quantity released.

Assuming the release to be confined to the period 12 GMT 10 October to 12 GMT 11 October, as indicated by the local monitoring, Crabtree carried out an air-trajectory analysis in order to reconstruct the plume and its movement over the United Kingdom. It was found that the most realistic results were obtained by using observed surface winds, after smoothing these and increasing the speeds by 25–30 per cent, so implying a vertical spread of the effluent cloud of at least some hundreds of metres. In accordance with the sequence of weather conditions, particularly the existence of a south-west wind early in the period, veering to north-west after the passage of a cold front over Windscale near 01 or 02 hr on 11 October, the reconstructed plume took on the shape of a letter V extending across the north of England. This plume as a whole moved from the north-west to the south-east of England, and was then blown across the southern part of England and Wales by the easterly winds developed in the ridge of high pressure which rapidly intensified behind the cold front. Comparison of the plume positions with the actual distribution of activity in the air, as indicated by 24-hr or 48-hr collections on filters exposed in industrial areas for ordinary air pollution surveys, gave support to the view that the release was virtually confined to the period 15 hr 10 October to 12 hr 11 October, with peak discharge occurring about 15 hr and 24 hr 10 October and 09 hr 11 October.

Only the broadest features of an obviously complex large-scale distribution are indicated by the air-activity data, but more detail of the distribution in north-west England was provided by measurements of the deposition of iodine-131, the methods and results of which are described by Chamberlain. One particularly interesting feature is the narrow band of deposited activity running south-east from Windscale along the coast of Cumberland, evidently associated with the discharge after the passage of the cold front. From the distribution across this band Chamberlain gives half-value widths, i.e. widths between points at which the total deposition fell to one-half of the peak value. Assuming Gaussian distribution these are easily converted to the more familiar plume-width specification in which fall to one-tenth of the peak value is the criterion. At a distance of 10 km the converted width is 2·3 km. This width is somewhat smaller than those observed on average in measurements of the cross-wind distribution of airborne material at similar range from a source (see 4.6 and Fig. 4.12). Moreover, between 3 and 34 km there is an increase of width approximately as the square root of the distance, which is appreciably less than that indicated in Fig. 4.12.

The interpretation of the foregoing results on cross-wind spread is not straightforward. Not only were the meteorological conditions somewhat complex, but also it seems possible (see Chamberlain's discussion) that the plume of iodine-131 was entrained in the plume of water vapour and droplets from the cooling towers of the power station almost exactly down-wind of Windscale.   In this case the spray or condensate from the latter plume might have enhanced the axial deposition, so emphasising the narrowness of the band affected.   Furthermore, the deposition did not diminish with distance in an entirely simple way, there being a substantial and general increase over the relatively high ground 20 km down-wind of Windscale. The reality of the latter feature was confirmed by subsequent measurements of the deposition of caesium-137.

An assessment of the total discharge of iodine-131 follows from a direct integration of the deposition up to a specified distance, together with an estimate of the amount blown beyond that distance.   Chamberlain gives the total activity deposited, within the 0·1 microcurie/m² isopleth of deposition, as 5000 curies.   This isopleth runs to approximately 150 km SSE of Windscale, and for this distance Crabtree was able to derive an approximate cross-wind distribution of the activity in surface air using the filter data mentioned previously.   It was then assumed that the vertical distribution was of Gaussian form, and that the top of the plume (where the concentration fell to one-tenth of the ground value) was at the base of the inversion which existed (at a height of 1500 m) in the air behind the front.   Using the wind speed obtaining during the passage of the plume the windborne flux of iodine-131 activity beyond the distance of approximately 150 km was computed as 22,000 curies.   The estimated total release was therefore about 27,000 curies.

From the simultaneous observations of deposition and air-activity at five sites in Lancashire and Yorkshire Chamberlain gives deposition velocities ranging from 0·24 to 0·52 cm/sec with an arithmetic mean of 0·4 cm/sec, and compares this with the theoretical value to be expected [Eq. (6.20)] if the surface is assumed to be a perfect sink for iodine-131. Chamberlain suggests that the friction velocity u_* probably did not exceed 20 cm/sec, and taking $z_1 = 500$ obtains $v_d = 0.8$ cm/sec, which is fairly consistent with that derived from the activity data.   However, it has since been pointed out by Chamberlain (1961) that the above observation of deposition velocity, and also the much lower value of 0·1 cm/sec obtained in the Harwell area, may be too high, because of inefficiency in the collection of the iodine from the air.   It is stated that the iodine was probably adsorbed on nuclei of sub-micron size during the travel of the cloud, which would account for low values of deposition velocity.   On the other hand observations at ranges up to 30 km, in desert country at Hanford in the U.S.A., gave values of v_d averaging 2·8 cm/sec.

A further test of some interest may be made by using the value of deposition velocity observed in Lancashire and Yorkshire (0·4 cm/sec) in Eq. (6.35), which gives the reduction of windborne material with time (or distance) of travel for the idealized case of instantaneous vertical spread throughout a finite depth $\bar{h}$ of the atmosphere. For the present purposes this equation transforms to

$$\frac{Q}{Q_0} = \exp -\left(\frac{v_d x}{\bar{h}\bar{u}}\right) \tag{6.38}$$

where Q_0 is the total amount of iodine-131 discharged, and Q is the quantity carried by the air beyond a distance x. Taking $\bar{h} = 0.75$ km (i.e. the approximate equivalent height appropriate to Crabtree's assumption of 1·5 km as the height at which the activity fell to one-tenth of the ground value), $x = 150$ km and $u = 500$ cm/sec it follows that $Q/Q_0 = 0.85$, which is to be compared with the value 0·81 ($= 22,000/27,000$) implied by the estimates from the integration of the deposition and air-activity measurements. The agreement is a verification of the consistency of the activity data.

The travel of atomic bomb debris in the troposphere

Machta *et al.* (1957) have described observations of atomic debris made from aircraft on the occasion of the tests conducted by the United States Atomic Energy Commission in Nevada in January and February 1951. The aircraft were fitted with pairs of filters which were changed alternately every 15 min, so that collections referred to overlapping 30-min sections of the flights, which were made at altitudes between 8000 and 30,000 ft, usually along the 80th and 95th meridians (the position of the test site was 37°N 116°W). Assessment of the samples was made on a purely relative basis. The results provide in the first place some data on the actual trajectories of the clouds of radioactive debris, for comparison with trajectories subsequently computed from wind data at or near the heights of the sampling. When available, observed winds were used, otherwise geostrophic winds were derived from charts of the contours of constant-pressure surfaces, or occasionally those of pressure at a constant level. Figures are given for the differences between the latitude at which the peak activity was observed, and that intersected by the computed trajectory, at the 95th meridian in twelve cases and the 85th meridian in one case. These differences range from 0·2 to 2·6 degrees and average approximately 1 degree, which, allowing for the difference in latitude and longitude scales, corresponds to an average error in N–S position of about 6 per cent of the distance of travel. As Machta *et al.* note, such errors are considerably smaller than those shown by comparisons of computed trajectories with balloon flights at altitudes of 30,000 ft, and they suggest that this is mainly due to a better coverage in wind data at the lower heights mostly involved in the sampling data. The figures obtained from the sampling data support this in showing a trend for the error to increase at the greater altitudes.

Many of the activity profiles presented by Machta *et al.* contain irregularities and inconsistencies of a degree which are not surprising in view of the complexity of the diffusion processes and the difficulties of measurement. The implications regarding lateral spread were discussed for three of the profiles only, in terms of the classical Fickian coefficient of diffusion, which was found to range from $1\cdot6 \times 10^8$ to $4\cdot8 \times 10^8$ cm^2/sec. These values are an order of magnitude greater than those obtained from the spread of balloons travelling over similar distances. The suggestion is made that this may be a result of the three-dimensional nature of the debris cloud, the lateral spread of which would therefore be influenced by the variation of wind direction with height. As regards the expression of the results in terms of Fickian-type diffusion it is noteworthy that no indication is provided as to whether the results support the implied variation of spread with the square root of distance, and it will be recalled (see 4.6) that the bulk of the evidence otherwise available for distances of the same order is contrary to this form of variation. A subsequent analysis of six of the activity profiles reported by Machta *et al.*, together with six more profiles obtained during similar tests in October and November 1951, has been presented briefly by Wilkins (1958b). It is stated that the twelve profiles used were of near-Gaussian shape out to at least three standard deviations. Standard deviations of the profile distribution are quoted, and the ratios of these to the distances along the cloud trajectory lie in the range 0·022–0·053, with a mean value 0·035. In alternative terms the widths of cloud (as defined by fall to one-tenth of peak concentration) were on average 0·15 times the distance of travel. As already noted, interpretation of this data is complicated by the fact that effects of large-scale wind shear are probably involved, but it is interesting to consider the implication in terms of pure diffusion of a cluster as treated in the paper by Smith and Hay (1961). Smith's theoretical analysis leads to the approximate form given in Eq. (4.13), i.e.,

$$\frac{\Delta\sigma}{\Delta x} = \frac{2}{3}\beta i^2$$

for cluster sizes of the order of the scale of turbulence. With σ ranging up to about 50 miles this condition could have been satisfied (i.e. as far as the scale of turbulence in the horizontal plane was concerned). In this case with $\Delta\sigma/\Delta x$ equal to 0·035, $\beta i^2 \simeq 0\cdot05$. The quantity β, the ratio of the Lagrangian time-scale to the time-scale of the correlogram observed at a fixed point, has been roughly estimated to have values near unity for large-scale turbulence (see Hay and Pasquill, 1959), which gives an intensity of turbulence i of approximately 0·2. There is no check which can easily be made on the correspondence of this with the actual statistics of large-scale turbulence in the horizontal, but the value is not untenable.

Other discussions of the results of the monitoring of bomb debris in relation to the large-scale circulation in the troposphere have been published by Machta, List and Hubert (1956) and List (1957). Apart from being consistent on the whole with a travel according to the appropriate wind field, the results are not complete enough to provide any significant generalizations concerning diffusion, and in some cases (e.g. see List) there are indeed anomalies which have yet to be explained. In principle, the debris clouds from nuclear tests provide unprecedented opportunities of examining large-scale diffusion. In practice, the observations which are most easily made, i.e. measurements of deposition on suitable artificial surfaces, are related to airborne concentration in a complex way, and in any case the substantial deposition in association with rain means that the material property carried by the air is far from conservative.

A useful summary of the data on the deposition of fission products is contained in Chamberlain's 1961 paper. The overall impression is that *dry* deposition occurs at a rate of about 0·1 cm/sec, whereas the amounts of activity brought down in rain on Britain in the period 1956–9 correspond to effective deposition velocities of about 1 cm/sec. This latter figure is based on total deposition during a year; for any particular occasion when rain is falling much larger deposition velocities are therefore implied.

The distribution of long-lived fission products from thermo-nuclear tests

The slow deposition of the very fine dust injected into the stratosphere during the tests of thermo-nuclear devices (the delayed fall-out referred to previously) evidently involves transport processes which are not only on a bigger scale than those which have been the main subject of this book, but which are also probably of a totally different character, possibly involving systematic circulations throughout the depth of the atmosphere as a whole. For a more detailed view of the problems involved, reference may be made to the paper by the Committee on Meteorological Aspects of the Effects of Atomic Radiation, and to the discussion by Machta (1959).

An account of measurements of strontium-90 and other fission products at a world-wide network of rainwater-sampling stations has been given by Stewart *et al.* (1957). Apart from the persistent deposition of strontium-90 over several years, a feature which immediately reflects on the slow return of the material which penetrated into the stratosphere, their results contain two other features of particular interest in a meteorological context. Firstly, the concentration ($\mu\mu$c/litre) of strontium-90 in rainwater during 1955–7 follows a distinct systematic variation with latitude, over the range 60°N to 50°S examined.   Working southwards there is a rise to a maximum in the region of 40°N, a pronounced fall to relatively small values in equatorial latitudes, then a rise again in the 40°–50° region of the southern hemisphere, to moderate values about one-quarter of those in similar latitudes in the northern hemisphere.   Secondly, the measurements at Milford Haven in the United Kingdom and Ohakea in New Zealand show seasonal variations which are in opposite phase, with maxima occurring in the spring seasons and minima in the autumn seasons.

The general picture of the distribution of delayed fall-out which has emerged from the above measurements and other similar surveys is still far from complete, and no single interpretation of the data has yet found universal acceptance.   Stewart et al. argue that the deposition pattern is primarily a consequence of a slow feed into the troposphere, with a periodic variation determined by the large-scale circulation in the stratosphere and its interaction with the troposphere, generally speaking in a fashion similar to the large-scale transport of ozone.   The occurrence of a spring maximum of ozone content at high latitudes has been explained by Dobson (1956) in a general circulation model which involves the formation and subsequent sinking of a very cold pool of air in the stratosphere above the winter pole. Such a process would require a meridional transport of air in the stratosphere, possibly involving a flow from the summer to the winter hemisphere and this, together with ultimate sinking into the troposphere on lines suggested by Brewer (1949), could explain the geographical and seasonal variation in the amount of strontium-90 contained in rain.   Alternative interpretations have recently been summarized by Martell (1959), including that due to Libby in which the spring maximum in the northern hemisphere is ascribed to material released in the troposphere itself, and also his own suggestion that the maximum is substantially provided by stratospheric debris of short residence-time injected by the immediately preceding test in the U.S.S.R.   The sorting out of these conflicting ideas is made especially difficult by the lack of precise information on the initial distribution of the debris in the stratosphere and troposphere.

6.6   Agricultural, botanical and related interests

There are many cases of atmospheric transport involving the dispersion, on various scales, of dusts, seeds, pollens and spores introduced into the atmosphere by natural processes.   Certain aspects of the migration of flying insects are manifestly affected by the dispersive action of the atmosphere, and toxic dust and sprays applied as herbicides and insecticides may be transported down-wind.   In some of these examples safety problems and economic aspects of a more or less obvious nature are involved.   One example for which the significance of atmospheric transport is only beginning to be considered in detail is the redistribution of chemicals blown away from the land and sea surfaces (see Eriksson, 1956).   For most of the examples the information available on the properties of the source and the subsequent distribution is usually very indefinite, but some useful generalizations can be made, and a few quantitative results can be cited.

One feature which is particularly relevant to cases of transport over long distances is the actual trajectory followed by the material, and its relation to that which can be inferred from the available wind data.   For all practical purposes the latter must usually be estimated indirectly from synoptic charts of the pressure distribution, or of the contours of the isobaric surfaces.   Such wind data are incomplete and subject to appreciable error (see Durst and Davis, 1957).   Furthermore, the height or height range in the atmosphere at which the material is present is rarely known with precision.   Within the limitations set by these uncertainties the general impression, gained from tracer studies and from analyses of the travel of dust clouds and smoke palls, is one of a broad confirmation of the obvious expectation, namely that the velocity at any stage should be the vectorial mean through the height range encompassing the bulk of the material.

Gregory (1945) has given an extended discussion of *plant-disease gradients* in relation to the anticipated variation of spore deposition with distance from the source, assuming a deposition coefficient equal to that which he estimated from Stepanov's small-scale experiments on spore dispersal.   It was assumed that the distribution of disease as represented by numbers of spores or lesions per plant could be directly compared with deposition, but when the data were in the form of number of plants affected it was necessary to make from these a statistical estimate of the equivalent numbers of lesions.   As far as possible cases were selected for which the background level of disease from distant sources was negligible, and for which the complication of secondary spread from existing lesions had not been developed.   The data were plotted on separate graphs according as the source approximated to a point or assumed line.   While recognizing irregularities in the data Gregory concluded that there was an orderliness about the plant-disease gradients which was compatible with the expected deposition.   It would however be a very difficult matter to say whether the variations in observed gradients were a consequence of variations in atmosphere turbulence and deposition velocity, and the most that can be confidently said is that at distances of the order of 100 m from a source the fall of disease intensity with distance is broadly similar to that known to be followed by the concentration from a source of airborne material.

In general terms the extreme range to which material can be transported in effective quantity is determined by the wind speed, the rate and final amount of vertical spread, and the effective deposition velocity. The importance of the first of these factors is obvious, while the essential significance of the last two in combination is immediately seen from Eq. (6.35) for the idealized case of rapid vertical spread over some limited height range.   Clearly, for large range the quantity h/v_d must be large.   It follows from this that any remarkable case of the arrival of dust or pollen, say, from extremely distant sources, is most probably a consequence of rapid convection of the air at the source to considerable heights, in conjunction with or followed by strong winds.   An important example of such long-range transport arises in the continental spread of plant diseases, and in this connection Stakman (1947) has given brief reference to epidemics of rust disease in wheat, occasioned by movement of spores in one direction or the other between the north and south of the United States of America.   On the other hand, it is clear that when spores or pollen are released close to the ground, in more normal conditions of wind and turbulence, development of vertical spread will often be sufficiently slow to give relatively small h/v_d, and hence appreciable deposition of the particles within a short range. Gregory (1952) has emphasized this feature, which has the obvious implication that the spacing of crops is an important factor in controlling the spread of plant diseases.   Likewise, Hyde has made several references (e.g. 1950) to the obviously predominant local origin of pollen catches at various places in Britain, and states that there was a great falling-off in the catch with decreasing frequency and increasing distance of plants up-wind, though pollens of distant origin were also recognized.

Some observations on the drift of chemical spray released from a low-flying aircraft have been reported by Yeo and Thompson (1953), and by Yeo, Akesson and Coutts (1959).   In the earlier work a solution of DDT was released on a cross-wind flight at a height of 30 ft above open country, in the form of drops in the range 5–250 μ diameter.   Deposition was measured by collecting the spray on glass plates lying on the ground, and estimating the numbers and sizes of drops.   The quantity of DDT collected was also estimated by colorimetric estimation of a dye added to the solution.   Measurements in a number of trials were analysed to give the proportions of the original DDT deposited in given intervals of time ranging up to about 100 sec.   It was found that this proportion increased systematically with increasing stability as represented by a factor approximately equivalent to the Richardson Number, a result which was no doubt a conse-quence of the reduction in vertical spread in stable conditions.   For the extremes of stability studied, the ratio of the proportions deposited was approximately 3:1 irrespective of the time interval.   Preliminary studies suggested that the effect of stability was more marked for the smaller drops, which again would be expected, since the larger (heavier) drops would tend to experience less vertical dispersion by atmospheric turbulence.

The later work by Yeo *et al.* used a spray with a volume median diameter of approximately 200 μ, released from an aircraft flying 10 ft over open rolling grassland, in long runs at right angles to the wind direction. Deposits on the ground were collected on filter papers, and the concentra-tions in the air at a height of 3 ft were measured by cascade impactors. The results of two experiments in near-neutral conditions of stability show a rapid fall-off in ground deposit and airborne concentration with distance up to about 100 m.   It is evident that the deposit diminishes more rapidly than concentration, presumably a result of the larger proportion of small drops remaining airborne at the greater distances of travel.   From the graphical data it can be estimated that the effective deposition velocities (presumably the terminal velocities in these cases) were about 5 m/sec at 10 yd down-wind and 0·3 m/sec at 300 yd down-wind.   These values are compatible with the size of drops probably contained in the spray, though the paper does not give any detailed analysis of this aspect.   These and earlier observations are described only briefly, but they exhibit a systematic character which suggests that the down-wind displacement of fairly coarse spray can be satisfactorily related to drop size and the conditions of wind and turbulence.

In the operation of spraying a particular crop with a herbicide, one of the problems is to avoid drift of the spray on to surrounding crops which could be damaged by the agent used.   Spraying equipment is therefore designed to minimize the risk of unwanted spread (see Courshee, 1959), but as a further safeguard it has been the practice to recommend that the opera-tion should preferably be carried out in calm conditions.   This is a rule which will no doubt prove to be beneficial in many cases, but it disregards the possibility of erratic air currents, especially those caused by convection on nominally calm sunny days, in which the fine spray might be carried at high concentration in unexpected directions and to unexpected distances. Spraying in the presence of an appreciable wind has at least the advantage that the direction of travel of fine spray will usually be definable.

As regards the effect of atmospheric diffusion on flying insects a particu-larly noteworthy example is provided by the distribution of aphids, which are weak fliers.   Once in flight their trajectories are largely controlled by turbulent air currents.   Johnson (1957) has described observations of the reduction with height of aphid population, using traps carried on a captive balloon cable at heights up to 2000 ft.   The profile was found to be significantly correlated with lapse rate in unstable conditions, in the expected sense that the greater the instability the slower was the fall-off of aphid population with height.   However, some of the details of the variation of vertical gradient are not entirely explicable in simple terms, and are no doubt complicated by the daily pattern of take-off.   Flying locusts, which are much more vigorous fliers, have been the subject of much study in relation to control measures, and certain characteristic features of swarm behaviour in relation to airflow have been described and discussed by Rainey (1958).   The flying swarms observed in eastern Africa apparently always travelled directly down-wind, in relation to the vectorial mean wind throughout the vertical extent of the swarm, though the speed of travel was up to that of the wind only for relatively large swarms.   Swarms of 'stratiform' or 'cumuliform' structure occurred, the latter only in conditions of vigorous convection, but small stratiform swarms were also observed to occur in such conditions.   The few direct comparisons between the vertical extent of the cumuliform swarms and vertical temperature distribution indicated that the top of the swarm was close to the top of the layer with superadiabatic or adiabatic lapse rate.   In strange contrast to the obvious control exerted by the vertical component of the air motion on the vertical spread of the locusts, the swarms habitually preserved a remarkable degree of cohesion horizontally, over distances of hundreds of kilometres.   This apparent countering of the dispersive action of the atmosphere in a horizontal plane, though not in the vertical, has yet to be properly elucidated.

Bibliography

Absalom, H. W. L., 1954, Meteorological aspects of smog, *Quart. J. R. Met Soc.*, **80**, 261.

Angell, J. K., 1958, Lagrangian wind fluctuations at 300 mb derived from transosonde data, *J. Met.*, **15**, 522.

—— 1959, A climatological analysis of two years of routine transosonde flights from Japan, *Monthly Weather Review*, **87**, 427.

—— 1960, An analysis of operational 300 mb transosonde flights from Japan in 1957–1958, *J. Met.*, **17**, 20.

Angell, J. K. and Pack, D. H., 1960, Analysis of some preliminary low-level constant level balloon (tetroon) flights, *Monthly Weather Review*, **88**, 235.

Ball, F. K., 1958, Some observations of bent plumes, *Quart. J. R. Met. Soc.*, **84**, 61.

Barad, M. L., 1958, Project Prairie Grass, a field program in diffusion, *Geophysical Research Papers No. 59*, Vols I & II, G.R.D., A.F.C.R.C., Bedford, Mass.

—— 1959, Analysis of diffusion studies at O'Neill, Atmospheric Diffusion and Air Pollution, ed. by F. N. Frenkiel and P. A. Sheppard, *Advances in Geophysics*, **6**, 389, Acad. Press.

Barad, M. L. and Haugen, D. A., 1959, A preliminary evaluation of Sutton's hypothesis for diffusion from a continuous point source, *J. Met.*, **16**, 12.

Baron, T., Gerhard, E. R. and Johnstone, H. F., 1949, Dissemination of aerosol particles dispersed from stacks, *Ind. & Eng. Chem.*, **41**, 2403.

Batchelor, G. K., 1946, Double velocity correlation function in turbulent motion, *Nature*, **158**, 883.

—— 1947, Kolmogoroff's theory of locally isotropic turbulence, *Proc. Camb. Phil. Soc.*, **43**, 533.

—— 1949, Diffusion in a field of homogeneous turbulence, I. Eulerian analysis, *Aust. J. Sci. Res.*, **2**, 437.

Batchelor, G. K., 1950, The application of the similarity theory of turbulence to atmospheric diffusion, *Quart. J. R. Met. Soc.*, **76**, 133.

—— 1952, Diffusion in a field of homogeneous turbulence, II. The relative motion of particles, *Proc. Camb. Phil. Soc.*, **48**, 345.

—— 1953, *The Theory of Homogeneous Turbulence*, Cambridge University Press.

Batchelor, G. K. and Townsend, A. A., 1956, *Turbulent Diffusion, Surveys in Mechanics*, ed. G. K. Batchelor and R. M. Davies, 352. Cambridge University Press.

Benton, G. S. and Kahn, A. B., 1958, Spectra of large-scale atmospheric flow at 300 mb, *J. Met.*, **15**, 404.

Best, A. C., 1935, Transfer of heat and momentum in the lowest layers of the atmosphere, *Meteorological Office Geophysical Memoirs No. 65*.

—— 1954, Assessment of maximum concentration at ground level of gas from a heated elevated source, a paper of the Meteorological Research Committee (London), *M.R.P. No. 878*.

—— 1957, Maximum gas concentrations at ground level from industrial chimneys, *J. Inst. Fuel*, **30**, 329.

Blackman, R. B. and Tukey, J. W., 1958, The measurement of power spectra from the point of view of communications engineering, Part I. *The Bell System Technical Journal*, **37**, 185.

Booker, H. G., 1948, Some problems of radio-meteorology, *Quart. J. R. Met. Soc.*, **74**, 277.

Bosanquet, C. H., 1957, The rise of a hot waste gas plume, *J. Inst. Fuel*, **30**, 322.

Bosanquet, C. H., Carey, W. F. and Halton, E. M., 1950, Dust deposition from chimney stacks, *Proc. Inst. Mech. Eng.*, **162**, 355.

Bosanquet, C. H. and Pearson, J. L., 1936, The spread of smoke and gases from chimneys, *Trans. Faraday Soc.*, **32**, 1249.

Braham, R. R., Seely, B. K. and Crozier, W. D., 1952, A technique for tagging and tracing air parcels, *Trans. Amer. Geophys. Union*, **33**, 825.

Brewer, A. W., 1949, Evidence for a world circulation provided by the measurements of helium and water vapour distribution in the stratosphere, *Quart. J. R. Met. Soc.*, **75**, 351.

Brier, G. W., 1950, The statistical theory of turbulence and the problem of diffusion in the atmosphere, *J. Met.*, **7**, 283.

Brooks, C. E. P. and Carruthers, N., 1953, *Handbook of Statistical Methods in Meteorology*, H.M.S.O., London.

Brunt, D., 1941, *Physical and Dynamical Meteorology*, Cambridge University Press.

Bushnell, R. H. and Huss, P. O., 1958, A power spectrum of surface winds, *J. Met.*, **15**, 180.

Businger, J. A., 1959, Data reduction technique; Project Prairie Grass, a Field Program in Diffusion, *Geophysical Research Papers No. 59*, Edited by D. A. Haugen, III, 29, G.R.D., A.F.C.R.C., Bedford, Mass.

Businger, J. A. and Suomi, V. E., 1958, Variance spectra of the vertical wind component derived from observations with the sonic anemometer at O'Neill, Nebraska in 1953, *Archiv. f. Met. Geoph. und Biokl.*, A, **10**, 415.

Calder, K. L., 1949, Eddy diffusion and evaporation in flow over aerodynamically smooth and rough surfaces: a treatment based on laboratory laws of turbulent flow with special reference to conditions in the lower atmosphere, *Quart. J. Mech. & Applied Math.*, **II**, 153.

—— 1952, *Some Recent British work on the Problem of Diffusion in the Lower Atmosphere*, Air Pollution, Proc. U.S. Tech. Conf. Air Poll., p. 787, McGraw-Hill, New York.

Chamberlain, A. C., 1953, *Aspects of Travel and Deposition of Aerosol and vapour Clouds*, A.E.R.E., HP/R 1261, H.M.S.O.

—— 1959, Deposition of iodine-131 in Northern England in October 1957, *Quart. J. R. Met. Soc.*, **85**, 350.

—— 1961, Aspects of the deposition of radioactive and other gases and particles, *Int. J. Air Poll.*, **3**.

—— 1961a, *Dispersion of Activity from Chimney Stacks; Atomic Energy Waste, its Nature, Use and Disposal*, ed. E. Glueckauf, p. 308, Butterworth.

Chamberlain, A. C. and Chadwick, R. C., 1953, Deposition of airborne radioiodine vapour, *Nucleonics*, **II**, 22.

Charnock, H., 1951, Note on eddy diffusion in the atmosphere between one and two kilometres, *Quart. J. R. Met. Soc.*, **77**, 654.

Charnock, H. and Robinson, G. D., 1957, Spectral estimates from subdivided meteorological series, A paper of the Meteorological Research Committee (London) *M.R.P.* No. 1062.

Church, P. E., 1949, Dilution of waste stack gases in the atmosphere, *Ind. Eng. Chem.*, **41**, 2753.

Committee on meteorological aspects of the effect of atomic radiation, 1956, report in *Science*, **124**, 105, U.S.A.

Committee on Air Pollution, 1954, *Report of Beaver Committee*, Cmd 9322, London, H.M.S.O.

Courshee, R. J., 1959, Reducing drift from ground sprayers, *Shell Public Health and Agricultural News*, No. 4.

Crabtree, J., 1959, The travel and diffusion of the radioactive material emitted during the Windscale accident, *Quart. J. R. Met. Soc.*, **85**, 362.

Cramer, H. E., 1952, Preliminary results of a program for measuring the structure of turbulent flow near the ground. International symposium on atmospheric turbulence in the boundary layer. *Geophys. Res. Papers* No. 19, p. 187, G.R.D., Cambridge, Mass.

—— 1957, A practical method for estimating the dispersal of atmospheric contaminants, *Proceedings of the Conference on Applied Meteorology*, *Am. Met. Soc.*

—— 1959, Engineering estimates of atmospheric dispersal capacity, *Amer. Ind. Hyg. Ass. J.*, **20**, 183.

Cramer, H. E., Gill, G. C. and Record, F. A., 1957, Heated thermocouple anemometers and light bivanes, *Exploring the Atmosphere's First Mile*, Edited by H. H. Lettau and B. Davidson, **1**, 233, Pergamon Press.

Cramer, H. E., Record, F. A. and Vaughan, H. C., 1958, The study of the diffusion of gases or aerosols in the lower atmosphere, *M.I.T. Department of Meteorology, Final Report under Contract* No. AF 19(604)—1058.

Crane, H. L. and Chilton, R. G., 1956, Measurements of atmospheric turbulence over a wide range of wavelength for one meteorological condition, *N.A.C.A. Technical Note* 3702.

Crozier, W. D. and Seely, B. K., 1955, Concentration distributions in aerosol plumes three to twenty-two miles from a point source, *Trans. Amer. Geophys. Union*, **36**, 42.

Csanady, G. T., 1955, Dispersal of dust particles from elevated sources, *Aust. J. Phys.*, **8**, 545.

—— 1957, Dispersal of dust particles from elevated sources, *Aust. J. Phys.*, **10**, 559.

—— 1958, Deposition of dust particles from industrial stacks, *Aust. J. App. Sci.*, **9**, 1.

Davidson, B. and Halitsky, J., 1958, A method of estimating the field of instantaneous ground concentration from tower bivane data, *J. Air Poll. Cont. Ass.*, **7**, 316.

Davies, D. R., 1950, Three-dimensional turbulence and evaporation in the lower atmosphere, II, *Quart. J. Mech. & Applied Math.*, **3**, 64.

—— 1954, On diffusion from a continuous point source at ground level into a turbulent atmosphere, *Quart. J. Mech. & Applied Math.*, **7**, 168.

Deacon, E. L., 1949, Vertical diffusion in the lowest layers of the atmosphere, *Quart. J. R. Met. Soc.*, **75**, 89.

—— 1957, Wind profiles and the shearing stress—an anomaly resolved, *Quart. J. R. Met. Soc.*, **83**, 537.

Deacon, E. L., 1959, *The Measurement of Turbulent Transfer in the Lower Atmosphere, Atmospheric Diffusion and Air Pollution* edited by F. N. Frenkiel and P. A. Sheppard, Advances in Geophysics, **6**, 211, Academic Press, New York.

Department of Scientific and Industrial Research, 1945, *Atmospheric Pollution in Leicester, a Scientific Survey*, H.M.S.O.

Dobson, G. M. B., 1956, Origin and distribution of the polyatomic molecules, in the atmosphere, *Proc. Roy. Soc. London*, A, **236**, 187.

Durst, C. S., 1948, The fine structure of wind in the free air, *Quart. J. R. Met. Soc.*, **74**, 349.

Durst, C. S., Crossley, A. F. and Davis, N. E., 1957, Horizontal diffusion in the atmosphere in the light of air trajectories, a paper of the Meteorological Research Committee (London) *M.R.P.* No. 1058.

—— 1959, Horizontal diffusion in the atmosphere as determined by geostrophic trajectories, *J. Fluid Mech.*, **6**, 401.

Durst, C. S. and Davis, N. E., 1957, Accuracy of geostrophic trajectories, *Met. Mag.*, **86**, 138.

Edinger, J. G., 1952, A technique for measuring the detailed structure of atmospheric flow, International Symposium on atmospheric turbulence in the boundary layer, *Geophys. Res. Paper* No. 19, G.R.D., Cambridge, Mass.

Edinger, J. G. and Rapp, R. R., 1957, Dispersion in the upper atmosphere, *J. Met.*, **14**, 421.

Ellison, T. H., 1957, Turbulent transport of heat and momentum from an infinite rough plane, *J. Fluid Mech.*, **2**, 456.

Eriksson, E., 1956, The chemical climate and saline soils in the arid zone, Australia—*U.N.E.S.C.O. symp.*, *Arid Zone Climate*, Paper No. 45.

Etkes, P. W. and Brooks, C. F., 1918, Smoke as an indicator of gustiness and convection, *Monthly Weather Review, U.S. Weather Bureau*, **46**, 459.

Falk, L. L. *et al.*, 1954, Development of a system for predicting dispersion from stacks, *Air Repair*, **4**, 87, Pittsburg, Pa.

Frenkiel, F. N., 1952a, On the statistical theory of turbulent diffusion, International symposium on atmospheric turbulence in the boundary layer, *Geophysics Research Papers No. 19*, 415, G.R.D., Cambridge, Mass.

—— 1952b, Application of the statistical theory of turbulent diffusion to micrometeorology, *J. Met.*, **9**, 252.

Frenkiel, F. N. and Katz, I., 1956, Studies of small-scale turbulent diffusion in the atmosphere, *J. Met.*, **13**, 388.

Giblett, M. A. *et al.*, 1932, The structure of wind over level country, *Meteorological Office Geophysical Memoirs* No. 54.

Gifford, F., 1953, A study of low-level air trajectories at Oak Ridge, Tenn., *Monthly Weather Review, U.S. Weather Bureau*, **81**, 179.

—— 1955, A simultaneous Lagrangian-Eulerian turbulence experiment, *Monthly Weather Review, U.S. Weather Bureau*, **83**, 293.

—— 1956, The relation between space and time correlations in the atmosphere, *J. Met.*, **13**, 289.

—— 1957a, Relative atmospheric diffusion of smoke puffs, *J. Met.*, **14**, 410.

—— 1957b, Further data on relative atmospheric diffusion, *J. Met.*, **14**, 475.

—— 1959a, The interpretation of meteorological spectra and correlations, *J. Met.*, **16**, 344.

—— 1959b, *Statistical Properties of a Fluctuating Plume Dispersion Model, Atmospheric Diffusion and Air Pollution*, edited by F. N. Frenkiel and P. A. Sheppard, Advances in Geophysics, 6, 117, Academic Press.

—— 1959c, Smoke plumes as quantitative air pollution indices, *Int. J. Air Poll.*, **2**, 42.

—— 1960, Peak to average concentration ratios according to a fluctuating plume dispersion model, *Int. J. Air Poll.*, **3**, 253.

Godson, W. L., 1958, The diffusion of particulate matter from an elevated source, *Archiv. f. Met. Geoph. und Biokl.*, A, **10**, 305.

Gosline, C. A., 1952, Dispersion from short stacks, *Chemical Engineering Progress*, **48**, 165.

Green, H. L. and Lane, W. R., 1957, *Particulate clouds: Dusts, Smokes and Mists*, Spon, London.

Greenfield, S. M., 1957, Rain scavenging of radioactive particulate matter from the atmosphere, *J. Met.*, **14**, 115.

Gregory, P. H., 1945, The dispersion of airborne spores, *Trans. Brit. Myc. Soc.*, **28**, 26.

—— 1951, Deposition of airborne *Lycopodium* spores on cylinders, *Ann. Appl. Biol.*, **38**, 357.

—— 1952, Fungus spores, *Trans. Brit. Myc. Soc.*, **35**, 1.

Griffiths, H. L., Panofsky, H. A. and Van der Hoven, I., 1956, Power spectrum analysis over large ranges of frequency, *J. Met.*, **13**, 279.

Gurvic, A. S., 1960, An experimental investigation of the frequency spectra of the vertical component of the wind velocity in the bottom layer of the atmosphere, *Akad. Nauk, Doklady*, **132**, 806.

Hay, J. S. and Pasquill, F., 1957, Diffusion from a fixed source at a height of a few hundred feet in the atmosphere, *J. Fluid Mech.*, **2**, 299.

Hay, J. S. and Pasquill, F., 1959, *Diffusion from a Continuous Source in Relation to the Spectrum and Scale of Turbulence. Atmospheric Diffusion and Air Pollution*, edited by F. N. Frenkiel and P. A. Sheppard, Advances in Geophysics, **6**, 345, Academic Press.

Haugen, D. A., 1959, Project Prairie Grass, a Field Program in Diffusion, *Geophysical Research Papers* No. 59, Vol. III, G.R.D.A.F.C., Bedford, Mass.

Hawkins, J. E. and Nonhebel, G., 1955, Chimneys and the dispersal of smoke, *J. Inst. Fuel*, **28**, 530.

Henry, R. M., 1959, A study of the effects of wind speed, lapse rate and altitude on the spectrum of atmospheric turbulence at low altitude, *Institution of the Aeronautical Sciences*, Report No. 59–43.

Hesselberg, T. L. and Bjorkdal, E., 1929, The law of distribution of eddy velocities, *Beitr. z. Phys. d. Fr. Atmos.*, **15**, 1929.

Hewson, E. W., 1945, The meteorological control of atmospheric pollution by heavy industry, *Quart. J. R. Met. Soc.*, **71**, 266.

Hilst, G. R., 1957a, Observations of the diffusion and transport of stack effluents in stable atmospheres, Ph.D. thesis, University of Chicago.

—— 1957b, The dispersion of stack gases in stable atmospheres, *J. Air Poll. Cont. Ass.*, **7**, 205.

Hilst, G. R. and Simpson, C. L., 1958, Observations of vertical diffusion rates in stable atmospheres, *J. Met.*, **15**, 125.

Hoecker, W. H., 1949, Contribution in Air Pollution in Donora, Pa., epidemiology of the unusual smog episode of October 1948, *Public Health Bulletin* No. 306. p. 126, U.S.A.

Holland, J. Z., 1953, A meteorological survey of the Oak Ridge Area, *U.S.A.E.C. Report ORO*–99, Tech. Inf. Ser., Oak Ridge, Tenn., U.S.A.

Holzman, B., 1943, The influence of stability on evaporation, *Ann. New York Acad. Sci.*, **44**, 13.

Hosler, C. R., Pack, D. H. and Harris, T. B., 1959, Meteorological Investigation of diffusion in a valley at Shippingport, Pennsylvania, U.S. Dept. of Commerce, Weather Bureau.

Hutchings, J. W., 1955, Turbulence theory applied to large-scale atmospheric phenomena, *J. Met.*, **12**, 263.

Hyde, H. A., 1950, Studies in atmospheric pollen. IV Pollen distribution in Great Britain, 1943, Part II. The composition of the pollen catch. *The New Phytologist*, **49**, 407.

Inoue, E., 1950, On the turbulent diffusion in the atmosphere (I), *J. Met. Soc. Japan*, **28**, 13.

Inoue, E., 1951, On the turbulent diffusion in the atmosphere (II) *J. Met. Soc. Japan*, **29**, 32.

Jalu, R., 1955, Exemples de situations météorologiques à pollution anormale, *La Météorologie*, July–September, 247.

Johnson, C. G., 1957, The vertical distribution of aphids in the air and the temperature lapse rate, *Quart. J. R. Met. Soc.*, **83**, 194.

Jones, J. I. P. and Butler, H. E., 1958, The measurement of gustiness in the first few thousand feet of the atmosphere, *Quart. J. R. Met. Soc.*, **84**, 17.

Jones, J. I. P. and Pasquill, F., 1959, An experimental system for directly recording statistics of the intensity of atmospheric turbulence, *Quart. J. R. Met. Soc.*, **85**, 225.

Jones, R. A., 1957, A preliminary examination of the spectrum and scale of the vertical component at 2000 ft., a paper of the Meteorological Research Committee (London) *M.R.P.* No. 1044.

Kahn, A. B., 1957, A generalization of average-correlation methods of spectrum analysis, *J. Met.*, **14**, 9.

Kampé de Fériet, M. J., 1939, Les fonctions aléatoires stationnaires et la théorie statistique de la turbulence homogène, *Ann. Soc. sci. Brux.*, **59**, 145.

Kazanskii, A. B. and Monin, A. S., 1957, The forms of smoke trails, *Izv. Akad. Nauk. U.S.S.R. (Ser. Geofiz.)*, No. 8, 1020.

Kellogg, W. W., 1956, Diffusion of smoke in the stratosphere, *J. Met.*, **13**, 241.

Kellogg, W. W., Rapp, R. R. and Greenfield, S. M., 1957, Close-in fallout, *J. Met.*, **14**, 1.

Laikhtman, D. L., 1944, Wind profile and interchange in the surface layers of the atmosphere, *Bull. Acad. Sci. U.R.S.S.*, 8.

Lappe, U. O., Davidson, B. and Notess, C. B., 1959, Analysis of atmospheric turbulence spectra obtained from concurrent airplane and tower measurements, *Institute of the Aeronautical Sciences, Report* No. 59–44.

Leonard, B. P., 1959, Long range cloud diffusion in the lower atmosphere, *J. Air Poll. Control Ass.*, **9**, 77.

Lettau, H. H. and Davidson, B., 1957, *Exploring the Atmosphere's First Mile;* Vol. I, *Instrumentation and Data Evaluation;* Vol. 2, *Site Description and Data Tabulation;* Pergamon Press.

List, R. J., The concentration of nuclear debris in the air as a meteorological variable, *Bull. Am. Met. Soc.*, **39**, 276.

Lowry, P. H., 1951, Microclimate factors in smoke pollution from tall stacks, *Am. Met. Soc. Met. Monographs*, **1**, 24.

Lowry, P. H., Mazzarella, D. A. and Smith, M. E., 1951, Ground level measurements of oil-fog emitted from a hundred-meter chimney, *Am. Met. Soc., Met. Monographs*, **1**, 30.

Lucas, D. H., 1958, The atmospheric pollution of cities, *Int. J. Air. Poll.*, **1**, 71.

Lucas, D. H., Spurr, G. and Williams, F., 1957, The use of balloons in atmospheric pollution research, *Quart. J. R. Met. Soc.*, **83**, 508.

MacCready, P. B., 1953a, Atmospheric turbulence measurements and analysis, *J. Met.*, **10**, 325.

—— 1953b, Structure of atmospheric turbulence, *J. Met.*, **10**, 434.

McCully, C. R., *et al.*, 1956, Scavenging action of rain in air-borne particulate matter, *Ind. Eng. Chem.*, **48**, 1512.

Machta, L., 1959, *Transport in the Stratosphere and through the Tropopause, Atmospheric Diffusion and Air Pollution*, ed. by F. N. Frenkiel and P. A. Sheppard, Advances in Geophysics, **6**, 273, Academic Press.

Machta, L., Hamilton, H. L., Hubert, L. F., List, R. J., and Nagler, K. M., 1957, Airborne measurements of atomic debris, *J. Met.*, **14**, 165.

Machta, L., List, R. J. and Hubert, L. F., 1956, World-wide travel of atomic debris, *Science*, **124**, 474.

Martell, E. A., 1959, Atmospheric aspects of strontium-90 fallout, *Science*, **129**, 1197.

Mason, B. J., 1957, *The Physics of Clouds*, O.U.P.

May, F. G., 1958, The washout by rain of *lycopodium* spores, *Quart. J. R. Met. Soc.*, **84**, 451.

Mazzarella, D. A., 1952, An all-weather remote-recording bi-vane, *Bull. Am. Met. Soc.*, **33**, 60.

McCormick, R. A., 1954, The partition and intensity of eddy energy at the 91 m level during unstable conditions as observed at Brookhaven National Laboratory, *Quart. J. R. Met. Soc.*, **80**, 359.

Meade, P. J., 1959, Smogs in Britain and the associated weather, *Int. J. Air Poll*, **2**, 87.

—— 1960, The estimation of ground level concentration from an elevated source, *Int. J. Air. Poll.*, **2**, 303.

Meade, P. J. and Priestley, C. H. B., 1956, The bent-over plume of hot gas, *Quart. J. R. Met. Soc.*, **82**, 526.

Meade, P. J. and Pasquill, F., 1958, A study of the average distribution of pollution around Staythorpe, *Int. J. Air Poll.*, **1**, 60.

Meetham, A. R., 1950, Natural removal of pollution from the atmosphere, *Quart. J. R. Met. Soc.*, **76**, 359.

—— 1952, *Atmospheric Pollution*, Pergamon Press.

Meetham, A. R., 1954, Natural removal of atmospheric pollution during fog, *Quart. J. R. Met. Soc.*, **80**, 96.

Mickelsen, W. R., 1955, An experimental comparison of the Lagrangian and Eulerian correlation coefficients in homogeneous isotropic turbulence, *N.A.C.A. Washington, Tech. Note No.* 3570.

Monin, A. S., 1955, The equation of turbulent diffusion, *Dokl. Akad. Nauk.*, **105**, 256.

—— 1959, *Smoke Propagation in the Surface Layer of the Atmosphere, Atmospheric Diffusion and Air Pollution*, edited by F. N. Frenkiel and P. A. Sheppard, Advances in Geophysics, **6**, 331, Academic Press.

Monin, A. S. and Obukhov, A. M., 1954, Basic regularity in turbulent mixing in the surface layer of the atmosphere, *Trud. Geofiz. Inst. Akad. Nauk, U.S.S.R.*, No. 24(151).

Morton, B. R., Taylor, G. I. and Turner, J. S., 1956, Turbulent gravitational convection from maintained and instantaneous sources, *Proc. Roy. Soc.*, A, **234**, 1.

Niemeyer, L. E., 1960, Forecasting air pollution potential, *Monthly Weather Review*, **88**, 88.

Obukhov, A. M., 1941, Energy distribution in the spectrum of turbulent flow, *Izv. Akad. Nauk, Geogr. i Geofiz*, **5**, 453.

Obukhov, A. M. and Yaglom, A. M., 1959, On the micro-structure of atmospheric turbulence—a review of recent work in the U.S.S.R., *Quart. J. R. Met. Soc.*, **85**, 81.

Ogura, Y., 1952, The theory of turbulent diffusion in the atmosphere, *J. Met. Soc. Japan*, **30**, 23.

—— 1953, The relation between the Space- and Time-correlation functions in a turbulent flow, *J. Met. Soc. Japan*, **31**, 355.

—— 1957, The influence of finite observation intervals on the measurement of turbulent diffusion parameters, *J. Met.*, **14**, 176.

—— 1958, On the isotropy of large-scale disturbances in the upper troposphere, *J. Met.*, **15**, 375.

—— 1959, *Diffusion from a Continuous Source in Relation to a Finite Observation Interval, Atmospheric Diffusion and Air Pollution*, edited by F. N. Frenkiel and P. A. Sheppard, Advances in Geophysics, **6**, 149, Academic Press.

Panofsky, H. A., 1953, The variation of the turbulence spectrum with height under superadiabatic conditions, *Quart. J. R. Met. Soc.*, **79**, 150.

—— 1961, An alternative derivation of the diabatic wind profile, *Quart. J. R. Met. Soc.*, **87**, 109.

Panofsky, H. A., Blackadar, A. K. and McVehil, G. E., 1960, The diabatic wind profile, *Quart. J. R. Met. Soc.*, **86**, 390.

Panofsky, H. A., Cramer, H. E. and Rao, V. R. K., 1958, The relation between Eulerian time and space spectra, *Quart. J. R. Met. Soc.*, **84**, 270.

Panofsky, H. A. and Deland, R. J., 1959, *One-dimensional Spectra of Atmospheric Turbulence in the Lowest 100 Metres, Atmospheric Diffusion and Air Pollution*, edited by F. N. Frenkiel and P. A. Sheppard, Advances in Geophysics, 6, 41, Academic Press.

Panofsky, H. A. and McCormick, R. A., 1952, The vertical momentum flux at Brookhaven at 109 meters, *Geophys. Res. Papers* No. **19**, 219, G.R.D., Cambridge, Mass.

—— 1954, Properties of spectra of atmospheric turbulence at 100 meters, *Quart. J. R. Met. Soc.*, **80**, 546.

—— 1960, The spectrum of vertical velocity near the surface, *Quart. J. R. Met. Soc.*, **86**, 495.

Panofsky, H. A. and Rao, V. R. K., 1958, Structure of atmospheric turbulence close to the surface over smooth terrain; *Pennsylvania State University, report prepared under contract No. AF* 19(604)–2252, Air Force Cambridge Research Center.

Panofsky, H. A. and Van der Hoven, I., 1955, Spectra and cross-spectra of velocity components in the mesometeorological range, *Quart. J. R. Met. Soc.*, **81**, 603.

Pasquill, F., 1949, Eddy diffusion of water vapour and heat near the ground, *Proc. Roy. Soc.*, A, **198**, 116.

—— 1950, The aerodynamic drag of grassland, *Proc. Roy. Soc.*, A, **202**, 143.

—— 1955, Preliminary studies of the distribution of particles at medium range from a ground-level point source (summary only) *Quart. J. R. Met. Soc.*, **81**, 636.

—— 1956, Meteorological research at Porton, *Nature*, **177**, 1148.

—— 1961, The estimation of the dispersion of windborne material, *Met. Mag.*, **90**, 33.

Pemberton, C. S., 1961, Scavenging action of rain on non-wettable particulate matter suspended in the atmosphere, *Int. J. Air Poll.*, **3**.

Pemberton, J., Clifton, M., Donoghue, J. K., Kerridge, D. and Moulds, W., 1959, The spatial distribution of air pollution in Sheffield, 1957–59, *Int. J. Air Poll.*, **2**, 175.

Perkins, W. A., Leighton, P. A., Grinnell, S. W. and Webster, F. X., 1952, A fluorescent atmospheric tracer technique for mesometeorological research, *Proc. 2nd National Air Pollution Symposium*, Pasadena, U.S.A.

Priestley, C. H. B., 1953, Buoyant motion in a turbulent environment, *Australian J. Phys.*, **6**, 279.

—— 1955, Free and forced convection in the atmosphere near the ground, *Quart. J. R. Met. Soc.*, **81**, 139.

—— 1956, A working theory of the bent-over plume of hot gas, *Quart. J. R. Met. Soc.*, **82**, 165.

—— 1959, *Turbulent Transfer in the Lower Atmosphere*, Univ. of Chicago Press.

—— 1959a, *The Isotropic Limit and the Microscale of Turbulence*, Atmospheric Diffusion and Air Pollution, edited by F. N. Frenkiel and P. A. Sheppard, Advances in Geophysics, **6**, 97, Academic Press.

—— 1960, A determinant hypothesis for the superadiabatic wind and temperature profiles, *Quart. J. R. Met. Soc.*, **86**, 232.

Priestley, C. H. B. and Ball, F. K., 1955, Continuous convection from an isolated source of heat, *Quart. J. R. Met. Soc.*, **81**, 144.

Rainey, R. C., 1958, Some observations of flying locusts and atmospheric turbulence in Eastern Africa, *Quart. J. R. Met. Soc.*, **84**, 334.

Richardson, L. F., 1926, Atmospheric diffusion shown on a distance-neighbour graph, *Proc. Roy. Soc.*, A, **110**, 709.

Richardson, L. F. and Proctor, D., 1925, Diffusion over distances ranging from 3 km to 86 km, *Memoirs of the Royal Meteorological Society*, Vol. **1**, No. 1.

Rider, N. E., 1954, Eddy diffusion of momentum, water vapour, and heat near the ground, *Phil. Trans. Roy. Soc.*, A, **246**, 481.

Roberts, O. F. T., 1923, The theoretical scattering of smoke in a Turbulent Atmosphere, *Proc. Roy. Soc.*, A, **104**, 640.

Rossby, C-G., 1932, A generalization of the theory of the mixing length with applications to atmospheric and oceanic turbulence, *Massachusetts Institute of Technology Meteorological Papers*, **1**, No. 4.

Rossby, C-G. and Montgomery, R. B., 1935, The layer of frictional influence in wind and ocean currents, *Papers in Physical Oceanography and Meteorology*, M.I.T. and Woods Hole Oceanographic Institution, **3**, No. 3.

Rounds, W., 1955, Solutions of the two-dimensional diffusion equations. *Trans. Amer. Geoph. Union*, **36**, 395.

Schmidt, F. H., 1957, On the diffusion of stack gases in the atmosphere, *Koninkl. Nederlands Met. Inst., Med. en Verhandelingen*, No. 68.

Schmidt, W., 1925, *Der Massenaustausch in freier Luft und verwandte Erscheinungen*, Probleme der Kosmischen Physik, Hamburg, Verlag von Henri Grand.

Scorer, R. S., 1955, Plumes from tall chimneys, *Weather*, **10**, 106.

Scorer, R. S., 1958, *Natural aerodynamics*, Pergamon Press. London.

—— 1959a, The behaviour of chimney plumes, *Int. Journ. Air Poll.*, **1**, 198.

—— 1959b, *The Rise of Bent-over Hot Plumes, Atmospheric Diffusion and Air Pollution*, edited by F. N. Frenkiel and P. A. Sheppard, Advances in Geophysics, **6**, 399. Academic Press.

Scrase, F. J., 1930, Some characteristics of eddy motion in the atmosphere, *Meteorological Office Geophysical Memoirs* No. 52.

Sheppard, P. A., 1947, The aerodynamic drag of the earth's surface and the value of von Kármán's constant in the lower atmosphere, *Proc. Roy, Soc.*, A, **188**, 208.

—— 1958, Turbulent transfer through the earth's surface and through the air above, *Quart. J. R. Met. Soc.*, **84**, 205.

Singer, I. A. and Smith, M. E., 1953, Relation of gustiness to other meteorological parameters, *J. Met.*, **10**, 121.

Smith, F. B., 1957a, The diffusion of smoke from a continuous elevated point-source into a turbulent atmosphere, *J. Fluid Mech.*, **2**, 49.

—— 1957b, Convection-diffusion processes below a stable layer, a paper of the Meteorological Research Committee (London) *M.R.P.* No. 1048.

—— 1957c, Convection-diffusion processes below a stable layer—Part II, a paper of the Meteorological Research Committee (London) *M.R.P.* No. 1073.

—— 1959, *The Turbulent Spread of a Falling Cluster, Atmospheric Diffusion and Air Pollution*, edited by F. N. Frenkiel and P. A. Sheppard, Advances in Geophysics, **6**, 193, Academic Press.

—— 1961, An analysis of vertical wind-fluctuations at heights between 500 and 5000 feet, *Quart. J. R. Met. Soc.*, **87**, 180.

Smith, F. B. and Abbott, P. F., 1961, Statistics of horizontal gustiness at 16 metres above ground, *Quart. J. R. Met. Soc.*, **87**.

Smith, F. B. and Hay, J. S., 1961, The expansion of clusters of particles in the atmosphere, *Quart. J. R. Met. Soc.*, **87**, 82.

Smith, M. E., 1951a, The forecasting of micrometeorological variables, *Met. Monogr.*, **1**, *Amer. Met. Soc.*, 50.

—— 1951b, Meteorological factors in atmospheric pollution problems, *Am. Ind. Hyg. Ass. Quart.*, **12**, 151.

Solot, S. B. and Darling, E. M., 1958, Theory of large-scale atmospheric diffusion and its application to air trajectories, *Geophysical Research Papers No. 58*, G.R.D., A.F.C.R.C., Bedford, Mass.

Spurr, G. and Priestley, C. H. B., 1957, The bent-over plume of hot gas (correspondence), *Quart. J. R. Met. Soc.*, **83**, 269.

Stakman, E. C., 1947, Plant diseases are shifty enemies, *American Scientist*, **35**, 321.

Stewart, N. G., Gale, H. J. and Crooks, R. N., 1954, The atmospheric diffusion of gases discharged from the chimney of the Harwell Pile (Bepo). *A.E.R.E. HP/R* 1452, H.M.S.O. (in shortened version *Int. J. Air Poll.*, **1**, 87, 1958).

Stewart, N. G., Osmond, R. G. D., Crooks, R. N. and Fisher, E. M., 1957, The world-wide deposition of long-lived fission products from nuclear test explosions, *A.E.R.E. HP/R* 2354, H.M.S.O.

Stratmann, H., 1956, Investigation of sulphur dioxide emission from a bituminous coal-fired power station with very high chimneys. *Mitt. Var. Grosskessel-besitzer* **40**, 49.

Sutton, O. G., 1932, A theory of eddy diffusion in the atmosphere, *Proc. Roy. Soc.*, A, **135**, 143.

—— 1934, Wind structure and evaporation in a turbulent atmosphere, *Proc. Roy. Soc.*, A, **146**, 701.

—— 1947a, The problem of diffusion in the lower atmosphere, *Quart. J. R. Met. Soc.*, **73**, 257.

—— 1947b, The theoretical distribution of airborne pollution from factory chimneys, *Quart. J. R. Met. Soc.*, **73**, 426.

—— 1949, *Atmospheric Turbulence*, Methuen's Monographs on Physical Subjects.

—— 1950, The dispersion of hot gases in the atmosphere, *J. Met.*, **7**, 307.

—— 1953, *Micrometeorology*, McGraw-Hill, New York.

Sutton, W. G. L., 1943, On the equation of diffusion in a turbulent medium, *Proc. Roy. Soc.*, A, **182**, 48.

Swinbank, W. C., 1951, The measurement of vertical transfer of heat and water vapour and momentum in the lower atmosphere with some results, *J. Met.*, **8**, 135.

—— 1955, An experimental study of eddy transports in the lower atmosphere, *Technical Paper No. 2, Melbourne, C.S.I.R.O., Div. Meteorological Physics*.

Tank, W. G., 1957, The use of large scale parameters in small scale diffusion studies, *Bull. Am. Met. Soc.*, **38**, 6.

Taylor, G. I., 1915, Eddy motion in the atmosphere, *Phil. Trans. Roy. Soc.*, A, **215**, 1.

—— 1921, Diffusion by continuous movements, *Proc. London Math. Soc.*, Ser. 2, 20, 196.

—— 1927, Turbulence, *Quart. J. R. Met. Soc.*, **53**, 201.

Taylor, G. I., 1935, Statistical theory of turbulence, Pts 1–4, *Proc. Roy. Soc.*, A, **151**, 421.

—— 1938, The spectrum of turbulence, *Proc. Roy. Soc.*, A, **164**, 476.

—— 1959, *The Present Position in the Theory of Turbulent Diffusion*, Atmospheric Diffusion and Air Pollution, ed. by F. N. Frenkiel and P. A. Sheppard, Advances in Geophysics, **6**, 101, Academic Press.

Taylor, R. J., 1952, Locally isotropic turbulence in the lower layers of the atmosphere, International symposium on atmospheric turbulence in the boundary layer. *Geophys. Res. Papers* No. 19, p. 231, G.R.D., Cambridge, Mass.

—— 1955, Some observations of wind velocity autocorrelation in the lowest layers of the atmosphere, *Aust. J. Phys.*, **8**, 535.

—— 1960, Similarity theory in the relation between fluxes and gradients in the lower atmosphere, *Quart. J. R. Met. Soc.*, **86**, 67.

Thomas, F. W., 1954, T.V.A. Air Pollution Studies Program, *Air Repair*, **4**, 59–65.

Thomas, M. D., Hill, G. R. and Abersold, J. N., 1949, Dispersion of gases from tall stacks, *Ind. & Eng. Chemistry*, **41**, 2409.

Tukey, J. W., 1950, The sampling theory of power spectrum estimates. Symposium on application of autocorrelation analysis to physical problems. Woods Hole, Mass., Office of Naval Research, Washington, D.C.

United States Weather Bureau, 1955, *Meteorology and Atomic Energy*, U.S. Government Printing Office.

Webb, E. K., 1955, Autocorrelations and energy spectra of atmospheric turbulence. *Tech. Paper No. 5, Melbourne, C.S.I.R.O., Div. Met. Physics.*

Wilkins, E. T., 1954, Air Pollution aspects of the London fog of December 1952, *Quart. J. R. Met. Soc.*, **80**, 267.

Wilkins, E. M., 1958a, Observations on the separations of pairs of neutral balloons and applications to atmospheric diffusion theory, *J. Met.*, **15**, 324.

—— 1958b, Effective coefficients of diffusivity for atomic bomb clouds at one thousand to two thousand miles, *Trans. Amer. Geoph. Union*, **39**, 58.

World Meteorological Organisation, 1958, Turbulent diffusion in the atmosphere. *WMO-No. 77 TP.31.*

Yeo, D. and Thompson, B. W., 1953, Deposition of a coarse aerosol released from a low-flying aircraft. *Nature*, **172**, 168.

Yeo, D., Akesson, N. B. and Coutts, H. H., 1959, Drift of toxic chemicals released from a low-flying aircraft. *Nature*, **183**, 131.

Yudine, M. I., 1959, *Physical Considerations on Heavy-particle Diffusion*, Atmospheric Diffusion and Air Pollution, edited by F. N. Frenkiel and P. A. Sheppard, Advances in Geophysics, **6**, 185, Academic Press.

Zbrozek, J. K., 1958, Some effects of atmospheric turbulence on aircraft, *Weather*, **13**, 215.

Index